JOHN CATT'S

Which School? for
Special Needs
2013/14

Twenty-second Edition
Editor: Jonathan Barnes

JOHN
CATT
EDUCATIONAL
LIMITED

Published in 2013 by John Catt Educational Ltd, 12 Deben Mill Business Centre, Old Maltings Approach, Melton, Woodbridge, Suffolk IP12 1BL UK

Tel: 01394 389850   Fax: 01394 386893
Email: enquiries@johncatt.com   Website: www.johncatt.com

Designed and typeset by John Catt Educational Limited
Printed and Bound in Great Britain by Cambrian Printers.

A CIP catalogue record for this book is available from the British Library.

ISBN: 978 1 908095 78 7
eISBN: 978 1 908095 79 4

Contents

Editor
Jonathan Barnes
Email: jonathanbarnes@johncatt.com

Advertising & School Profiles
Tel: +44 (0) 1394 389850
Email: sales@johncatt.com

Distribution/Book Sales
Tel: +44 (0) 1394 389863
Email: booksales@johncatt.com

Contents

Contents

Introduction

by Jonathan Barnes, Editor

Welcome to the 2013/14 edition of *Which School for Special Needs?*

We're delighted to give a platform to so many excellent special schools in this important guidebook and we hope you will be inspired to investigate further into what they have to offer. Our aim is to provide a one-stop service for parents looking for the right school for their children. It's hard to think of a more important decision to make than choosing a school for a child with special needs, and if we can help make that decision-making process a little easier, then we will have achieved our aim!

It continues to be a time of great change in the Special Educational Needs sector, as new Government legislation makes it way through the Houses of Parliament. It can be terribly confusing to work out what the reforms mean to families of SEN children and for that reason we have invited experts in the field to give their thoughts and advice. They include Claire Dorer, chief executive of the National Association of Independent Schools and Non-Maintained Special Schools, and Malcolm Reeve, chair of the Federation of Leaders in Special Education and National Director of Education for SEND at the Academies Enterprise Trust, who have both written excellent pieces providing both a snapshot of the current situation and a look at the opportunities presented by the changes. As Claire points out in her article, 'The year ahead will be full of challenges but there is rarely a dull moment in the world of special education!'

In previous editions of *Which School for Special Needs?* we have tracked the progress of the British Paralympic Association in the build-up to the Paralympic Games in London last summer. As we now know, the 2012 Games were a stunning triumph, creating national heroes and putting disability sport 'on the map'. Now they've had a chance to catch their breath and come back down to earth, the BPA have given us a post-Paralympics rundown on how they are building on that success.

We also have editorial from Options Group, the National Autistic Society, the Royal National Institute for Blind People and SpaceKraft; educational psychologist Ruth Birnbaum gives some key pointers on choosing a special needs school; and Katie Emsley, of Langley Wellington LLP Solicitors, provides an update on the legal aspects to consider.

Finding an establishment that will address the needs of your child is extremely important, as it will have a significant impact on their development, the level of independence they are able to achieve and the opportunities they are able to embrace in life. The search for the right school can be a complex and emotional journey and so, to help the reader, we have tried to make this guide as informative, interesting and easy to use as possible.

This guide also provides the reader with detailed information about the range of provision for children with SEN, helping you to make an informed, confident choice of school or college according to your child's individual needs. As well as featuring listings and information of independent schools and colleges we also provide up-to-date details of all the maintained special schools in the UK. With each new edition we do our best to ensure that our resource is up-to-date with current data, research, classification and opinion, and that each special needs sector is fairly and accurately represented in the guide. We welcome, however, suggestions from readers as to how we could further improve this resource.

Melton, Suffolk, April 2013

How to use this guide

Here are some pointers on how to use this guidebook effectively

Which School? for Special Needs is divided into specific sections:

1. Editorial

This includes articles, written by experts in their fields, explaining various aspects of special needs education. There are also case studies and other interesting articles.

2. Profiles

Here the schools and colleges have been given the opportunity to highlight what they feel are their best qualities in order to help you decide whether this is the right school for your child. They are presented in sections according to the needs they specialise in:

- sensory or physical impairment
- social interaction difficulties (autism, ASD & ASP)
- learning difficulties (including dyslexia/SPLD)
- emotional, behavioural and/or social difficulties.

Within these sections, schools and colleges are listed by region in alphabetical order.

3. Directory

Here you will find basic up-to-date information about every independent or non-maintained special needs school and college, and further education colleges, in England, Northern Ireland, Scotland and Wales, giving contact details, size of school and which specific needs are catered for. (You will find a key to the abbreviations at the start of each directory section) The directory is divided into four sections:

- sensory or physical impairment
- social interaction difficulties (autism, ASD & ASP)
- learning difficulties (including dyslexia/SPLD)
- emotional, behavioural and/or social difficulties.

Within these sections, each establishment is listed by region in alphabetical order and those that have entries in the profiles section are cross-referenced to allow you to find further detailed information. Against each entry you will find a number of symbols indicating any SEN speciality, including an icon to indicate if the school is DfE approved.

4. Useful associations and websites

In this section we provide a list of useful organisations and websites relevant to special educational needs, which may be useful to parents looking for specific help or advice.

5. Maintained schools

Here we have included basic details of all maintained special schools in England, Northern Ireland, Scotland and Wales. They are listed according to their Local Authority.

6. Index

Page numbers preceded by a D indicate a school appearing in the directory, those without will be found in the profiles section.

How to use this guide effectively

John Catt's *Which School? for Special Needs* can be used effectively in several ways according to the information you are looking for. For example, are you looking for:

A specific school? If you know the name of the school but are unsure of its location simply go to the index at the back of the guide where you will find all schools listed alphabetically.

A particular type of school? Both the profiles and directories are divided into sections according to the type of provision. **See also the appendix on page 183,** which lists specific special needs and the schools that cater for them.

A school in a certain region? Look first in the relevant directory. This will give you the basic information about the schools in each region, complete with contact details and which specific needs are catered for. More detailed information can be found in the profiles section for those schools who have chosen to include a full entry.

More information on relevant educational organisations? At the end of the directories you will find a list of useful organisations and websites relevant to special educational needs.

Please note: regional divisions

To facilitate the use of this guide, we have included the geographical region 'Central & West'. This is not an officially designated region and has been created solely for the purposes of this publication.

One final thing, on the next page you will find a list of commonly used SEN abbreviations. This list can be found repeated at various points throughout the guide.

Abbreviations – a full glossary can be found at page 325

ACLD	Autism, Communication and Associated Learning Difficulties	LD	Learning Difficulties
ADD	Attention Deficit Disorder	MLD	Moderate Learning Difficulties
ADHD	Attention Deficit and Hyperactivity Disorder	MSI	Multi-sensory Impairment
ASD	Autistic Spectrum Disorder	OCD	Obsessive Compulsive Disorder
ASP	Asperger Syndrome	PD	Physical Difficulties
AUT	Autism	PH	Physical Impairment
BESD	Behavioural, Emotional and Social Difficulties	Phe	Partially Hearing
		PMLD	Profound and Multiple Learning Difficulties
CCD	Complex Communication Difficulties	PNI	Physical Neurological Impairment
CLD	Complex Learning Difficulties	SCD	Social and Communication Difficulties
CP	Cerebral Palsy	SCLD	Severe to Complex Learning Difficulties
D	Deaf		
DEL	Delicate	SEBD	Severe Emotional and Behavioural Difficulties
DYS	Dyslexia		
DYSP	Dyspraxia	SEBN	Social, Emotional and Behavioural Needs
EBD	Emotional and Behavioural Difficulties	SLD	Severe Language Difficulties
EPI	Epilepsy	SLI	Specific Language Impairment
GLD	General Learning Difficulties	SPLD	Specific Learning Difficulties
HA	High Ability	SP&LD	Speech and Language Difficulties
HI	Hearing Impairment	VIS	Visual Impairment

We are grateful to all the individuals and associations who have assisted in the publication of this guide. Special thanks go to: Claire Dorer; Malcolm Reeve; Katherine Allin at the British Paralympic Association; Geoff Evans and Jaspreet Sogi at Options Group; Vicky Ramsay at SpaceKraft; Gabriella Brooks and Liz Gutteridge at the RNIB; Ruth Birnbaum; Sally Li at the National Autistic Society; and Katie Emsley, of Langley Wellington LLP Solicitors.

'Many challenges and changes to come...'

Claire Dorer, chief executive of the National Association of Independent Schools and Non-Maintained Special Schools (NASS), offers her thoughts on the ongoing developments in SEN provision

As I am writing this, the Government has just launched a new Children and Families Bill in Parliament – for the most of the life of this edition of *Which School for Special Needs?* it will be making its way through scrutiny and debate in the House of Commons and House of Lords before coming into force towards the end of 2014.

Many of us in the field of SEN expected these reforms to bring major changes to policy and practice. The published Bill suggests a more moderate approach, where parents might not see a great deal of difference when their child's Statement of Special Educational Needs morphs into an Education, Health and Care Plan. When the Bill was first published, there were no plans to create a duty for health providers to deliver the services identified as being needed in their area. Lobbying from SEN groups has led to the Government amending this, creating a duty to deliver health services for the first time. This is an exciting and welcome development. Parents will get the chance to hold a personal budget for their child, which will give them some additional controls over the services that they receive. However, this will not include allocating funding for a full school placement, which was what many parents had hoped for. There are chances for personal budgets to make a real difference for families but it is a change which will come with challenges too as parents will take on more responsibility for the services which they choose to purchase.

However, there are significant changes particularly relevant to readers of this guide. When the Bill becomes law, non-maintained and independent special schools will become Local Authority statutory partners. This means that, for the first time, parents will have the right to express a preference for a non-maintained or independent special school in exactly the same way that they can now express a preference for a Local Authority maintained special school. Instead of parents having to prove why a placement in a school from our sector would be the right option, Local Authorities will now have to prove why that placement is not the right option. It's a subtle change on paper but, in practice, we hope this will give parents a real choice of special school provision, across all types of school.

Within schools, we face the challenge of proving that the non-maintained and independent special school sector represents a cost-effective placement option. Historically, we have been accused of being more expensive than maintained provision but have suffered from a failure to make like-for-like comparisons of provision. In 2012, research from the accountants Baker Tilly[1] indicated that day and weekly boarding provision in non-maintained and independent special schools is actually cheaper than the Local Authority

Some Challenges Need Ambitious and Innovative Solutions!

"Four years ago I could never have imagined I would have changed so much!"

Josh is now employed at the Ruskin Glass Centre Café following three invaluable years at Glasshouse College

Our young people learn and achieve through practical, real-life activities and accredited courses to progress onto greater independence, further education and employment.

While our provision for day and residential students is ranked Good to Outstanding by Ofsted and 97% of students successfully complete their courses, of which 95% achieve recognised qualifications, their real achievement is to leave with the confidence and skills to know they have a place in their communities.

To find out more about our innovative, holistic and personalised curriculum, delivered by trained and expert staff, contact our nearest provision or visit our website: www.rmt.org

Ruskin Mill Trust transforms lives for people with ASD including Asperger's Syndrome, learning difficulties and/or disabilities, mental health issues and challenging behaviour.

Ruskin Mill Trust is an educational charity and draws its inspiration from the insights of Rudolf Steiner, John Ruskin and William Morris.

Charity No: 1137167

providing equivalent packages of support. We know that our schools are the choice of many parents because of the extra support they offer beyond education, through access to therapies and a range of short-break and social care options. For parents used to fighting to co-ordinate all of the services that their child accesses, having all services in one place can save a lot of time and effort.

The impact of securing the right placement is huge. All schools have anecdotes of young people whose lives have been transformed by the receiving the right support at the right time. A second report by Baker Tilly[2] looked at the 'social return on investment' that a good school placement makes. The report considers the financial value of a school placement by considering the impact that it has both during and after that placement. We know that the impact on the young person themselves is huge – young people who have their special educational needs addressed are more likely to go on to further and higher education and employment. They are less likely to be one of the 40% of young people with SEN who develops a mental health problem and less likely to become involved in criminal behaviour. However, the benefits of the placement extend further, to the family of the child or young person. The parents of children with SEN have a higher than average chance of developing mental health problems and are less likely to be in employment. The siblings of children with SEN have a higher than average chance of being disengaged from education. Parents of children in our schools tell us that finding the right placement for their child has made family life less stressful. For some parents, there is finally an opportunity to begin a part-time or full-time job or study for further qualifications. In financial terms, across the non-maintained and independent special school sector this represents annual savings in the region of £600 million. Of course, such benefits are not unique to our sector but this study does show the consequences of making the right school placement.

Nationally, finances remain tight and schools and Local Authorities need to work closely together to ensure we have enough specialist provision in the right places. We are hoping for opportunities to work more closely with maintained schools to help share some of the specialist knowledge and experience within our sector. We also need to learn more about the interventions which really make a difference for our children and young people. We know that access to speech and language therapy is a key issue for many parents and we expect that this will be one area where personal budgets might be used to good effect. However, we still know relatively little about exactly how much input makes a difference and whether this is always best delivered through one-to-one sessions as opposed to group work or training other school staff.

The year ahead will be full of challenges but there is rarely a dull moment in the world of special education! I know that our schools will be looking forward to adapting to this new landscape alongside you. Who knows what next year's edition will bring?

Notes

1. Clifford, J. And Theobald, C. (2012) National Association of Independent Schools and Non-maintained Special Schools: Summary of Findings: Extension of the 2011 Cost Comparison methodology to a wider sample www.nasschools.org.uk

2. Clifford, J. And Theobald, C. (2012) National Association of Independent and Non-Maintained Special Schools: Social Impact Evaluation of Non-Maintained and Independent Special schools using Social Return on Investment www.nasschools.org.uk

The key to finding the right place is having the right choice.

WILSIC HALL SCHOOL

FULLERTON HOUSE SCHOOL

Everyone at Hesley Group is here to enable people with complex needs achieve their full potential.

To do this we believe in creating stable placements in safe environments. In places where care and education plans can be built around the individual, focused on their needs and goals. We also believe in offering children and young adults with autism, a learning disability and associated complex needs the choice of where they want to live, learn and grow in confidence. After all, finding a place that's right for them is everything.

We offer a choice of two schools. Both offer a wealth of experience and specialist expertise on hand together with high-quality therapeutic environments and resources. Which one is right is often a personal thing. So why not visit both?

Fullerton House School
The school supports 8 to 19 year olds. Situated in the village of Denaby Main, near Doncaster, it has a real 'heart of the community' feel.

Wilsic Hall School
Situated in its own picturesque 14 acre countryside setting five miles south of Doncaster, Wilsic Hall School supports young people from 11 to 19 years of age.

We've made it easier for families, carers, professionals, and the people we can support, find all the information they need to know about our services.

www.hesleygroup.co.uk

SEE OUR NEW WEBSITE

Referral enquiries freephone
0800 055 6789

Hesley Group

Everyone has a part to play in SEN reforms

Malcolm Reeve, chair of the Federation of Leaders in Special Education and national director of education for SEND at the Academies Enterprise Trust, believes the new educational landscape offers a time of hope and opportunity that we must all seize upon...

We are experiencing the biggest changes in the field of SEN education in a generation. The government, through the Department for Education, is encouraging the academisation and free school process and in that context a multiplicity of partnerships, federations and trusts have formed, accompanied by a revised role for local authorities as they adapt to the changing educational landscape. There is greater scrutiny of provision than ever before; local authorities will soon face 'school improvement' inspections from Ofsted and academy 'chains' are surely soon to follow. Ofsted itself has a greater focus than ever on special educational needs and is particularly concerned about the progress of 'vulnerable' children. At the same time there are significant reforms to the funding of schools and the funding which any education provision will receive for its SEN students. The Children and Families Bill, with its far-reaching section in Part 3 on SEN reforms, has just received its second reading in Parliament. Truly this is a time of great change but it is also a time of great opportunity and of hope.

> Truly this is a time of great change but it is also a time of great opportunity and of hope

There is no doubt that changes to the ways in which we educate children with SEN and their families are sorely needed. The number of children identified as having SEN in English schools is five times the EU average and yet:

- The extent of training for teachers who wish to work in the field of SEN has been systematically neglected for years. It is a travesty that our most vulnerable children are taught by teachers who often have received no formal training in the field and learn 'on the job'.

- The ready availability of therapy and social care services to support children with SEN and their families is historically poor in local authority specialist provisions and even worse in mainstream provision.

There are additional problems when children reach school-leaving age:

- 30% of young people with a statement of special educational need at 16 years of age are not in employment, education or training by the time they are eighteen (source: National Audit Office, Sept 2011).

- 'The choice of education and training opportunities at 16 was limited for many young people with learning difficulties and/or disabilities.' (source: Ofsted – A statement is not enough'

Nevertheless, across our country are some of the most outstanding specialist provisions in the world. I have had the privilege of visiting many of them and the dedication and commitment of staff as well as the quality of their service to the child and family/carers is a pleasure to behold. However, all of us who work in the field know that there is so much to achieve. The Children and Families Bill, which arose out of the Green Paper proposals of 2011, is currently making its way through Parliament and will become legislation next year.

The notion of a single Education, Health and Care plan to replace statements of SEN is laudable. It recognises both the challenges which young people face when they reach the end of statutory schooling and the need to integrate the services around a single plan. The question that almost everyone is asking is will the plan have the 'teeth' it needs. The proposals place a 'duty to jointly commission' services but they do not place a legal duty on health and social care to deliver the services. In Parliament, just as I prepared this piece, the Minister for Children and Families announced that a new legal duty would be placed on commissioning groups to ensure that children and young adults receive the health services identified in their Education, Health and care plans. This is a significant and welcome shift but as the saying goes, 'the proof of the pudding will be in the eating'! The FLSE has said, 'Therapy services in schools across the country need to improve and this must be seen as the absolute goal of joint commissioning.'

Having said that, there is no point in having outstanding specialist provision if young people 'fall off the cliff-edge' at the end of statutory education. The EHC plans, their force in law and the obligations placed upon services to deliver what is stated in them will be the key to whether the SEN reforms bring about the necessary changes for those with more severe needs. The development of effective post-16 and post-19 provisions for young people is paramount. Too often young people and their families are faced with limited choices that are not socially inclusive. For years I have been concerned about what happens to the most vulnerable at the end of statutory education. The end of a 'one-size fits all' approach has to come and the right for a young adult to both have a say in their provision and to have an ongoing personalised pathway is vital. The SEN reforms go some way towards addressing this and the education funding reforms do allow for greater flexibility in developing provisions.

The training and development of the workforce, both teachers and support staff, is critical to ensuring that children have the targeted support they need. Specialist training needs to improve and all teachers need to have significant SEN elements as part of their training. Those who advocate for children with SEND must continue to push for changes in this area.

The vast majority of young people with SEN are in mainstream education and a new SEN Code of Practice, yet to be released, will apply. Whilst specialist provisions continue to develop their services, radical reforms are needed to address the needs of those with SEN in mainstream provisions. Mainstream provisions have conflicting demands placed upon them that sometimes mitigate against the needs of those with SEND. The flexibility of mainstream responses to SEN is an area which can be improved. Special schools and specialist services have the opportunity to further develop their support for SEN children in mainstream in the new landscape through partnership working.

Some of the changes will come through the Children and Families Bill but others will have to be led and driven by parents/carers, teachers, schools, voluntary services and most importantly the young people themselves all working together to bring about change in a new landscape. Everyone has their part to play but most of all I would like to see greater powers placed in the hands of parents/carers and young people, combined with legal obligations placed on all services to actually deliver personalised provision for those with SEN. For now we must concentrate on ensuring that the SEN Reforms indeed have 'teeth' and make the necessary difference to lives.

Disability sport thrives after 2012 triumph

The British Paralympic Association tell us how they are building on the success of the London Games

The London 2012 Games were the biggest Paralympic Games in history. Over the course of 11 days of sporting action, 4000 athletes from more than 170 countries competed in stadia and venues which were packed to the rafters with cheering fans. Record ticket sales meant that many events sold out.

The Games showcased Paralympic sport in a way that had not been witnessed before, with increased coverage across TV, radio and print media making household names of British athletes such as Ellie Simmonds, David Weir (above) and Dame Sarah Storey. Channel 4 provided 16 hours of live TV coverage every day and 6.3 million viewers watched Jonnie Peacock win gold in the T44 100m, the highest ratings for a single Paralympic event.

ParalympicsGB took 301 athletes to compete at the London Games – their largest ever team. Together, they achieved the ambition of winning more medals across more sports, with a total of 34 gold, 43 silver and 43 bronze medals. British athletes competed in each of the 20 sports on the Paralympic programme, from archery to wheelchair tennis.

To be selected to compete at a Paralympic Games is the pinnacle of an elite disabled athlete's career. For British athletes, competing at London 2012 represented the culmination of years of hard work, training and commitment.

The BPA recognised that the performance of British athletes in London presented a fantastic opportunity to inspire a new generation of disabled people to get into sport. As the Games headed toward their conclusion, the BPA decided to capitalise on the interest generated by London 2012 and announced its

ambition to host a festival of Paralympic sport, which would provide opportunities for disabled people to take part in a multi-sport celebration and also serve to identify future generations of British athletes.

The inaugural ParalympicsGB Sports Fest took place in Surrey in December 2012. The event offered people the opportunity to participate in come-and-try sessions for the vast majority of summer and winter Paralympic sports. At a number of 'Meet the Medallists' sessions visitors also had the opportunity to find out more about the journey that Paralympic athletes had taken from grass-roots level to elite competition.

In total, over 1,000 people attended the two-day event. The BPA's ambition is now to take Sports Fest to other parts of the UK so that more people have the opportunity to get involved, and a series of events are planned for 2013 and 2014.

Another area of activity for the BPA coming out of the Games was Deloitte Parasport. Run jointly by the BPA and business advisory firm Deloitte, Parasport acts as the 'Yellow Pages' for disability sport. The website is designed to help users identify the sports for them and signpost them to clubs and opportunities in their local area. Through Parasport, users can also read and watch videos about existing Paralympic sports as well as a growing number of non-Paralympic sports.

Over 37,500 people logged on to Parasport during the London 2012 Paralympic Games, compared with 1,400 people during the same period the year before. This represented an increase of more than 2,000%. The majority of these visitors were using the 'Find a Club' function, suggesting that people were inspired by the performances of British athletes and were seeking to get more active.

Meanwhile, in schools across the country the Get Set programme continues to help engage young people in the Paralympic movement. The BPA has partnered with the British Olympic Association to ensure that Get Set, the official London 2012 education programme for schools and colleges across the UK, will continue into 2013 and beyond.

The programme provides free learning resources for 3-19 year olds, offering materials and resources for teachers to use in the classroom, in assembly and in wider activities. Get Set enables students to find out more about the Games and explore the Olympic values of excellence, friendship and respect, and the Paralympic values of determination, inspiration, courage and equality.

There are currently over 26,000 schools and colleges registered with Get Set, 91% of which have led Paralympic activities as part of their programme. Through the activities and conversations sparked by Get Set, the programme will continue to play a key role in engaging young people in the Paralympic Games.

The BPA remains dedicated to ensuring British athletes are best prepared to succeed as part of ParalympicsGB at Sochi 2014, Rio 2016 and beyond, to maintain their position as a leading Paralympic nation.

At the same time, through initiatives such as Sports Fest, Parasport and Get Set, the organisation is continuing to work hard to maximise engagement and awareness of Paralympic sports and athletes, with the aim of using the inspirational performances of British athletes during London 2012 to encourage the next generation of Paralympians to take up sport.

To become a fan of ParalympicsGB please visit the ParalympicsGB Facebook page or follow on Twitter at twitter.com/paralympicsgb. For further information, contact:

British Paralympic Association
60 Charlotte Street
London
W1T 2NU
Telephone: 020 7842 5789
Fax: 020 7842 5777
Email: info@paralympics.org.uk
Website: www.paralympics.org.uk
Parasport: www.parasport.org.uk
Get Set: www.getset.co.uk

Registered charity number 802385

Sensory project builds links with community

SpaceKraft reports on the completion of its innovative Environments Project at the Bridge Special School in Telford

SpaceKraft has completed work on a major four-year project to design and install an extensive array of multi-sensory equipment across 20 separate areas of the purpose-built Bridge Special School in Telford, Shropshire, a centre for children with severe and profound learning and physical disabilities.

Formerly based at two restrictive and increasingly unsuitable sites in Brookside and Stirchley, The Bridge School was relocated at the new purpose-built facilities on the Hadley campus. Serving the whole of the Borough of Telford and Wrekin, the school provides for 162 severe/profound learning disability pupils aged five to 19 years, many of whom have additional needs including physical disabilities, sensory impairment and autism. In addition the school runs an assessment nursery where up to 40 part-time pupils from as young as 2½ years undergo statutory assessment.

SpaceKraft became involved with the Bridge School project from its inception working closely with the headteacher and deputy headteacher. SpaceKraft developed the design and specification of 20 sensory areas that would become a vital part of the school's curriculum. The headteacher, Una Van-Den-Berg, and deputy headteacher Heather Davis had a clear brief for the sensory equipment which would be included in the new school.

Heather Davis explains: "All our staff were very heavily involved in the design of the new school, really thinking through the needs of the pupils now and what was going to be an effective provision for them in the future. We went back to what was going to be the best way to help them to learn and then built the

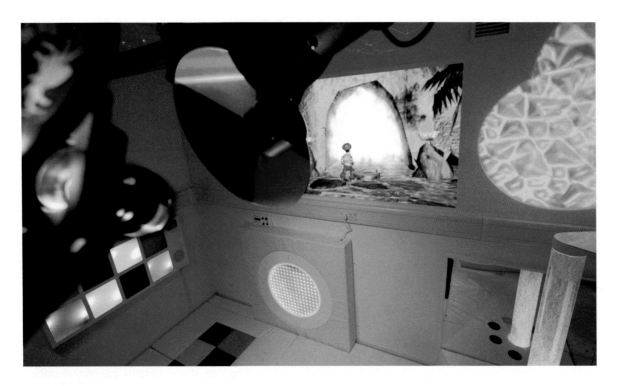

facilities around that. We had to project into the future because the school has been built with an expected 25 to 30-year lifespan, so we had to also think about the changing needs of the changing population that we can see coming through early years, and think about how that will affect educational provision much further down the line.

"We had a very extensive knowledge of who we were providing for – knowledge of the children and how best to help them to learn. We had a really clear idea of how we wanted to plan the curriculum and how we felt it was best to reduce the barriers to learning that our children have. We had worked with SpaceKraft before on two very small rooms at the old school sites, so we had already established a professional relationship with them. Because of this, we were able to go to SpaceKraft and say, 'This is what we are trying to achieve and this is what we feel the children really need – what have you got that will help us to do that?' Obviously, they knew their product, so they were able to show us all sorts of things that matched our ideas of what we wanted."

An essential part of the brief was that the five key stages of primary and secondary education would each have their own Whiteroom and Blackroom, with each room designed to support the differing requirements of the pupils as they advance through the school. In addition, it was important that pupils who would remain at the same level throughout their education were also provided for, enabling them to benefit from working with a changing variety of sensory equipment pitched at that level. The moderate sizes of the rooms were deliberately chosen, to enable the teachers to work with individual children or with small groups of children, as the school's staff have found this to be the most effective way of working with their pupils in multi-sensory environments such as these.

SpaceKraft designed and installed five multi-sensory Whiterooms, equipping each with SpaceKraft's exclusive Sensory Show Magic interactive sound video and lighting system. The rooms also incorporate a wide variety of sensory equipment such as bubble tubes, fibre-optic sideglows, infinity tunnels and musical hopscotch pads. Similarly, the five Blackrooms were fitted with interactive switch controls, a range of SpaceKraft UV and fibre-optic products as well as a variety of other Blackroom equipment such as sound-activated Catherine wheels, interactive infinity tunnels and various wall-mounted panels including LED bubble panels, sound-to-light panels, UV tactile panels and touch panels.

Two different Softplay rooms were developed for the school. One room was designed for younger children undertaking simple play activities in the safe soft play environment, and was furnished with Softplay dens, steps, stepping stones and a geometric jungle. The other room was designed to encourage more interactive play by including Softplay Noisy products with auditory rewards – stepping blocks, steps and slides – in addition to space tubes and a Softplay Den. Both rooms were lined with Softplay walls and floors, which also formed the structure of four Soft Calming rooms at the school.

> **'**We had a really clear idea of how we wanted to plan the curriculum and how we felt it was best to reduce the barriers to learning that our children have**'**

SpaceKraft fitted the school's hydrotherapy pool with Sensory Show Magic interactive sound and lighting, and the Show Magic System was also installed in the music room, the school's music and drama hall, and a science classroom. As the Show Magic System enables the teachers to design flexible programs of learning, entertainment or play, the endless possibilities for providing students with interactive audio-visual experiences has proved to be a vital teaching aid, greatly enhancing understanding in maths and science lessons and encouraging participation in drama and music activities. With the Show Magic technology being common to all of the sensory areas of the school, the teachers only required training in the one system before they were capable of programming and operating the audio-visual equipment throughout the school.

In addition to its primary function at the core of The Bridge School's curriculum, the multi-sensory equipment installed by SpaceKraft has also greatly benefited the school's inclusion work. Local therapists are invited to use the hydrotherapy pool and the multi-sensory rooms for assessments or ongoing work with their own clients, while teachers and pupils from the two nearby mainstream schools are also encouraged to visit and use the Show Magic audio-visual facilities for projects and learning programmes of their own, helping to engage mainstream pupils in mathematics, science and literacy.

Heather Davis explains: "Our vision, in terms of inclusion, is that the facilities that we have here should be available to the community as a whole, bringing our pupils into social contact with members of the community and vice versa. Interaction of this kind is very important to our pupils' understanding of the world beyond the walls of the school, as well as promoting understanding of our pupils in the minds of the visitors, the majority of whom would otherwise have no contact with youngsters with severe and profound learning and physical disabilities. The facilities that SpaceKraft have provided are fantastic tools for encouraging a meaningful social interaction between our pupils and the mainstream community."

Educating children with autism – a holistic approach

Geoff Evans, of Options Group, outlines strategies, methods and approaches for the SEN classroom

In order to effectively educate children with autism, we must not only develop and maximise educational opportunities, but also adopt a more holistic approach that addresses their individual needs in a planned and integrated way. This approach usually includes recognising and responding to the needs arising from autism, such as addressing sensory differences and developing social and communication abilities. The maximising of physical well-being and development of practical strategies for managing stress and anxiety are seen as an essential component of such an approach. A holistic approach begins with developing learning methods and interventions based upon abilities, strengths and special interests.

Developing methods and approaches based upon abilities and strengths

Very often the starting point is an assessment where we concentrate on understanding the whole picture, including both needs and abilities. For example, needs could include the development of communication, social interaction, organisation and generalisation skills. Such assessments can be used to develop programmes, which motivate and provide a vehicle with which to deliver the curriculum. At Options Group, we work with each child's strengths and abilities. By doing this, we have seen real progress in the areas of learning new skills and behaviours in children with a history of failed placements.

Addressing sensory processing differences

Recently, there has been a greater emphasis put upon sensory issues and autism. In practice, there is still a need for schools to take into consideration the sensory processing differences and styles of children with autism. Addressing sensory issues in the classroom and the wider school can impact upon a child's learning experience. At Options Group, each service has a dedicated Professional and Clinical Multi-disciplinary Team (PCMT), which includes Occupational Therapists with the knowledge and expertise of facilitating living and learning for those who may process sensory information differently. The PCMTs advise on the appropriate strategies and approaches to enhance the learning process, for example providing the child with the right coloured paper to write or read from or organising classrooms to minimise distraction. Even relatively small planned changes resulting from individual assessments can impact upon a child's success.

A holistic approach recognises the importance of developing children's knowledge and experience of the world in which they live and learn

Opening up the world for children with autism

A holistic approach recognises the importance of developing children's knowledge and experience of the world in which they live and learn. Many children come to Options Group's specialist schools with a limited experience of the world and are gradually invited and supported to explore the wider world and learn the skills necessary to not only function but also to achieve. These skills are dependent upon the individual child, but may include learning to move around school independently to eventually accessing the local community with the right levels of support. For others, it may include experiencing different environments through an outdoor education programme.

Meeting social and communication needs

This area requires an individual approach based upon detailed assessment and often involves working with experienced staff in intensive interaction. It may also involve the use of social skills groups, circle time and drama lessons. Whatever the approach you take, all will need enhancing with incidental social skills and communication teaching throughout the waking day.

The maximising of physical well-being

Children with autism may experience difficulty with gross and fine motor skills, poor muscle tone together with vestibular and proprioceptive difficulties. These difficulties mean that completing everyday tasks such as participating in playground activities, sports and other physical activities are challenging. Extra time spent developing and implementing simple individual exercise programmes can produce benefits not only in the classroom but in all areas of a child's life. Where possible, such programmes are more effective when developed in co-operation with parents and the wider family. Exercise programmes do not need to be complex and could include walking, cycling, swimming or one-to-one sessions in the gym.

Providing practical strategies for managing stress and anxiety

One of the factors that has the most dramatic effect upon children with autism, as learners is high levels of worry and anxiety. Anxiety can impact upon children's ability to learn effectively and function in and out of school, with many experiencing withdrawal, increase in repetitive behaviours and difficulty in communicating and engaging.

A holistic approach to educating children with autism focuses on managing environments and equipping them with a range of techniques to manage their own raising levels of anxiety. Simple techniques for combating anxiety can include controlled breathing and creating safe havens within the school. Such an approach will also equip staff with the knowledge and skills to recognise the signs of increased worry and anxiety and help them to respond appropriately.

Addressing the autism

A holistic approach must address the impact and needs arising from autism. This will mean addressing communication, social interaction and social imagination difficulties. Whilst these difficulties and differences should be addressed in an integrated way through the curriculum, there is also a need for the use of specialist approaches and interventions. Such approaches will often include the use of structure, visual approaches, Picture Exchange Communication System (PECS) and the use of script based approaches, such as social stories.

Conclusion

In this short article it has only been possible to identify and briefly discuss some of the components of a holistic approach to educating children with autism.

Do feel free to contact me at geoffe@optionsgroup.co.uk or call me on 01789 767800.

Creative, flexible education for young people with autism

We believe that every child and young person with autism has a right to the tailored education they need to prepare for a fulfilling adulthood.

With our educational services expanding this year we are proudly supporting an ever growing number of children and young people from four to 25 years old across eight schools.

Opportunities range from day and residential placements to short breaks and outreach services - all supported by caring and experienced staff working in modern facilities.

- **Primary and secondary education**
- **Post-16 provision**

- **Day, termly and year-round provision**
- **24-hour curriculum**

- **Outreach services**
- **Transition service**
- **Short break services**

For enquiries or referrals contact us on **0117 974 8430**
Or visit **www.autism.org.uk/educationenquiries**

The National
Autistic Society

Accept difference. Not indifference.

Specialist support that is closer to home

The National Autistic Society looks at whether specialist autism support can be offered in every local area

In the 1960s, a group of parents set up the Sybil Elgar School, a specialist school for children with autism in Middlesex. At the time, understanding and knowledge of autism was far more limited than it is today, and these parents had been told that their children were uneducable. They begged to differ.

Education has come a long way since then, but far too many families still have to battle to secure the right education for their child with autism. Nationally, one in five children with autism has been excluded from mainstream school, and 67% of these have been excluded more than once. The most common reason given to parents when their child is excluded is that the school cannot cope with them.

Those children who are able to access appropriate autism-specialist education often have to travel long distances every day, while some have no choice but to leave home and live at their school.

The issues surrounding educational placements are complex. For some children with autism, being sent to a school that is a long way from home can be detrimental to their wellbeing, while any local support that their family received can quickly fall away. In some cases, young people struggle to build support networks in their new location, while others find it difficult to return after school to an area where they no longer have any links. But the alternative may be just as difficult, because if the right educational provision is not available in a child's local area, this can have an equally serious impact on them and their family.

It's vital that children with autism have a choice in their education, and are able to attend a suitable school near to their home, if they wish, so that they can remain part of their own community.

In order for this to happen, children need to be able to access support locally that is tailored to their individual needs – meaning a flexible, personalised approach to education is of the utmost importance. The Sybil Elgar School, a trailblazer in the 1960s that still flourishes today, is establishing a new house for pupils who need to live in an autism-specialist home throughout the year. This will be the first of its kind in London and will allow young people who have autism and highly complex support needs to remain close to their families.

Meanwhile, the Robert Ogden School in South Yorkshire has a house in the local village so that any pupils who need a weekly residential option, a short break or an occasional overnight stay, can live in a homely, high-quality environment and, just like most of their peers, have a short walk or ride to school.

The Government's free school initiative could usher in a new generation of autism-specific schools. The National Autistic Society (NAS) runs seven schools across the UK and is working with several local communities on plans for free schools where there is an identified need for specialist autism provision, with the first set to open later this year, in Berkshire.

While there will always be some children who need to attend specialist schools for pupils with autism and to stay at these schools for all of their years in education, there are also many children who need a much more flexible approach, attending a specialist school for a specific, dedicated amount of time.

Emma, who is mother to David, a 17-year-old with autism, explains how this approach has benefited her son:

"The combination of mainstream and special school has definitely been the best set-up for David. Integration into mainstream school is very important to him. [The special school] focuses mainly on his wellbeing and personal skills, and mainstream on his academic needs. Everyone – including the schools, the local authority, David's family and, of course, David himself – has worked together and I think this is why it has succeeded."

The key to offering flexible support lies with local authorities being supported to develop a comprehensive, integrated system of support for young people and their families. As well as this, organisations such as the NAS can work with parents, local schools, colleges and services to share practice; provide outreach; and support mainstream and special school partners to identify pupils at risk and prevent placement breakdown.

It is also important for pupils to retain links with their local community, wherever possible. As well as taking part in activities in the community, such as sports clubs or social groups, if a pupil starts at a specialist school, such as one run by the NAS, a partner school can be identified near to the pupil's home. The partner school is informed of the pupil's progress and, if appropriate, the pupil will be able to take up academic and social opportunities in that school. If the time comes when the pupil is ready to be permanently re-included into their local school, the young person, their parents and staff from both schools can work together to bring about a successful transition.

Ultimately, a 'mixed menu' of support that recognises pupils' changing needs should allow children and young people with autism to develop the knowledge and skills they need to lead full and meaningful adult lives. Further study, university and employment may all become realistic, achievable goals – and who would not want children with autism, or any other disability, to have these opportunities?

As understanding of autism continues to develop among education professionals and local authorities, so the need for personalised learning that builds on the strengths of individual pupils becomes ever more apparent. By putting the needs of pupils at the centre of all that we do, we can help young people with autism to thrive in school and achieve their aspirations. When we think that, just 50 years ago, children with autism were labelled uneducable, this is progress indeed.

The National Autistic Society runs specialist schools in the UK for children and young people with autism. To find out more see page 48 or contact us on:

Tel. 0117 974 8430

Email: naseducationgroup@nas.org.uk or visit our website: www.autism.org.uk/eduationgroup

The National Autistic Society is the UK's leading charity for people affected by autism. We were founded in 1962, by a group of parents who were passionate about ensuring a better future for their children. Today we have over 18,000 members, 80 branches and provide a wide range of advice, information, support and specialist services to 100,000 people each year. A local charity with a national presence, we campaign and lobby for lasting positive change for people affected by autism.

Adapting the curriculum for young people with sight loss and complex needs

Sharon Macleod, Qualified Teacher of the Visually Impaired (QTVI), and Emily Hayes, Deputy Head Teacher of the Royal National Institute of Blind People (RNIB) Pears Centre for Specialist Learning, explain the centre's ongoing work

Here at RNIB Pears Centre for Specialist Learning, we support children and young people (up to the age of 19) who have multiple disabilities, complex health needs as well as sight loss, for example learning disabilities, autism, physical disabilities and communication difficulties. We consider literacy in its broadest sense: we look at the potential of our young people, their targets and also what they will need as they move into adulthood. This can encompass a range of considerations, from those young people for whom an ability to intentionally communicate their basic needs and wishes is the objective, through to those for whom a lifelong aspiration is to be an independent reader. At all levels, the use of literacy to enhance the ability of our young people to communicate and be active participants in their own decision making is essential.

It is easy in the current educational climate to establish a reactive curriculum that ticks all of the boxes, but doesn't actually work in practice to guarantee students make good or better progress. Throughout any school's curriculum it is vital to provide opportunities for young people to engage in activities and opportunities to enhance their literacy skills and to enable them to read. In addition to this, a focus within your curriculum specifically on literacy can support student progress, if it is done in a considered way that reflects the needs of young people.

We adapt our literacy curriculum to make it meaningful for our young people and this provides opportunities for personalisation. This is especially the case in reading lessons. At times this means that classes are grouped according to their level of understanding and communication. We have three main reading groups in key stage 4 and the sixth form, which are:

1. Sensory Stories group

2. Interactive Reading group

3. Supported Reading group

Sensory Stories group

The Sensory Stories group are largely pre-verbal students for whom reading is a challenge. However, by grouping the students together, we can deliver the reading curriculum through the whole sensory experience: tactile, auditory, olfactory, gustatory or visual stimuli wherever possible. Through this they can not only experience reading, but also start to explore their likes and dislikes and display emergent responses. In terms of technology, this group may also use Big Mac switches and 4talk4 switches (such as those from Inclusive Technology).

We consider literacy in its broadest sense: we look at the potential of our young people, their targets and also what they will need as they move into adulthood

Interactive Reading group

The Interactive Reading group includes both pre-verbal students and those students who may vocalise, but not verbalise coherently. There is some overlap with the sensory aspects of the group above. These students are encouraged to interact with reading activities, either by page turning, selecting an audiobook track or touchpad, and selecting objects that represent the key features of the story. During these lessons, there is also a critical focus on turn-taking and wider social skills that can be explored through reading activities. These students may never read entirely without support, but will be able to eventually participate actively in reading.

Supported Reading group

Our Supported Reading group is made up of students where some form of independent reading in adulthood is an aspiration and within their potential. We are always looking at new ways of helping our students to realise this potential. The introduction of various technologies has contributed massively to the development of independence in our young people in many areas of school life.

This group is benefitting from using 'Clear Reader' and 'Clear Reader+' from Optelec, which not only acts as a 2D full colour magnifier with high definition, but can also take a photo of text and read it back to a young person. We have also recently started working with Apple iPads and are not only using Apps, but

also basic voice recording software that can be used to record audio stories in familiar voices. Additionally, we use RNIB's 'PenFriend' which supports independence by allowing the reader to scan labels on the pages and listen to the text being read, with very little support. The 'PenFriend' can also be used to re-record stories in a more familiar voice for students who display any noise hyposensitivity.

Impact on pupil progress

When we thought about meeting the challenge of a meaningful literacy curriculum for our young people, we thought about the outcomes they required. We will of course review our literacy policy regularly, but so far this method of working is paying real dividends. Pupils are not only making progress across their 'academic' literacy targets, but also in their wider communication targets and social skills.

Get in touch

For further information please do not hesitate to contact us:

- Call 024 7636 9500

- Email pearscentre@rnib.org.uk

- Visit rnib.org.uk/pearscentre

See also page 62 for more information about the RNIB Pears Centre for Specialist Learning

Choosing a special needs school

Educational psychologoist and author Ruth Birnbaum offers practical advice on seeking effective education for children with special educational needs

No-one is prepared for having a special needs child and developmental difficulties know no boundaries. Whilst parents may be given a list of schools they are still left in a quandary about whether a school is appropriate and suitable for their individual child. In writing my book, *Choosing a School for a Child with Special Needs*, I hoped to demystify the process and empower parents to ask questions of schools which they visit, so that a more balanced view can be reached and an objective decision can be made. Parents need to work together with schools and other professionals to decide what their child needs and how their strengths can be realised in a school context. While parents live with their child every day and have much to offer, they also have to listen to advice. Weighing up what really matters is possible and choices can be made on the best evidence available. Choosing a school is such an important decision that it cannot be left to chance.

What kind of information is needed? Here are some helpful pointers:

1. Look at the primary area of need

Is it communication and interaction? Cognition and learning? Behavioural, emotional and social Development? Sensory and physical? Medical or complex needs?

2. Understand the background

Understand the role of psychological assessment and draw up a list of schools which state they can meet the assessed need and then obtain the documents that will help you restrict your list to those schools that need to be visited.

3. Set up a visit

Make sure a visit is set up with the right people; look at the general physical school environment, as well as the classroom environment. Make a record of the school visit.

4. Look at specific provision/intervention

Consider the type of provision in both mainstream and special schools. Probe and analyse what is available in reality and the professional support the child will receive. What are the qualifications which are needed? What type of intervention could be available? Does the school offer help with specific learning difficulties/sensory needs/autistic provision; are different therapies available *eg* art therapy; music therapy; drama therapy; play therapy or psychotherapy? Does the school offer counselling and mentoring? Can the child access speech and language therapy, occupational therapy and physiotherapy?

5. Consider other important issues

Levels of integration and inclusion; Religious beliefs; co-education; school size; small classes; transition; equality and discrimination. In all cases, there will be practical questions to ask.

6. Think about other school models available

There can be a range of different school models to consider, depending on the need; such as mainstream, special units in mainstream, special schools, dual-placements, pupil referral units, residential schools, home education, hospital schools, studio schools and virtual schools.

7. Summarise your thoughts

Evaluate findings on a spreadsheet with your own comments and compare school visits. Trust your first impressions and feelings but be open to other views. Use websites, resources and organisations in the area you are researching.

Perhaps, a few selective questions from my book will offer some examples:

- A key question, when looking at special schools, is to determine whether all teachers share the specialism, or only some of them; *eg.* if a child is placed in a specialist dyslexic school, will the child receive lessons in history and geography at secondary level from specialist teachers in their subject area, who have also undertaken SpLD training? If not, one must consider whether the value of attending such a school outweighs a mainstream experience.

- What happens to the class work that the child misses when they are in the special unit? How do they catch up or will they be following the same curriculum in the unit? If the unit has a number of different aged children, are lessons taught across the age ranges in the unit or will children be taught separately?

- Is the occupational therapist trained or certified in the use of any standardised diagnostic tools that are used to assess children who might have sensory processing disorder?

- How often is the speech and language therapist (SaLT) in school? Is the focus on individual or group therapy? Does the SaLT spend time in the classroom? How much time?

- In a special school, how many staff have a recognised qualification in the area of need? *eg.* ASD.

- Is there any special equipment already being used in specific subjects; such as food technology, maths, science, PE, *etc*?

- In the classroom, note the class sizes and the physical space. Is there room for additional resources; *eg.* a work station or wheelchair? Note the organisation and the way in which lessons start and finish. Are the goals and objectives of the lessons clearly set out in a visual format and do the children understand them? Are different strategies used for children who cannot access the usual format?

For parents, who are thinking about choosing a school for a child with special needs, it is possible to have confidence with knowledge. By making a decision, based on factual evidence where possible, a parent should be able to accept or reject a school on the basis of impartial evaluation. Using the combination of this guidebook and *Choosing a School for a Child with Special Needs*, parents will be able to make an informed choice and act as advocates for their children who may not be able to speak for themselves.

We only have one opportunity at education and we need to make sure nothing is overlooked.

Ruth Birnbaum (2010) Choosing a School for a Child with Special Needs (Jessica Kingsley – ISBN No: 978-1-84310-987-7)

Ruth Birnbaum is a Chartered Educational Psychologist in independent practice with 30 years experience in education. She visits schools across the UK to consider provision and advise parents and legal consultants on which schools are most appropriate for which children.

Statementing and the Special Educational Needs and Disability Tribunal

Katie Emsley, Chartered Legal Executive, examines the legal aspects

Statementing is the process by which Local Authorities (LAs) assess and provide for children with Special Educational Needs (SEN). The statutory framework in England is contained primarily within the Education Act 1996 (Part IV and Schedules 26 and 27) and the Special Educational Needs and Disability Act 2001. In addition, there are Regulations, most notably the Education (Special Educational Needs) (England) (Consolidation) Regulations 2001. A Special Educational Needs Code of Practice, published in 2001, to which LAs and schools must have regard, provides an overview of SEN.

A Green Paper on SEN was published by the Government in March 2011 proposing changes to the current SEN system and framework. Draft Legislation was subsequently published in September 2012, setting out in detail the proposed provisions. In February 2013 amended provisions were included in the Children and Families Bill 2013 which is now subject to the parliamentary process. The Bill covers a range of areas affecting children, young people and families and sets out proposed new law and proposed changes to current legislation. In the case of SEN, the proposed changes include extending the SEN system from birth to 25 years, replacing Statements and Statutory Assessments (explained below) with a new Education, Health and Care Plan, extending protection to young people in further education and training and offering families personal budgets. Some of the main proposed provisions have been tested by 31 Local Authorities and funding for these 'pathfinders' has now been extended to September 2014. How the proposed provisions may work in practice is not explored here. However, it is of note that the Government states in its response to pre-legislative scrutiny of its SEN proposals that 'existing protections and rights for parents will be protected within the new system' and that parents' statutory right of appeal against decisions made about their child's SEN will remain in place. It is anticipated that changes will come into effect from September 2014 at the earliest, following new legislation. Until then, the current statutory framework remains in place and this is explored below.

Statementing begins with a Statutory Assessment of a child's needs by their LA and, where deemed appropriate, leads to the issue of a Final Statement of Special Educational Needs (a Statement). The needs of the majority of children with SEN are provided for in school without a Statement.

A parent or a child's school can ask the LA to undertake a Statutory Assessment if no such Assessment has been made within the previous six months. The LA should comply with such a request, or undertake the Assessment of its own volition, if the child has special educational needs and it is necessary for the LA to determine the special educational provision which any learning difficulty the child may have calls for.

The LA must make a decision as to whether to undertake a Statutory Assessment within six weeks of receiving a request from a parent or school. In order to undertake a Statutory Assessment, the LA is required to seek advice from the child's parents and school, a registered medical practitioner, an educational psychologist and Social Services. The LA has 10 weeks to gather this advice and complete the Assessment and a further two weeks to issue a draft of the Statement (known as a Proposed Statement) or to notify the child's parents that it will not issue a Statement.

A Statement must follow a prescribed format:

Part 1: Basic information about the child, including name and date of birth.

Part 2: A description of the child's special educational needs.

Part 3: The special educational provision to meet the needs set out in Part 2.

Part 4: The type of school or specific school where the provision will be delivered.

Part 5: A description of the child's non-educational needs.

Part 6: The non-educational provision which may be made available (the LA is under no obligation to deliver this provision).

When sending a copy of the Proposed Statement, the LA must notify parents of their right to request a meeting with the LA and to make representations about the contents of Parts 2 and 3. Parents can also express a preference for a maintained (*ie* state) school (which can be a mainstream or a special school) or make representations for any other school (*eg* a non-maintained or independent school). Part 4 of the Proposed Statement will therefore be left blank. A LA is only required to have regard to a parental request for a non-maintained or independent school in so far as that is compatible with the efficient education of the child and in so far as it avoids unreasonable public expenditure. However, the LA must name a school which is appropriate for the child and which can deliver the provision required and it may be that that cannot be achieved within the maintained sector.

A Final Statement should be issued within eight weeks of the Proposed Statement and will specify, in Part 4, the school where the provision will be delivered. The LA has a statutory duty to arrange the provision specified in the Final Statement, unless the child's parents are making their own suitable arrangements.

The statementing process, from the date of a request for a Statutory Assessment to the issue of a Final Statement should take 26 weeks in total. An Annual Review of the Statement must be carried out each year.

Disputes between parents and LAs may arise at any stage of the statementing process and, as a result, obtaining a satisfactorily worded Statement can take significantly longer than 26 weeks. A LA may decide that it is not necessary to undertake a Statutory Assessment or decide not to issue a Statement. Parents have a statutory right of appeal against a decision made by a LA when it:

a) refuses to undertake a Statutory Assessment or a further Statutory Assessment.

b) decides not to issue a Statement.

c) refuses a parental request to change the school named if the Statement is at least one year old (this right of appeal only applies to maintained schools and where the parents' preferred school is the same type of school currently named).

d) issues a Final Statement or issues an amended Final Statement.

e) decides not to amend a Statement having carried out a further Statutory Assessment.

f) decides not to amend a Statement following an Annual Review.

g) decides to cease to maintain a Statement.

Appeals are heard by the Special Educational Needs and Disability Tribunal (the SEND Tribunal). Appeals must be lodged with the Tribunal within two months of the date of the LA's decision letter. Parents are required to provide sufficient grounds of appeal, setting out their case, and robust, comprehensive and up to date evidence to support their position should be obtained and served in accordance with the Tribunal directions. Appeals are usually listed for hearing 20 weeks following registration of the appeal and are heard by a panel of three; a Tribunal judge and two specialist lay members. The Tribunal will consider the written and oral evidence submitted by both parties to the appeal and make its determination. It can draw on its own expertise when reaching a decision and will usually issue a written decision within two weeks of the hearing.

Where a LA has refused to undertake a Statutory Assessment the Tribunal can either dismiss the appeal or order the LA to undertake the Statutory Assessment. Where a LA has decided not to issue a Statement, the SEND Tribunal can dismiss the appeal, order the LA to issue a Statement (it cannot order what that statement should say at this point) or order the LA to reconsider its position.

In the case of points d) – g) above, a parent will have a right of appeal against the description of their child's needs, the provision specified to meet those needs and the named school. The Tribunal can dismiss the appeal, order the LA to make changes to Parts 2, 3 and/or 4 or order the LA to cease to maintain the Statement.

Provision in Part 3 should normally be quantified (in terms of hours and staff) and be specific and clear so as to leave no room for doubt as to what is to be delivered. The provision of speech and language therapy, occupational therapy and physiotherapy is often a significant area of dispute. LAs often determine that such input is non-educational and will only specify it in Part 6 of a Statement, if at all. This removes any statutory duty from the LA to deliver the provision to the child and in many cases it should be specified as an educational need in Part 3. It is generally necessary to successfully challenge Parts 2 and 3 of a Statement in order to secure a change to the school named in Part 4. There is continuing emphasis in SEN law that children should be educated primarily within mainstream schools, particularly when this is the wish of parents. However, for those children with the most severe and complex needs, placement within the special school sector (including the independent special school sector) may be required.

Katie Emsley is a Chartered Legal Executive at Langley Wellington LLP
Solicitors which has an Education Department experienced in dealing
with all aspects of education and SEN law

PROFILES

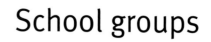

School groups

3 The Boulevard, Ascot Road
Watford WD18 8AG
Tel: 0300 123 2112

Email: ask.us@actionforchildren.org.uk
Website: www.actionforchildren.org.uk

Action for Children Headlands School

2 St Augustine's Road, Penarth, Vale of Glamorgan
CF64 1YY
Tel: 02920 709771
Fax: 02920 700515
Email: headlands.school@actionforchildren.org.uk
Website: www.actionforchildren.org.uk/headlands
Principal: Matthew Burns

*For full details about Action for Children Headlands
School see page 110*

Action for Children Parklands Campus

Action for Children Parklands Campus, Near
Appleton, Abingdon, Oxfordshire OX13 5QB
Tel: 01865 390436
Email: parklands.campus@actionforchildren.org.uk
Website: www.actionforchildren.org.uk/parklands
Principal: Raymond Wilson

*For full details about Action for Children Parklands
Campus see page 93*

Action for Children Penhurst School

New Street, Chipping Norton, Oxfordshire OX7 5LN
Tel: 01608 642559
Fax: 01608 647029
Email: penhurst.school@actionforchildren.org.uk
Website: www.actionforchildren.org.uk/schools
Principal: Derek Lyseight-Jones

Central Services, Hesley Hall, Tickhill
Doncaster DN11 9NH
Tel: 01302 866906
Fax: 01302 861661
Email: enquiries@hesleygroup.co.uk
Website: www.hesleygroup.co.uk

Community Solutions
49 King Street

Thorne, Doncaster, South Yorkshire DN8 5AU
Tel: 01405 818580
Fax: 01405 743110
Email: enquiries@hesleygroup.co.uk
Website: www.hesleygroup.co.uk
Registered Care Manager: Eileen Champion

Hesley Village

Tickhill, Doncaster, South Yorkshire DN11 9HH
Tel: 01302 866906
Fax: 01302 965473
Email: enquiries@hesleygroup.co.uk
Website: www.hesleygroup.co.uk
Principal: David O'Connor

Low Laithes Village

Old Farm Lane, Wombwell, Barnsley, South
Yorkshire S73 8SU
Tel: 01226 272050
Fax: 01226 272068
Email: enquiries@hesleygroup.co.uk
Website: www.hesleygroup.co.uk
General Manager: David Little

Fullerton House School

Tickill Square, Denaby, Doncaster, South Yorkshire
DN12 4AR
Tel: 01709 861663
Fax: 01709 869635
Email: enquiries@hesleygroup.co.uk
Website: www.fullertonhouseschool.co.uk
Head: David Whitehead

*For full details about Fullerton House School see page
108*

Wilsic Hall School

Wadworth, Doncaster, South Yorkshire DN11 9AG
Tel: 01302 856382
Fax: 01302 853608
Email: enquiries@hesleygroup.co.uk
Website: www.wilsichallschool.co.uk
Head: Geoff Turner

For full details about Wilsic Hall School see page 109

helps children
communicate
REGISTERED CHARITY 210031

8 Wakley Street
London EC1V 7QE
Tel: 0845 225 4073
Fax: 0845 225 4072

Website: www.ican.org.uk

I CAN'S Dawn House School

Helmsley Road, Rainworth, Mansfield,
Nottinghamshire NG21 0DQ
Tel: 01623 795361
Fax: 01623 491173
Email: dawnhouse@ican.org.uk
Website: www.dawnhouseschool.org.uk or
www.ican.org.uk
Principal: Angela Child

For full details about I CAN'S Dawn House School see page 96

I CAN's Meath School

Brox Road, Ottershaw, Surrey KT16 0LF
Tel: 01932 872302
Fax: 01932 875180
Email: meath@meath-ican.org.uk
Website: www.meathschool.org.uk or
www.ican.org.uk
Headteacher: Janet Dunn OBE, MA,
AdvDipSpecEduc

For full details about I CAN's Meath School see page 102

Fourth Floor, 43-45 Dorset Street
London W1U 7NA
Tel: 020 3434 1090
Fax: 020 7160 5375

Website: www.kedlestonuk.com

Arc School

Church End, Ansley, Nuneaton, Warwickshire CV10 0QR
Tel: 024 7639 4801
Headmistress: Pauline Garret

Donyland Lodge School

Fingringhoe Road, Rowhedge, Colchester, Essex CO5 7JL
Tel: 01206 728869
Email: admin@donyland.org.uk
Website: www.donyland.org.uk
Director: Lesley Woodhouse

Leaways School London

Theydon Road, Clapton, London, London E5 9NZ
Tel: 020 8815 4030
Email: info@leawaysschool.co.uk
Website: www.leawaysschool.co.uk
Headmaster: Richard Gadd

Shapwick Prep

Mark Road, Burtle, Bridgwater, Somerset TA7 8NJ
Tel: 01278 722012
Fax: 01278 723312
Email: prep@shapwickschool.com
Website: www.shapwickschool.com
Joint Headmasters: D C Walker BA(Hons) & J P Whittock CertEd

Wings School, Cumbria

Whassett, Milnthorpe, Cumbria LA7 7DN
Tel: 01539 562006
Fax: 01539 564811
Email: info@wingsschool.co.uk
Website: www.wingsschool.co.uk
Director of Education & Care: Mrs Pam Redican

For full details about Wings School, Cumbria see page 122

Wings School, Nottinghamshire

Kirklington Hall, Kirklington, Newark, Nottinghamshire NG22 8NB
Tel: 01636 817430
Fax: 01636 817435
Email: info@wingsnottsschool.co.uk
Website: www.wingsschool.co.uk
Director of Education & Care: Mrs Pam Redican

For full details about Wings School, Nottinghamshire see page 121

The Old Vicarage, Swinderby
Lincoln LN6 9LU
Tel: 01522 868279
Fax: 01522 866000

Website: www.kisimul.co.uk

Cruckton Hall

Cruckton, Shrewsbury, Shropshire SY5 8PR
Tel: 01743 860206
Fax: 01743 860941
Email: pdm@cruckton.com
Website: www.cruckton.com
Head Teacher: P D Mayhew

For full details about Cruckton Hall see page 84

Kisimul School

The Old Vicarage, 61 High Street, Swinderby,
Lincoln, Lincolnshire LN6 9LU
Tel: 01522 868279
Fax: 01522 866000
Email: admissions@kisimul.co.uk
Website: www.kisimul.co.uk
Director of Education: Mr Danny Carter BA(Hons),
MA, MEd

For full details about Kisimul School see page 98

Kisimul School – Woodstock House

Woodstock Lane North, Long Ditton, Surbiton,
Surrey KT6 5HN
Tel: 020 8335 2570
Fax: 020 8335 2571
Email: admissions@kisimul.co.uk
Website: www.kisimul.co.uk
Director of Education: Mr Danny Carter BA(Hons),
MA, MEd

For full details about Kisimul School – Woodstock House see page 104

Kisimul Upper School

Acacia Hall, Shortwood Lane, Friesthorpe, Lincoln,
Lincolnshire LN3 5AL
Tel: 01673 880022
Fax: 01673 880021
Website: www.kisimul.co.uk

393 City Road
London EC1V 1NG
Tel: 020 7833 2299
Fax: 020 7833 9666
Email: nas@nas.org.uk
Website: www.nas.org.uk

NAS Anderson School

Rookery Lane, Pilning, Bristol, Bristol BS35 4JN
Tel: 01454 632532
Fax: 01454 634907
Email: nasanderson@nas.org.uk
Website: www.autism.org.uk/andersonschool
Head of Education: Simon Cartwright

For full details about NAS Anderson School see page 73

NAS Broomhayes School & Children's Centre

Kingsley House, Alverdiscott Road, Bideford,
Devon EX39 4PL
Tel: 01237 473830
Fax: 01237 421097
Email: broomhayes@nas.org.uk
Website: www.autism.org.uk/broomhayes
Principal: Ben Higgins

NAS Daldorch House School

Sorn Road, Catrine, East Ayrshire KA5 6NA
Tel: 01290 551666
Fax: 01290 553399
Email: daldorch@nas.org.uk
Website: www.autism.org.uk/daldorch
Principal: Shona Pinkerton DCE, DPSE(SEN),
MEdSEN

For full details about NAS Daldorch House School see page 88

NAS Daldorch Satellite School

St Leonards, East Kilbride, South Lanarkshire G74
Tel: 01355 246242
Fax: 01290 553399
Email: daldorch@nas.org.uk
Website: www.autism.org.uk/daldorch
Principal: Shona Pinkerton

For full details about NAS Daldorch Satellite School see page 89

NAS Helen Allison School

Longfield Road, Meopham, Kent DA13 0EW
Tel: 01474 814878
Fax: 01474 812033
Email: helen.allison@nas.org.uk
Website: www.autism.org.uk/helenallison
Executive Principal: Dr Jacqui Ashton Smith

For full details about NAS Helen Allison School see page 81

NAS Radlett Lodge School

Harper Lane, Radlett, Hertfordshire WD7 9HW
Tel: 01923 854922
Fax: 01923 859922
Email: radlett.lodge@nas.org.uk
Website: www.autism.org.uk/radlett
Principal: Jo Galloway

For full details about NAS Radlett Lodge School see page 76

NAS Robert Ogden School

Clayton Lane, Thurnscoe, Rotherham, South
Yorkshire S63 0BG
Tel: 01709 874443
Fax: 01709 870701
Email: robert.ogden@nas.org.uk
Website: www.autism.org.uk/robertogden
Executive Principal: Dr Jacqui Ashton-Smith

*For full details about NAS Robert Ogden School see
page 87*

NAS Sybil Elgar School

Havelock Road, Southall, Middlesex UB2 4NR
Tel: 020 8813 9168
Fax: 020 8571 7332
Email: sybil.elgar@nas.org.uk
Website: www.autism.org.uk/sybilelgar
Principal: Chloe Phillips

*For full details about NAS Sybil Elgar School see page
78*

NAS Thames Valley Free School

Conwy Close, Tilehurst, Reading, Reading RG30
4BZ
Tel: 0117 9748 430
Email: naseducationgroup@nas.org.uk
Website: www.thamesvalleyfreeschool.co.uk
Principal Designate: Fiona Veitch

*For full details about NAS Thames Valley Free School
see page 82*

Options Group
making a difference

Turnpike Gate House, Alcester Heath
Alcester B49 5JG
Tel: 01789 767800
Fax: 01789 767801
Email: info@optionsgroup.co.uk
Website: www.optionsgroup.co.uk

AALPS Cymru

Llanerach-y-mor, Holywell, Flintshire CH8 9DX
Tel: 01745 562570
Email: info@aalpscymru.co.uk
Website: www.optionsgroup.co.uk
Registered Manager: Shian Thomas

AALPS Midlands

The Rhydd, Hanley Castle, Worcestershire WR8 0AD
Tel: 01684 312 610
Email: info@aalpsmids.co.uk
Website: www.optionsgroup.co.uk
Registered Manager: Darren Goodwin

AALPS North

Winterton Road, Roxby, Scunthorpe, North
Lincolnshire DN15 0BJ
Tel: 01724 733777
Fax: 01724 733666
Email: info@aalpsnorth.co.uk
Website: www.optionsgroup.co.uk
Centre Head: Mr Russell Leese

Barton School

Barrow Road, Barton-upon-Humber, Lincolnshire
DN18 6DA
Tel: 01652 631280
Fax: 01652 637419
Email: info@bartonschool.co.uk
Website: www.optionsgroup.co.uk
Headteacher: Mark Eames

For full details about Barton School see page 86

Higford School

Higford Hall, Higford, Shifnal, Shropshire TF11 9ET
Tel: 01952 630600
Fax: 01952 630605
Email: info@higfordschool.co.uk
Website: www.optionsgroup.co.uk
Headteacher: Anne Adams

For full details about Higford School see page 83

Kinsale School

Kinsale Hall, Llanerch-y-Mor, Holywell, Flintshire
CH8 9DX
Tel: 01745 562500
Fax: 01745 562501
Email: info@kinsaleschool.co.uk
Website: www.optionsgroup.co.uk
Headteacher: Emma Keyworth

For full details about Kinsale School see page 90

Young Options College

Lamledge Lane, Shifnal, Shropshire TF11 8SD
Tel: 01952 468220
Fax: 01952 468221
Email: info@youngoptions.co.uk
Website: www.optionsgroup.co.uk
Headteacher: Louise De-Hayes

For full details about Young Options College see page 127

Young Options Pathway College Stoke

Phoenix House, Marlborough Road, Longton, Stoke-on-Trent, Stoke-on-Trent ST3 1EJ
Tel: 01782 377270
Fax: 01782 313667
Email: info@pathwaystoke.co.uk
Website: www.optionsgroup.co.uk
Headteacher: Mel Callaghan

For full details about Young Options Pathway College Stoke see page 128

105 Judd Street
London WC1H 9NE

Website: www.rnib.org.uk

RNIB College Loughborough

Radmoor Road, Loughborough, Leicestershire LE11 3BS
Tel: 01509 611077
Fax: 01509 232013
Email: enquiries@rnibcollege.ac.uk
Website: www.rnibcollege.ac.uk
Principal: Tony Warren MA(Cantab), MBA, PGCE

RNIB Pears Centre for Specialist Learning

Wheelwright Lane, Ash Green, Coventry, West Midlands CV7 9RA
Tel: 024 7636 9500
Fax: 024 7636 9501
Email: pearscentre@rnib.org.uk
Website: www.rnib.org.uk/pearscentre
Head of Education: Andy Moran

For full details about RNIB Pears Centre for Specialist Learning see page 62

RNIB Sunshine House School and Children's Home

33 Dene Road, Northwood, Middlesex HA6 2DD
Tel: 01923 822538
Fax: 01923 826227
Email: shsadmin@rnib.org.uk
Website: www.rnib.org.uk/sunshinehouse
Head: John Ayres

For full details about RNIB Sunshine House School and Children's Home see page 58

Old Bristol Road, Nailsworth
Stroud GL6 0LA
Tel: 01453 837 521
Fax: 01453 837 621

Website: www.rmt.org

Brantwood Specialist School

1 Kenwood Bank, Nether Edge, Sheffield, South
Yorkshire S7 1NU
Tel: 0114 258 9062
Email: admin@brantwood.rmt.org
Website: www.rmt.org
Headteacher: Constantin Court

*For full details about Brantwood Specialist School see
page 129*

Clervaux Trust

Clow Beck Eco Centre, Jolby Lane, Croft on Tees,
North Yorkshire DL2 2TF
Tel: 01325 729860
Email: info@clervaux.org.uk
Website: www.clervaux.org.uk
Executive Director: Cate McQueen

Freeman College

Sterling Works, 88 Arundel Street, Sheffield, South
Yorkshire S1 2NG
Tel: 0114 252 5940
Fax: 0114 252 5996
Email: enquiries@fmc.rmt.org
Website: www.rmt.org
Principal: Bonny Etchell-Anderson

For full details about Freeman College see page 117

Glasshouse College

Wollaston Road, Amblecote, Stourbridge, West
Midlands DY8 4HF
Tel: 01384 399400
Fax: 01384 399401
Email: enquiries@ghc.rmt.org
Website: www.rmt.org
Principal: Ollie Cheney

For full details about Glasshouse College see page 116

Plas Dwbl Farm College

Mynachlog-ddu, Clunderwen, Pembrokeshire SA66
7SE
Tel: 01449 419420
Email: info@plasdwbl.rmt.org
Website: www.rmt.org
Principal: Elisabeth Johnson

*For full details about Plas Dwbl Farm College see page
111*

Ruskin Mill College

The Fisheries, Horsley, Gloucestershire GL6 0PL
Tel: 01453 837500
Fax: 01453 837506
Email: enquiries@rmc.rmt.org
Website: www.rmt.org
Principal: Elisabeth Johnson

For full details about Ruskin Mill College see page 115

School and colleges specialising in sensory or physical impairment

Royal School for the Deaf Derby

(Founded 1894)

Ashbourne Road, Derby DE22 3BH
Tel: 01332 362512   Email: principal@rsdd.org.uk
Fax: 01332 299708   Website: www.rsd-derby.org

Principal: Cheryll Ford BA, BPhil, NPQH
School type: Coeducational Day & Boarding
Age range of pupils: 3–19
No. of pupils enrolled as at 1.1.13: 140
Boys: 97 Girls: 43
Fees per annum as at 1.1.13: Day: £21,696
Boarding: £33,474

Royal School for the Deaf Derby welcomes profoundly and severely deaf young people from the United Kingdom and other countries. It values British Sign Language (BSL) and English equally and respects the cultures of deaf and hearing people. The curriculum is delivered through English and BSL and progress is rigorously monitored through formal assessment and by external examinations. The school promotes a positive sense of identity for each pupil, preparing them for the opportunities of adult life and for full participation in their local community.

The National Curriculum is followed throughout the school and is adapted to suit the needs of the individual child through personalised learning programmes. It is taught by phase or subject specialist teachers of the deaf to small class groups. Examinations offered include GCSE, DIDA and Entry Levels.

Post-16 students follow individual programmes of study at mainstream colleges with courses ranging from vocational options through to A levels and Level 3 BTEC National. They are supported by Transition Support Communicators. Key Skills, Wider Key Skills and Skills for Life, including literacy and numeracy, are delivered by teachers of the deaf at base.

Free places are offered to deaf children aged three to five in the Foundation Stage.

Residence, for weekly and part-time boarders, offers a 24-hour curriculum that includes developing life skills, managing money and, at Post-16, driving theory and lessons. The residential houses are designed to promote a feeling of belonging and security while living away from home.

Speech and language therapists support pupils individually and in small class-based groups. The school's audiologist is based in a modern well-equipped suite. Medical services are provided by an on-campus nurse and the local practice surgery.

For further information, contact Cheryll Ford or Anne Muller at the school.

Royal School for the Deaf Derby is a registered charity (no. 1062507) whose object is the education of deaf children aged 3 to 19.

RNIB Sunshine House School and Children's Home

33 Dene Road, Northwood, Middlesex HA6 2DD
Tel: 01923 822538   Email: shsadmin@rnib.org.uk
Fax: 01923 826227   Website: www.rnib.org.uk/sunshinehouse

Head: John Ayres
School type: Coeducational
Non-maintained Special School
Age range of pupils: 2–11
Fees per annum as at 1.1.13:
Enquire for details
Average size of class: 8
Teacher/pupil ratio: 2:3
From September 2014 we are increasing our age
range to 2-14.

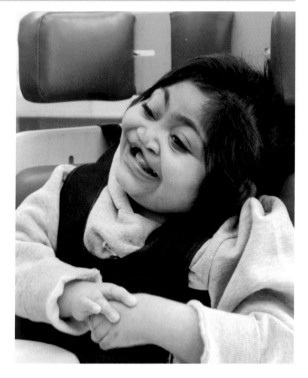

RNIB Sunshine House School and Children's Home,
in Northwood, Middlesex, is a specialist primary
school, children's home and service for families
supporting blind and partially sighted children with
significant learning difficulties and disabilities.

Boasting a range of specialist indoor and outdoor
facilities, Sunshine House provides a safe and
supportive environment for children to meet their
full potential.

Everyone at Sunshine House is treated as an
individual with their own set of needs and learning
goals. Working together with parents and specialists
we ensure that achievements go beyond the
classroom into everyday life.

Our specialist primary school educates children from
two to 11 years who have a range of physical,
learning and sensory needs. Children follow an
individually tailored curriculum supporting their
special education needs. Most children are working
between P levels 1 and 8. Each class has no more
than eight children with a minimum support ratio of
two adults for every three children.

Our team of in-house therapists combine their work
with a child's learning, making therapies a part of
everyday school life. We also have a paediatric

community nurse who visits daily to ensure that all
medical needs are met.

Our children's home offers a range of flexible day
care, overnight and short stay options, including an
after school club, play days, theme days, sleepovers
and overnight stays where children aged between two
and 14 years can stay up to four nights per week
(Monday to Thursday) for up to 50 weeks per year
during the school term and holidays. We welcome
children who attend school elsewhere, providing we
can meet their needs.

Find out more online at rnib.org.uk/sunshinehouse or
call 01923 82 25 38.

Chailey Heritage School

(Founded 1903)

Haywards Heath Road, North Chailey, Lewes, East Sussex BN8 4EF
Tel: 01825 724444   Email: schooloffice@chs.org.uk
Fax: 01825 723773   Website: www.chs.org.uk

Principal: Sylvia Lamb
Headteacher: Simon Yates
Director of Social Care: Denise Banks
School type: Coeducational Boarding & Day
& Children's Home
Age range of pupils: 3–19
plus Futures@Chailey Heritage for young adults
aged 19-25
No. of pupils enrolled as at 1.1.13: 73
Fees per annum as at 1.1.13:
Please contact the school for details

Chailey Heritage School is a non-maintained special school for children and young people aged 3 to 19 with a wide range of complex physical, communication, sensory and learning difficulties and health needs.

The school is a registered children's home and offers flexible care packages for up to 52 weeks of the year. Chailey Heritage School was judged to be outstanding by Ofsted in September 2009.

Flexible residential care

There are six purpose-built residential bungalows designed for pupils who require residential provision in order to attend school. Each bungalow has specialist equipment and can accommodate pupils for short break and flexible care packages of up to 52 weeks boarding.

The bungalows are led by a registered children's home manager supported by residential team managers who lead and manage highly trained staff providing 24-hour care together with NHS nurses.

On site clinical services

Chailey Heritage School shares its location with Chailey Heritage Clinical Services (CHCS) – a specialist clinical team and part of the Sussex Community NHS Trust. Pupils' clinical needs are overseen by specialists in paediatric conditions, neurological problems and long-term disabilities. Therapists from CHCS make up part of the school's multidisciplinary team, which offers a unique

combination of education, residential, therapy and health services on a single site.

Education

The school offers a broad and balanced curriculum adapted to each pupil according to age and ability. This is alongside integrated therapy from a highly skilled team that includes expert teachers, paediatric medical consultants, speech and language therapists, physiotherapists, occupational therapists, nurses and rehabilitation engineers. This holistic approach ensures that learning programmes can be designed to suit each individual.

The school is divided into three departments: Pre-School/Primary Department (PSP) for nursery age children up to 11 years old; Secondary Department (11-16 years); 16+ Department for students up to 19 years old. For some pupils the school can set up and support dual placements with pupils' local mainstream schools.

Transition

Futures@Chailey Heritage is an exciting new transition provision for young adults with physical disabilities, aged 19-25. For more information visit www.futureschailey.org.uk

Chailey Heritage School and Futures@Chailey Heritage are part of Chailey Heritage Foundation. Registered Charity Number 1075837. Registered in England as a Charitable Company limited by Guarantee No. 3769775

The School for Profound Education (formerly St Margaret's School)
Non-Maintained Special School

(Founded 1985)

The School
for Profound Education
education, care & therapy for learners with pmld

formerly St Margaret's School, Tadworth

The Children's Trust, Tadworth, Surrey KT20 5RU
Tel: 01737 365810   Email: profoundeducation@thechildrenstrust.org.uk
Fax: 01737 365819   Website: www.thechildrenstrust.org.uk/profoundeducation

Head: Mrs Sylvia Kerambrum
School type: Coeducational Boarding
Residential up to 52 weeks and day places.
Profound and multiple learning difficulties.
Physical disabilities, sensory impairments and
complex medical or care needs.
Member of: NASS
Age range of pupils: 5–25
No. of pupils enrolled as at 1.1.13:
Boys: 25 Girls: 17
Fees per annum as at 1.1.13:
On application

The School for Profound Education (formerly known
as St Margaret's School) is one of the few special
schools in the UK that works exclusively with
learners with profound and multiple learning
difficulties (PMLD) and complex health needs. The
school is a non-maintained residential special school
that provides education, care and therapy in a safe,
caring and happy environment in which each
learner's needs can be met. The school has its own
doctor and small team of nurses, and provides 24-
hour medical cover. The school has developed
particular expertise in catering for learners with Rett
syndrome and acquired brain injury.

Curriculum

All learners use The Profound Education Curriculum,
which has been specially developed by the school. It
is a broad, balanced curriculum designed to be
relevant to individual needs, delivered to a 24-hour
model. The curriculum emphasises sensory awareness,
the importance of developing precursors to learning,
intentional communication and interactions. It has a
holistic approach, integrating all therapy procedures.
Since its publication The Profound Education
Curriculum has been adopted by dozens of special
schools across the UK and internationally.

Residential provision has now been extended to
young adults aged 19 to 25 at The College for
Profound Education, where learners continue to use
the curriculum as part of their chosen courses and
age-appropriate activities.

Both the school and college can offer residential
placements of up to 52 weeks a year.

*The school is part of The Children's Trust, a national
charity that provides education, care and therapy to
children with multiple disabilities and rehabilitation to
children and young people with acquired brain injury.
Charity no. 288018.*

WESC Foundation – The Specialist School for Visual Impairment
for young people with little or no sight
(Founded 1838)

Countess Wear, Exeter, Devon EX2 6HA
Tel: 01392 454200   Email: info@wescfoundation.ac.uk
Fax: 01392 428048   Website: www.wescfoundation.ac.uk

Chief Executive: Mrs Tracy de Bernhardt-Dunkin
School type: Non-maintained Special School and College
Day and boarders
Member of: NATSPEC
Age range of pupils: 5–16
Fees per annum as at 1.1.13:
On request

WESC Foundation specialises in meeting the needs of young people with visual impairment, including many with complex needs. The school offers an excellent academic curriculum that follows the National Curriculum syllabus ranging from P scales to GCSE. Each pupil receives mobility and therapy sessions where a need has been identified (occupational therapy, physiotherapy, speech and language therapy, music therapy). Specialist ICT equipment and adapted access technology is tailored for each pupil.

The school residences offer homely, comfortable accommodation for weekly boarders and those wishing to stay occasionally. Accommodation comprises comfortable bedrooms and areas for socialising with friends and visitors. Groundfloor areas are wheelchair accessible and suitable adaptations are made for individuals.

Our 14-acre campus provides space for pupils to enjoy the sensory garden, swimming pool, gym and library and adapted playing areas. Situated on the outskirts of Exeter – city in the country by the sea – the campus offers radial access to a huge range of activities and experiences. Extended curricular activities include trips to the beach, park, ten pin bowling and even residential trips abroad.

Pupils are totally involved in planning for their future with many of them continuing their studies and development at our college, which is situated on the same campus.

Candidates for both the school and college need to come for an assessment. This is free and is usually held over a period of two days. The assessment process is an opportunity for you to take an in-depth look at what we have to offer and allows our specialist staff to determine how best to meet a young person's needs. Please call or email for more information on assessment and admissions quoting WHM/01/13.

Registered charity no. 1058937

RNIB Pears Centre for Specialist Learning
(Formerly RNIB Rushton School and Children's Home)
(Founded 1957)

Wheelwright Lane, Ash Green, Coventry, West Midlands CV7 9RA
Tel: 024 7636 9500   Email: pearscentre@rnib.org.uk
Fax: 024 7636 9501   Website: www.rnib.org.uk/pearscentre

Head of Education: Andy Moran
Appointed: September 2007
School type: Coeducational Boarding & Day
Age range of pupils: 4–19
No. of pupils enrolled as at 1.1.13: 20

We offer individually-tailored education, care, healthcare and therapies to young people with multiple disabilities and complex needs who are blind or partially sighted. We also support young people with high health needs who may require long-term ventilation or who have life-threatening or life-limiting conditions.

We support children and young people to maximise their potential for learning, independence and fulfilment. Both our school and children's home are graded "Outstanding" by Ofsted.

Education and curriculum

We are the only non-maintained special school in England to be awarded specialist SEN status for cognition and learning. Our broad, balanced and relevant curriculum is differentiated to meet individual needs and learning styles.

Classes are kept to a small number of usually no more than seven pupils. National Curriculum core and foundation subjects are taught and are highly personalised to the needs of each student. From the age of 14, students study AQA accredited units, which focus on life skills and vocational studies. Students also participate in the Duke of Edinburgh's Award Scheme.

Our developing outreach service called 'Periscope' provides educational advice, guidance and practical support to pupils, parents and service providers locally and nationally.

Living and leisure

Our children's home offers up to 52-week care. We also offer short breaks and respite care to children and young people from pre-school age, whether of not they attend our school. Our comfortable and homely environment is both stimulating and supportive. Each young person living with us has their own bedroom, which is made safe and personal to them.

Young people plan and choose their social and leisure activities, like pop concerts and swimming. This enhances their self-esteem and sense of identity. They also have the opportunity to go on holidays and enjoy new challenges and experiences.

Therapies and healthcare

Our in-house team offers specialist expertise including learning disabilities, physiotherapy, speech and language therapy, behaviour management and mobility/habilitation. Water and music therapies, clinical psychology and occupational therapy are also part of our provision.

New purpose-built facilities

A major redevelopment has provided a newly-built school and bungalow-style accommodation. Our fully accessible modern facilities are helping to develop and encourage independence as well as cater for individual needs.

Visit us!

We welcome visits from parents, carers, children, other family members and professionals. Call us on 024 7636 9500 or email pearscentre@rnib.org.uk.

Doncaster School for the Deaf

(Founded 1892)

Doncaster School for the Deaf

Leger Way, Doncaster, South Yorkshire DN2 6AY
Tel: 01302 386733   Email: principal@ddt-deaf.org.uk or secretary@ddt-deaf.org.uk
Fax: 01302 361808   Website: www.deaf-trust.co.uk

Executive Principal: Mr Alan W Robinson
School type: Non-maintained (Special)
Coeducational Boarding and Day
(Enrolment throughout the year. Please contact us to arrange an informal visit)
Member of: NASS
Age range of pupils: 5–19
No. of pupils enrolled as at 1.1.13: 27
Boys: 18 Girls: 9
No. of boarders: 3
Fees per annum as at 1.1.13:
Fees on request
Religious denomination: Non-denominational

We offer a broad and balanced curriculum which is accessible to all our pupils, providing smooth progression and continuity through all Key Stages.

The language and communication policy at Doncaster School for the Deaf is a pupil-centred approach, based on their method of preferred communication. We aim to meet the needs of pupils who communicate through British Sign Language (BSL) or English.

The School has a full-time Audiologist, Speech and Language Therapist, Mental Health Nurse and a team of Learning Support Assistants as well as a visiting Doctor and an on-site fully qualified Nurse.

Provision for resident pupils is in a modern comfortable house sympathetically converted to provide high standards of living accommodation.

Qualifications include GCSE, Entry Level Certificate of Achievement, ASDAN, CoPE (Certificate of Personal Effectiveness) and Signature (BSL). The school believes that the school curriculum should be broad, balanced and personalised in order to reflect the needs of each pupil and to nurture a lifelong desire to learn. In addition to curriculum subjects pupils access speech therapy, BSL lessons and Deaf Studies. Some KS4 pupils are able to access vocational courses as part of the 14-19 curriculum.

The School works in partnership with Little Learners Day Nursery and Communication Specialist College Doncaster (formerly Doncaster College for the Deaf) which share the same campus.

We have close links with parents, and regular events at the school.

The school occupies a large, pleasant site. A superb sports hall, heated indoor swimming pool and extensive playing fields. The school welcomes visitors.

St John's Catholic School for the Deaf

(Founded 1870)

Church Street, Boston Spa, Wetherby, West Yorkshire LS23 6DF
Tel: 01937 842144   Email: info@stjohns.org.uk
Fax: 01937 541471   Website: www.stjohns.org.uk

Headteacher: Mrs A Bradbury BA(Hons), MSc
School type: Coeducational Boarding & Day
Age range of pupils: 4–19
No. of pupils enrolled as at 1.1.13: 80
Fees per annum as at 1.1.13:
On application
Religious denomination: Catholic, welcoming
pupils of all denominations

St John's school for the deaf is a day and boarding school for hearing impaired pupils aged 4 to 19. In 2007 we became a specialist school for sensory and physical impairments.

St John's is an oral school where pupils are taught by specialist teachers of hearing impaired children. There is great emphasis on supporting the

development of pupils' spoken language as well as reading and writing. This approach is underpinned by our commitment to the use of technology to provide children with maximum access to speech. We have a resident audiologist, all classrooms are acoustically treated and pupils have speech therapy delivered by a team of therapists.

Some pupils have special needs in addition to deafness such as visual and physical impairments, dyslexia, dyspraxia, autism and ADHD. Most pupils arrive with linguistic levels significantly below their hearing peers but have the opportunity to study a wide range of GCSE and other nationally accredited courses. Post-16 students go on to university, further education or employment.

The primary department uses a unique approach to reading and language development, the Maternal Reflective Method. This uses the pupils' own conversations to develop a reading text and matches the child's interest level with their linguistic development, providing a bridge into literacy.

In the secondary department, there are three curricular strands to match pupils' needs. These lead to GCSE and Entry Level qualifications while pupils with complex needs are taught by teachers of hearing impaired children with additional qualifications. Pupils with unusual patterns of strengths and weaknesses study in a mixture of the three stands. Other professionals such as physiotherapists, occupational therapists and psychologists work together to provide a holistic approach to meeting pupils' needs.

Our Post-16 students attend mainstream colleges supported by our own note takers and a teacher of the deaf. Students receive additional tutorial support at school as well as continuing with speech therapy and courses in English and maths. Support in the residential setting enables pupils to develop an individual study culture and independent living skills.

A unique part of the pastoral work of the school is our link with the York team, a group of mental health professionals specialising in deafness who offer individual and family counselling and advice and training for school staff.

St John's Catholic School for the Deaf is a registered charity (No 529319) that offers an oral education to deaf pupils aged 4 to 19 years.

Colleges of further education specialising in sensory or physical impairment

WESC Foundation – The Specialist College for Visual Impairment
for young people with little or no sight

(Founded 1838)

Countess Wear, Exeter, Devon EX2 6HA
Tel: 01392 454200   Email: info@wescfoundation.ac.uk
Fax: 01392 428048   Website: www.wescfoundation.ac.uk

Principal: Mrs Tracy de Bernhardt-Dunkin
School type: Non-maintained Special School and College
Member of: NATSPEC
Age range of pupils: 16+
Fees per annum as at 1.1.13:
On request

The WESC Foundation provides a wide range of Post-16 academic and vocational courses and specialist training and support to help young people with a visual impairment make a successful transition to adult life. Many pupils from the school move directly to the college.

Tailored to the needs of the individual our courses contain employability and work experience modules and are supported by work placements in our own social firms (shops and eBay centre) or with partner organisations.

We also work in partnership with other colleges of further education to provide our students with a unique academic and vocational experience.

The college offers:

- Specialist support tailored to the needs of each student
- A challenging curriculum
- A wide range of nationally accredited awards and qualifications
- A virtual learning support
- Work placements with local employers
- Professional specialists: speech and language therapists, physiotherapists, occupational therapists, music therapists, mobility tutors, qualified nurses and care staff
- Qualified and experienced teachers of the visually and multi-sensory impaired
- Individual learning plans

- High staff:learner ratio
- Purpose-built accommodation: from fully supervised to self-contained houses
- Day and residential placements
- Broad-base leisure programmes
- Specialist sensory environments

College accommodation comprises comfortable bedrooms with well-equipped areas for socialising with friends and visitors. Maple Lodge and Ash Lodge benefit from larger bedrooms and extra wide access for wheelchairs. Lodges feature adjustable height kitchen and bathroom appliances, talking kitchen equipment and an accessible laundry. The latest technologies, equipment and fittings help develop and support independent living skills. Campus facilities include: pool, gym, library, bar and social area.

Situated on the outskirts of Exeter – city in the country by the sea – the campus offers radial access to a huge range of activities and experiences. Extended curricular activities include trips to the beach, park, ten pin bowling and even residential trips abroad.

Please call or email for more information on assessment and admissions quoting WHM/0/13.

Registered charity no. 1058937.

Henshaws College

(Founded 1837)

Bogs Lane, Harrogate, North Yorkshire HG1 4ED
Tel: 01423 886451   Email: admissions@henshaws.ac.uk
Fax: 01423 885095   Website: www.henshaws.ac.uk

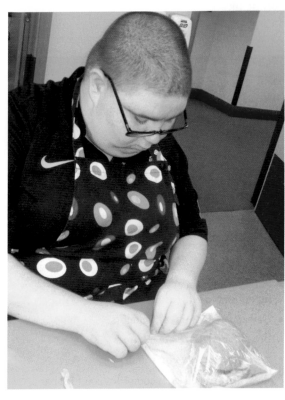

Principal: Nicki Eyre (acting)
School type: Coeducational Independent Specialist College
Age range of pupils: 16+
No. of pupils enrolled as at 1.1.13: 74
Boys: 42 Girls: 32
Fees per annum as at 1.1.13:
On application – according to support needs
Religious denomination: Non-denominational

Henshaws College supports students with learning difficulties and physical disabilities, with a specialism in visual impairment.

Curriculum

Each student follows an individual learning programme which focuses on Independence and Employability skills. Vocational pathways include Arts & Craft, Media & IT, Horticulture, Admin & Retail, and Hospitality. Work experience and social enterprise activities both on and off campus support training and skill development. Emphasis is on personal progression and practical application of skills, including communication, literacy, numeracy, independent travel and ICT. Our extended curriculum reinforces the transference of skills learned in the classroom into everyday living.

Accommodation

A range of accommodation is available on campus including en suite bedrooms and self contained flats, providing opportunities for students to experience a variety of living options as independence skills develop.

Specialist facilities

Specialist resources, teaching and training areas are fully accessible to all students, including the health, fitness and leisure centre with swimming and hydrotherapy pools, sauna, steam room and multigym. Our Assistive Technology Specialist ensures access to ICT and supports users of high-tech communication aids.

Student support services

Students are fully supported by our multi-disciplinary team of specialist staff, including physiotherapists, occupational therapists, speech and language therapists, rehabilitation and behaviour support. Each student has a personal tutor who offers support throughout their time at college to identify realistic options for the future. We work in close partnership with a number of agencies including social services and specialist careers advisors to guide students through the transition process. Ofsted judged that the care, guidance and support offered to students is "Outstanding".

Henshaws College is part of Henshaws Society for Blind People, a registered charity that exists to enable people with sight loss and other disabilities to build the skills and independence they need, to achieve the future they want. (Charity No. 221888)

School and colleges specialising in social interaction difficulties (Autism, ASD & ASP)

NAS Anderson School

NAS Anderson School, Rookery Lane, Pilning, Bristol BS35 4JN

Tel: 01454 632532
Fax: 01454 634907

Email: nasanderson@nas.org.uk

Web:
www.autism.org.uk/andersonschool

Head of Education: Simon Cartwright

School type: mixed independent day and residential school and outreach service for children and young people on the autism spectrum, including Asperger syndrome

Catchment area: South West England and South Wales

Support offered: flexible day, weekly, and year-round residential provision; short breaks and holiday play scheme; outreach support for maintained/non-maintained schools

Age range of students: 10-19
Capacity: 20
Founded: 2012

- waking day curriculum

- high staff to student ratio

- multi-sensory rooms

- fully equipped teaching/catering kitchens

- horticultural teaching zone

- wide range of local amenities

Anderson School opened its doors in 2012 and provides pioneering specialist autism education, working collaboratively with local parents, schools and services. We provide high-quality education and care for students with autism in a 24-hour learning environment.

School days are clearly structured, and the curriculum builds on students' skills and talents and addresses the particular challenges they face. This model allows young people with autism to thrive. Students also participate in a wide variety of enrichment activities which take advantage of our tranquil location on the outskirts of Bristol.

Our provision is innovative; some students will remain with the school for the whole of their secondary education whilst others are supported to move back into mainstream education.

'Our exciting provision is steeped in innovation and intervention. We promote and celebrate success through individualised pathways.'

Simon Cartwright, Head of Education

The National Autistic Society (NAS) is the UK's leading charity for people affected by autism.

Prior's Court School

(Founded 1999)

Hermitage, Thatcham, West Berkshire RG18 9NU
Tel: 01635 247202   Email: mail@priorscourt.org.uk
Fax: 01635 247203   Website: www.priorscourt.org.uk

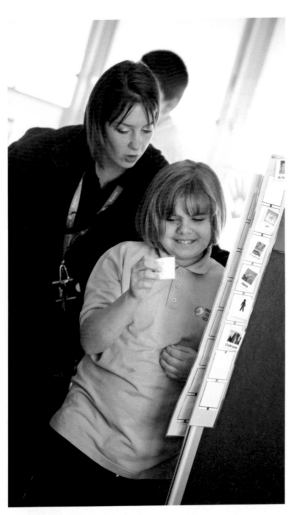

Director of Education and Learning: Sue Piper
Appointed: September 2011
School type: Coeducational Boarding & Day
Age range of pupils: 5–19
No. of pupils enrolled as at 1.1.13: 56
Boys: 42 Girls: 14 Sixth Form: 22
No. of boarders: 53
Fees per annum as at 1.1.13:
on application

Prior's Court School is an independent specialist school for students with autism, learning difficulties and complex needs from 5 to 19 years, offering day, weekly and termly 38, 44 and 52 week placements.

The school operates a person-centred approach, uniting autism expertise and knowledge with an understanding of each individual to support and maximise their potential and achieve real progress. A meaningful and functional curriculum with individualised learning programmes used throughout the waking day is built around students' interests and skills. The school has a strong focus on developing independence, personal care and life skills, communication, choice-making and social skills as well as building vocational skills and providing work placement opportunities on-site and in the community. The rich programme of activities on and off-site enables students to practice skills in a variety of settings and supports as inclusive a life as possible.

Set in over 50 acres, the sensory swimming pool, trampolines, trim trail and adventure playground, zip wire, swings, activity track, outdoor gym and the abundant space form part of the emphasis on physical exercise that is placed in our approach. Our approach combines a selection of methodologies and best practice, carefully moulded to suit the special needs of the students.

A large on-site therapy and multi-disciplinary team includes speech & language therapy, occupational therapy, clinical psychology, registered nurses, horticulture, animal husbandry, swimming and ICT instructors. The highly trained and dedicated staff work closely with families and professionals to create a co-ordinated and consistent programme of education and care whose success is recognised worldwide.

Prior's Court also offer a provision for young adults up to 25, providing a transitional step towards a more inclusive life for individuals with autism, as well as specialist autism training and conferences.

Registered charity no. 1070227

Swalcliffe Park School Trust

(Founded 1965)

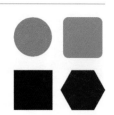

Swalcliffe, Banbury, Oxfordshire OX15 5EP
Tel: 01295 780302   Email: admin@swalcliffepark.co.uk
Fax: 01295 780006   Website: www.swalcliffepark.co.uk

Principal: Mr Kiran Hingorani
School type: Boys' Boarding & Day
Member of: NASS, NAES, WMLG, PACT, IIP,
SWALSS, NASEN, FLSE
Age range of pupils:
Boys: 11–19
No. of pupils enrolled as at 1.1.13: 45
Day: 7
Maximum number of boarders: 57
Fees per annum as at 1.1.13:
are available on request or set according to
individual needs

Swalcliffe Park School is a non-maintained charitable trust providing specialist education and care for boys aged 11-19 yrs. All students have a diagnosis of Autistic Spectrum Disorder (ASD) – mainly Asperger's Syndrome. Many having additional needs arising from other diagnoses including ADHD, Dyslexia, Dyspraxia and language impairment.

Placements are funded by Local Authorities from across the UK for a 38 week school year on a day, two weekly or termly boarding basis.

The school offers single room accommodation and has recently completed a significant renovation of its residential facilities.

Swalcliffe Parkhas a large, well-qualified staff team including teachers, learning support assistants, residential staff, speech and language therapists, occupational therapists, an educational psychologist, nurse, consulting psychiatrist, counsellor and massage therapist. Staff work collaboratively to create a wide range of learning opportunities during the school day, into the evenings and at weekends. These are designed to promote Communication, Independence, Self-Management and Achievement.

Communication

Weekly social communication groups are designed to improve our students' perspective taking skills.

Through school day and residential activities students learn about the importance of developing meaningful relationships and about communicating for different purposes. They are encouraged to share their own ideas and feelings and to respect and value those of others.

Independence

The Independence curriculum offers a variety of activities and opportunities for students to develop essential life skills in a range of settings. Students are supported to care for themselves and to manage their personal affairs and safety. They are encouraged to problem solve and to take an active role in their local communities.

Self-Management

We give special emphasis to Self-Management strategies to reflect the complexity of our students' needs. We help students to recognise their emotions and reactions to different situations and to manage these positively in order to behave in an expected way. Students are encouraged to use strategies to manage their anxieties and to look after their own physical and emotional well-being.

Achievement

We offer an extensive range of curricular activities throughout the school day, into the evenings and at weekends. Personalised learning pathways enable students to plan and prepare for their futures beyond school. Students choose pathways that build upon their strengths, interests, talents and ambitions. They achieve a wide range of vocational and academic qualifications.

The reports from our most recent Ofsted inspections in January 2012 (education and residential) and November 2012 (residential) describe the school as **'Outstanding'**.

The National Autistic Society

NAS Radlett Lodge School

NAS Radlett Lodge School,
Harper Lane, Radlett,
Hertfordshire WD7 9HW

Tel: 01923 854922
Fax: 01923 859922

Email: radlett.lodge@nas.org.uk
Web: www.autism.org.uk/radlettlodge

Principal: Jo Galloway

School type: mixed independent day and residential school for children and young people on the autism spectrum, including Asperger syndrome

Support offered: day, weekly & termly boarding; residential provision (38-week and 43 week); short breaks and outreach services; 24-hour curriculum

Age range of students: 4-19
Number of students enrolled: 55
Catchment area: national
Founded: 1974

- **over 35 years' experience**

- **high staff to student ratio**

- **art and design area**

- **gymnasium and sports facilities**

- **teaching kitchen**

- **1:1 teaching area**

- **sensory room**

- **soft play area**

At Radlett Lodge School, our ultimate aim is to enable every one of our students to become as independent as possible. We emphasise developing communication and social skills through a curriculum which meets the specific needs of students with autism.

We have a high staff to student ratio which enables students to access all areas of the National Curriculum at the right level. Through a structured and supportive learning environment and friendly, approachable staff, students develop social relationships and receive a broad and balanced education.

We prepare students for adult life by supporting them to enjoy activities in the wider community and to learn life and independent living skills; we also make everything we teach relevant to the real world. Some students are encouraged to visit other local schools for specific sessions.

'The provision is outstanding. The school continues to provide excellent high quality 24 hour care and education. Students receive outstanding support enabling them to progress at school.'

Ofsted, 2011 (www.ofsted.gov.uk)

The National Autistic Society (NAS) is the UK's leading charity for people affected by autism.

Potterspury Lodge School

(Founded 1956)

Towcester, Northamptonshire NN12 7LL
Tel: 01908 542912   Email: mail@potterspurylodge.co.uk
Fax: 01908 543399   Website: www.potterspurylodge.co.uk

Principal: Mr John W D Brown
Appointed: September 2004
School type: Boys' Termly Boarding, Weekly Boarding and Day
Member of: NASS, NASEN, SEBDA
Age range of pupils:
Boys: 8–18
No. of pupils enrolled as at 1.1.13: 44 Sixth Form: 6
No. of boarders: 13
Fees per annum as at 1.1.13: Day: £50,000
Boarding: £75,000
Termly Boarding: £80,000
Average size of class: up to 9

Potterspury Lodge is a charitable trust, which offers high quality education for boys aged between eight to eighteen years who have autistic spectrum disorders and a variety of emotional, social and behavioural difficulties and associated learning difficulties.

We teach the full National Curriculum, with the exception of a modern foreign language. Class sizes are kept to around eight or nine students and in addition to the subject teachers there are also learning support assistants in every class.

For boarders, the accommodation is organised so that they live in small groups of five or six in self contained houses, with them all enjoying the benefit of their own care staff and sharing in the day to day living arrangements, as one would in a family.

From year ten, pupils follow a life skills programme, In year eleven, some students are able to take part in work based training and all year 10 and year 11 students undertake two week-long periods of work experience.

We have provision for students in years 12 and 13 in The Stables Further Education Centre. Education and Residential support managers enable students to follow programmes of education and training according to their individual needs, using our own resources and those of local colleges, amenities and workplace training providers.

The School enables children to develop and grow in a caring and supportive atmosphere, and gives them the perfect opportunity to socialise and enjoy life. We organise trips for the pupils on a regular basis, including skiing holidays in Italy and outdoor pursuits expeditions in the UK and France. All pupils are given the opportunity to be fully included in activities.

The grounds are wonderful for sports and outdoor games, particularly when the weather is nice. The children are also encouraged to join in the wide number of after school clubs, which include such diverse activities as Badminton, Pottery, Football, Computers and Technology as well as our own Scout Group. We make full use of local recreational and Leisure facilities and some students are members of the local Sea Cadets Corps.

Potterspury Lodge School is a registered charity, which exists to provide pupils with Special Educational Needs with a wide range of opportunities to experience success. These are designed to help them progress towards being better integrated into society and then to go on to meet the demands of independent adult life.

Charity No. 1103356

The National
Autistic Society

NAS Sybil Elgar School

NAS Sybil Elgar School,
Havelock Road, Southall,
Middlesex UB2 4NY

Tel: 020 8813 9168
Fax: 020 8571 7332

Email: sybil.elgar@nas.org.uk
Web: www.autism.org.uk/sybilelgar

Principal: Chloe Phillips

School type: mixed independent day and residential school for children and young people on the autism spectrum, including Asperger syndrome

Age range of students: 4-19

Support offered: day, 38-week and 52 week (from September) residential provision; short breaks and holiday play scheme; 24-hour curriculum

Capacity: 100

Catchment area: national

Founded: 1965

- **over 45 years' experience**

- **high staff to student ratio**

- **music therapy rooms**

- **fully equipped teaching/catering kitchens**

- **ICT and science laboratories**

- **multi-sensory room**

- **wide range of local amenities**

Children and young people come first at Sybil Elgar. We have created a warm and caring environment so that all students can focus on learning through a broad, balanced and autism-specific education.

We are ambitious on behalf of our students, aiming to provide them with the best education possible. Through individual educational programmes and a high staff to student ratio, we cater for a wide range of abilities and needs, nurturing each child's social and communication skills.

At the age of 16, students move into our specialist further education department located on the campus of Acton College, where they participate in an exciting curriculum that inspires and prepares them for adult life. We are known for being innovative, progressive and ambitious and our school is an exciting place for young people on their way to adulthood.

'Students learn exceptionally good life and social skills, which significantly increase their self-esteem and confidence... the curriculum is significantly enhanced by specialist approaches for students... with complex special educational needs.'
Ofsted, 2011 (www.ofsted.gov.uk)

The National Autistic Society (NAS) is the UK's leading charity for people affected by autism.

Riverston School
'Bespoke Learning for Life'

63-69 Eltham Road, Lee Green, London SE12 8UF
Tel: 020 8318 4327   Email: office@riverstonschool.co.uk
Fax: 020 8297 0514   Website: www.riverstonschool.co.uk

Riverston *Plus*

Headmistress: Mrs S E Salathiel
School type: Independent Non-Selective Day School for boys and girls of all abilities from 1-19 yrs
Age range of pupils: 1–19
No. of pupils enrolled as of 5.1.13: 215
Boys: 155 Girls: 60
Fees per annum as at 5.1.13:
On application
Teacher/pupil ratio: 1:8

Riverston School has a reputation within the local and wider community of South London for its uniqueness. We are a small independent non-selective day school for boys and girls of all abilities including those with learning difficulties.

Riverston *Plus*, which is part of Riverston School, offers a well-designed and fully resourced learning support centre for pupils who have special educational needs. Although this special needs provision is delivered in a separate building of the school, the pupils are integrated into the school curriculum and attend mainstream lessons wherever possible. This is determined by their individual educational programmes.

Pupils are able to be nurtured in an environment tailor-made to meet their specific requirements, and for some, this means a specially designed curriculum that supports and meets the challenges associated with everyday life. This may include social and communication classes, speech and language sessions, occupational therapy help, 'Travel Safe' programmes and well differentiated teaching, all guided and monitored by a qualified director of SEN. Pupils within the Riverston *Plus* facility are thriving because they feel comfortable and confident, and are part of the mainstream school system. This is endorsed in a recent ISI Inspection, which stated:

'The well designed curriculum gives good support to pupils of all ages, abilities and needs, including those with LDD. The learning support is excellent. As a result, the needs of all individuals are met, strongly in line with the schools aims.' ISI Report 2010

Riverston *Plus* is supported by a speech and language therapist, educational psychologist, occupational therapist and physiotherapist together with experienced staff to support every child's needs. Links with external agencies, including health authorities, social services and educational welfare specialists are also well established.

The overall aims and objectives of Riverston *Plus* is to provide exceptional caring and professional teaching to pupils with special educational needs, enabling them to reach their true individual potential, and provide them with a 'Bespoke Learning for Life.'

A short film about Riverston *Plus*, showing exactly what makes us unique, can be accessed through our Riverston School website at: www.riverstonschool.co.uk

The Holmewood School

(Founded 2010)

The Holmewood School
London

88 Woodside Park Road, London N12 8SH
Tel: 020 8920 0660   Email: enquiries@thsl.org.uk
Fax: 020 8445 9678   Website: www.thsl.org.uk

Head of School: Lucia Santi
School type: Coeducational Day
Age range of pupils: 7–18
Fees per annum as at 1.1.13:
On request

The Holmewood School London caters for students who have speech, language and social communication difficulties and those associated with high functioning autism and Asperger's syndrome.

Our school offers a successful alternative to mainstream education. Class sizes are small with a high staffing ratio. Comprehensive programmes are planned and delivered by specialist staff to meet each child's needs.

Teaching ensures all learning styles are met and addresses our kinaesthetic, visual, auditory and multi-sensory learners so that maximum individual potential is achieved. A structured and tailored environment ensures students are supported and challenged in their learning and development.

The curriculum is designed using the National Curriculum up to GCSE. For those students more vocationally oriented we support a range of courses that develop interests, strengths and skills providing valuable career related experiences and qualifications.

Mainstream experiences with our link school support teaching and learning. The Holmewood School is part of a global network of schools within the Dwight family of schools offering an international perspective.

Learning is enhanced through our social skills and life skills curriculum. Planning and reflection time built into each day emphasises the importance that we place on students' personal development. Our whole school focus on celebrating student achievement is reflected in our approach to positive behaviour and rewards.

Therapies and practice are cutting edge and delivered by our multidisciplinary team. Comprehensive programmes are designed and integrated within our curriculum. The school benefits from a unique partnership with a Harley Street-based sensory integration clinic.

Located in North London the school has access to the rich cultural and educational experiences that the capital provides. Excellent local transport services makes learning in the community accessible for our students. Educational visits and offsite activities are incorporated within our programmes so students can consolidate and generalise the learning that takes place in the classroom.

If you think The Holmewood School would be the right place for your child, please contact our admissions director, Nadine Huseyin on 020 8920 0665 or nhuseyin@thsl.org.uk

The National
Autistic Society

NAS Helen Allison School

NAS Helen Allison School,
Longfield Road, Meopham,
Kent DA13 0EW

Tel: 01474 814878
Fax: 01474 812033

Email: helen.allison@nas.org.uk
Web: www.autism.org.uk/helenallison

Executive Principal:
Dr Jacqui Ashton Smith

Head of School: Susan Conway

School type: mixed independent day
and residential school for children and
young people on the autism spectrum,
including Asperger syndrome

Support offered: day and
38-week provision; respite and
short break services

Age range of students: 5-19
Capacity: 70
Catchment area: London,
South East and East Anglia
Founded: 1968

- **over 40 years' experience**

- **small classes**

- **high student to teacher ratio**

- **separate FE department**

- **senior students accommodation**

- **allotments where students grow and sell produce**

- **conservation area**

At Helen Allison School our goal is to create a safe and
structured environment so that each of our students can
be happy and make progress. We deliver a high quality and
enjoyable education and use our expert knowledge of autism to
find the best possible way for each student to learn.

Our class sizes are small and we deliver individual programmes
for each student allowing them to reach their full potential. We
believe in preparing our children and young people for fulfilling
adult lives and the main curriculum is enhanced with a wide
range of social activities and community-based learning.

Our further education department and residential buildings are
in nearby Gravesend, giving students easy access to a range of
shops, amenities and public transport.

'The quality of the leadership and management of the
residential provision is outstanding, resulting in outstanding
outcomes for boarders...The excellent quality of the
assessment of students' needs and abilities is a particular
strength of the school. The curriculum is outstanding.'

Ofsted, 2012 (www.ofsted.gov.uk)

The National Autistic Society (NAS) is the UK's leading charity for people
affected by autism.

NAS Thames Valley Free School

NAS Thames Valley Free School,
Conwy Close, Tilehurst, Reading,
Berkshire RG30 4BZ

Tel: 0117 9748 430

Email: naseducationgroup@nas.org.uk
Web: www.thamesvalleyfreeschool.co.uk

Principal Designate: Fiona Veitch

School type: Free school; mixed day provision

Age range of students: 5-16

Support offered: Standard and enhanced provision; enrichment activities.

Catchment area: Reading, Berkshire and neighbouring local authorities.

Opening: September 2013

- opening September 2013

- standard provision for young people of average to high ability struggling in mainstream education because of their autism

- enhanced provision for young people with very complex needs

- the Thames Valley Free School is independent of the National Autistic Society (NAS)

- the school is a collaboration of the NAS with local authorities, voluntary groups, schools and parents

- NAS has a key role in the quality assurance of the school as well as in training the staff

NAS Thames Valley Free School represents a new chapter in the provision of high quality education for children and young people with autism and Asperger syndrome.

Our educational model centres on truly personalised teaching that capitalises on an individual's strengths and removes barriers to learning. The curriculum will develop a core foundation of knowledge and skills for each student which will prepare them for the transition into further study or employment. We will also support all of our students to increase their inclusion in their community.

'We view each child as an individual and we will tailor our education provision to meet his or her needs and give them the best possible start in life.'

Fiona Veitch, Principal Designate, NAS Thames Valley Free School

Sponsored by

The National Autistic Society (NAS) is the UK's leading charity for people affected by autism.

Higford School

Higford Hall, Higford, Shifnal, Shropshire TF11 9ET
Tel: 01952 630600   Email: info@higfordschool.co.uk
Fax: 01952 630605   Website: www.optionsgroup.co.uk

Options Group
making a difference

Headteacher: Anne Adams
School type: Coeducational Residential & Day
Age range of pupils: 8–19
Fees per annum as at 1.1.13:
On application

Higford School provides integrated programmes of care, education and therapy for children and young people aged 8 to 19 with autism, Asperger's Syndrome, learning disabilities and associated complex needs including challenging behaviours.

Set in 28 acres of rolling Shropshire countryside, Higford School is an NAS-accredited service offering day, respite, outreach and residential placements.

Up to 52-week residential care is provided within homely, specially adapted accommodation. There is also dedicated respite provision on-site. Students have their own individual en-suite bedrooms which they are supported to personalise, shared lounges and kitchens.

Higford School adopts a person-centred and outcomes-focused approach to providing care and education that is designed to help each student exercise choice and control, increase their confidence and prepare for adulthood. Care and educational programmes are individually tailored and delivered in a variety of environments. Learning takes place throughout the waking day encouraging the development of communication, social and life skills alongside academic achievement. Higford School has an on-site Professional and Clinical Multi-disciplinary Team that works closely with the school and care staff to develop the communication and life skills of each student.

Higford School offers National Curriculum subjects for Key Stage 2, 3 and 4 students, a vocational-based curriculum for Post-16 students and teaching frameworks that have been specifically designed for children and young people with complex learning needs.

Each student's individual learning abilities, requirements and academic progression are consistently monitored to ensure that support remains proactive, that learning opportunities are maximised and that every individual achievement is celebrated.

The education, care and therapy staff teams utilise a range of teaching methods, communication systems and frameworks to ensure that learning is person-centred, consistent, stimulating, fun and meaningful. This multi-disciplinary working ensures a consistency of approach in meeting the diverse needs of every student.

Cruckton Hall
(part of the Kisimul Group)

(Founded 1981)

Cruckton, Shrewsbury, Shropshire SY5 8PR
Tel: 01743 860206   Email: pdm@cruckton.com
Fax: 01743 860941   Website: www.cruckton.com

Head Teacher: P D Mayhew
School type: Boys' Residential
Member of: NAS, NASS, NASEN
Age range of pupils:
Boys: 8–19
No. of pupils enrolled as at 1.1.13: 80
Fees per annum as at 1.1.13:
On application

Curriculum

For those pupils who are resident at Cruckton we provide a 24-hour approach. All boys at the school have an Individual Education Plan (IEP), a Placement and Care Plan, Health Plan and, from Year 9, a Transition Plan. The respective parts of these plans are discussed between the professionals at the school, the boy and his parents/carers. The school has a full range of specialist rooms to support all National Curriculum subjects. All pupils are prepared for GCSE examinations in English, maths and science. They can also choose to study for GCSE in history, geography, French, German, computer studies, art, home economics and design technology. In addition, we also offer ECDL, AQA Skills for Life Awards and a variety of Entry Level certificates.

Assessment and entry requirements

Entry is by interview and assessment. The multi-disciplinary team of professionals will carry out a baseline assessment on each student within the first six weeks of admission. Cruckton has a visiting consultant child and adolescent psychiatrist who visits the boys on a regular basis, as required. The multi-disciplinary team consists of a consultant educational psychologist, systemic psychotherapist, two speech and language therapists, occupational therapist and two paediatric nurses. They provide a variety of interventions and therapies to minimise the anxieties and maximise the development of our young people.

The wider environment

The hall is a listed building surrounded by ten acres of gardens that include woods, playing fields and play areas. The site is located within a friendly rural community, in beautiful countryside, four miles from the market town of Shropshire. The Welsh Marches provide a stunning backdrop and a rich source of options for our regular trips and adventures. The town of Shrewsbury offers excellent amenities for the school and is now linked to the motorway network of the West Midlands, greatly improving access.

Residential environment and activities

The structure that provides success for the boys in the classroom environment is replicated in the residential area and boys have a range of recreational activities provided, which reflect their needs and encourage their specialisms. Many boys choose an active leisure programme. This can be provided by activities such as skateboarding, swimming, football and cricket, and in the summer the Adventure Camp encourages team work amongst our student group through activities such as orienteering, mountain biking, rock climbing and raft building. For the more studious, a range of activities from *Warhammer* to chess club are provided. Links with local clubs and

'Cruckton Hall provides a good quality of education and offers good, "seamless", boarding provision.'

'It is outstanding in promoting pupils' personal development and does exceptionally well in "opening doors" for pupils, enabling them to learn, and preparing them for life after school in employment, college, university or in more sheltered environments.'

'The school's curriculum is outstanding and creates in pupils an excitement about learning which they have not experienced previously.'

'A key strength of the school is the way it supports pupils' transition, whether this is into the school, into courses or adult life. Pupils are particularly well informed through the wide range of support they receive, as well as formal careers guidance.'

Ofsted report 12-13 November 2008.

societies include the local stables, local army cadet force, Jiu Jitsu, Laser Quest, bowling alley, street dancing and swimming are well-established. The links between the IEP targets are shared across the 24-hour approach, both in the home and education setting, with a huge variety of enrichment activities and programmes. Forest school, Lego therapy, robotics, stable management, mountain biking, Blists Hill Museum and work experience are all part of the enrichment programme.

Behaviour management

It is accepted that many boys come to Cruckton Hall School exhibiting both difficult and challenging behaviour. The structural consistency of various approaches, combined with a consistent nurturing environment, has a track record of providing the boys with the ability to be accepted within social settings of their choice. The basis of the approach is to foster the following qualities: self-respect, respect for other students, respect for staff, courtesy, politeness, patience, tolerance and motivation to work. Boys will be encouraged and supported to meet as many of these expectations as is possible. Attendance at school is a non-negotiable requirement of a boy's placement at Cruckton Hall. School uniform is always worn.

Aims and philosophy

Cruckton Hall School aims to provide a warm, structured and caring learning environment in which each boy feels safe and secure, can succeed, is treated as an individual and is able to develop his skills and talents in order that he leaves school as an active participant in, and a positive contributor to, society.

Barton School

Barrow Road, Barton-upon-Humber, Lincolnshire DN18 6DA
Tel: 01652 631280   Email: info@bartonschool.co.uk
Fax: 01652 637419   Website: www.optionsgroup.co.uk

Options Group
making a difference

Headteacher: Mark Eames
School type: Coeducational Residential & Day
Age range of pupils: 8–19
Fees per annum as at 1.1.13:
On application

Barton School provides integrated programmes of care, education and therapy for children and young people aged 8 to 19 with autism, Asperger's Syndrome, learning disabilities and associated complex needs including challenging behaviours. Barton School is a DfE-registered special school and Ofsted registered children's home offering day, respite, outreach and residential placements.

Barton School adopts a person-centred approach to the delivery of care and educational programmes that are designed to help students express their needs and wants, and to become more independent. Particular priority is given to the development of communication and interpersonal skills and the use of regular physical activity to improve overall emotional and physical wellbeing. Following a holistic approach to care and education ensures that learning takes place throughout the waking day – not just in the classroom!

Situated in Barton-upon-Humber in North Lincolnshire, Barton School is a purpose-built service specially designed to meet the educational and developmental needs of children and young people with complex needs. Using a range of proven techniques, teaching frameworks and communications systems, Barton School provides high quality education including access to the National Curriculum and vocational based curriculums. Providing a waking day learning environment promotes the development of social, communication and life skills. Barton School has an on-site dedicated Professional and Clinical Multi-disciplinary Team that works closely with the school and care staff to develop the communication and life skills of each student.

Barton School has 5 communal living flats for 4 to 6 students that contain single bedrooms, with en-suite bathrooms, shared lounges and kitchens/diners. Built-in visual and auditory features help to create peaceful atmospheres where students with sensory needs can develop their life and social skills with confidence.

The National Autistic Society

NAS Robert Ogden School

NAS Robert Ogden School,
Clayton Lane, Thurnscoe, Rotherham,
South Yorkshire S63 0BG

Tel: 01709 874443
Fax: 01709 870701

Email: robert.ogden@nas.org.uk
Web: www.autism.org.uk/robertogden

Executive Principal:
Dr Jacqui Ashton Smith

Head of School: Dr Khursh Khan

School type: mixed independent day
and residential school for children and
young people on the autism spectrum,
including Asperger syndrome

Support offered: day, 38-week
and 52 week provisions; short
breaks; 24-hour curriculum

Age range of students: 5-19
Number of students enrolled: 80
Catchment area: national
Founded: 1976

- **over 30 years' experience**

- **staff to student ratio minimum of 1:2**

- **modern ICT facilities**

- **teaching kitchen and café**

- **working pottery stations**

- **horticultural gardens**

- **training flat**

The Robert Ogden School is one of the largest schools in the
UK for children and young people with autism. Our priority is for
every child to be happy enabling them to learn and grow from
primary to further education.

Every student accesses the National Curriculum in a way that
is tailored to their own educational needs and abilities whilst
remaining broad, balanced and challenging. The individual plan
of each child allows them to learn about the world around them
and to develop skills necessary for adulthood.

Our excellent facilities include specialist academic and leisure
suites which enable students to build their social confidence,
pursue their interests and learn a wide range of skills.

'The quality of the curriculum, teaching and assessment are
all outstanding. The curriculum is highly personalised so that
it meets individual students' needs exceptionally well...The
spiritual, moral, social and cultural development of students
is outstanding and is at the heart of the school's work.'

Ofsted, 2011 (www.ofsted.gov.uk)

The National Autistic Society (NAS) is the UK's leading charity for people
affected by autism.

NAS Daldorch House School

NAS Daldorch House School,
Sorn Road, Catrine,
East Ayrshire, KA5 6NA

Tel: 01290 551666
Fax: 01290 553399

Email: daldorch@nas.org.uk
Web: www.autism.org.uk/daldorch

Principal: Shona Pinkerton

School type: mixed independent day and residential school for children and young people on the autism spectrum, including Asperrger syndrome

Age range: 5- 21
Founded: 1998

Support offered: flexible, day and residential on a weekly, termly and 52-week basis; residential and day breaks; outreach service offering statutory education/social support, training assessment and consultancy

Catchment area: national

- **individual programmes**

- **high staff to pupil ratio**

- **extensive learning support**

- **year-round learning opportunities**

- **strongly influenced by Curriculum for Excellence**

- **extensive grounds**

- **sensory and soft play rooms**

- **music therapy**

- **vocational skills and enterprise activities**

- **sport and leisure facilities**

- **parent accommodation**

Developing communication, social and life skills is at the core of our 24 hour curriculum at Daldorch. All our pupils have access to a broad and balanced curriculum which is individually designed according to their abilities and meets their needs. We enrich each pupil's learning by capitalising on their interests and expanding their understanding of the world. The varied and rewarding educational opportunities that we offer provide our pupils with a stepping stone to a positive future.

Learning is an ongoing process at Daldorch and does not stop at the end of a school day. Evenings, weekends and holidays can present great learning opportunities. We wish our children to become successful learners and confident individuals who take an active part in society while enjoying their school life to the full.

We offer primary and secondary, day and residential education for pupils up to the age of 21.

Her Majesty's Inspectorate of Education in 2012 recognised the following strengths of the school:

- trusting relationships between staff and children and young people
- identification and knowledge of young people's learning needs
- staff knowledge and understanding of autism spectrum disorders
- progress in implementing Curriculum for Excellence for young people with autism
- close links and very good communication with parents and carers.

The National Autistic Society (NAS) is the UK's leading charity for people affected by autism.

The National Autistic Society

NAS Daldorch Satellite School
(South Lanarkshire Children's Services)

NAS Daldorch Satellite School, St Leonards, East Kilbride, South Lanarkshire

Tel: 01355 246 242
Fax: 01290 553399

Email: daldorch@nas.org.uk
Web: www.autism.org.uk/daldorch

Principal: Shona Pinkerton

School type: mixed independent residential school for children and young people on the autism spectrum, including Asperger syndrome

Support offered: 52-week residential provision

Age range: 5-19

Capacity: 5 students

Catchment area: South Lanarkshire

Founded: 2011

- **a small school with big resources**
- **same teaching staff as Daldorch House School**
- **home and education under one roof**
- **individual programmes**
- **high staff to pupil ratio**
- **specialist support**
- **excellent links to the community**
- **local school with national expertise**
- **24-hour curriculum**
- **modern facilities**
- **in association with South Lanarkshire Council**

At Daldorch Satellite School (South Lanarkshire) in East Kilbride, five young people with autism can benefit from everything our main school, Daldorch House School in Ayrshire, has to offer while being closer to home. Pupils benefit from the same level of specialist care and education (provided by the same teachers) as pupils at our main campus, whilst remaining in their familiar community. The satellite service combines care and education environments under one roof. Its autism-friendly design and up-to-date technology make it a wonderful place to live and learn.

Daldorch Satellite School (South Lanarkshire) offers each young person care and education tailored to their individual needs. We also offer behaviour support, speech and language therapy and full-time care for 365 days a year. Every pupil receives high level support from our staff and we encourage all pupils to make the most of other educational and leisure opportunities in the local area.

'Every young person with autism should have the best possible opportunity to live and learn in a setting that works for them.'

Shona Pinkerton, Principal of Daldorch House.

The National Autistic Society (NAS) is the UK's leading charity for people affected by autism.

Kinsale School

Kinsale Hall, Llanerch-y-Mor, Holywell, Flintshire CH8 9DX
Tel: 01745 562500   Email: info@kinsaleschool.co.uk
Fax: 01745 562501   Website: www.optionsgroup.co.uk

Options Group
making a difference

Headteacher: Emma Keyworth
School type: Coeducational Residential & Day
Age range of pupils: 8–19
Fees per annum as at 1.1.13:
On application

Set in a stunning rural location overlooking the Dee Estuary in North Wales, Kinsale School provides integrated programmes of care, education and therapy for children and young people aged 8 to 19 with autism, learning disabilities and associated complex needs including challenging behaviours.

Kinsale School is an NAS-accredited, Estyn "Excellent" rated school offering both day and up to 52-week residential placements.

Attendance at Kinsale School is often the first step of a longer journey through the Options Group Pathway, which enables young people to develop life skills and prepare for leaving care within safe, structured environments.

Kinsale School adopts a person-centred and outcomes-focused approach to learning and believes that education should be individually tailored and delivered in a variety of environments.

Using complementary techniques and approaches, the school offers high-quality education including access to the National Curriculum and vocational based curriculums. Providing a waking day curriculum means that education is promoted beyond the classroom to ensure that each student develops social, communication and life skills.

Kinsale School has a range of accommodation suitable for children and young people with varying needs. Residential accommodation is comprised of specifically designed communal flats for between 2 and 6 students, with a semi-independent living flat available for those who are ready to make the transition to more independent living or require this type of environment. Students have their own bedrooms, with en-suite facilities if appropriate and each flat has a large communal living/dining area and kitchen.

Kinsale School has a dedicated on-site Professional and Clinical Multi-disciplinary Team that works closely with the school and care staff to develop the communication and life skills of each student. Additional clinical support is provided through the wider network of Professional and Clinical Services available within Options Group.

Schools and colleges specialising in learning difficulties (including dyslexia/SPLD)

Action for Children Parklands Campus

Action for Children Parklands Campus, Near Appleton, Abingdon, Oxfordshire
OX13 5QB
Tel: 01865 390436   Email: parklands.campus@actionforchildren.org.uk
Website: www.actionforchildren.org.uk/parklands

Principal: Raymond Wilson
School type: Coeducational Day & Boarding
A non-maintained special school offering day and residential services.
Special needs provision: A range of needs including BESD, ASD, DYS, MLD, SPLD
Member of: NASS
Age range of pupils: 11–19

Action for Children Parklands Campus will provide you with a holistic approach to education and care, offering day and residential services to young people and their families. At the same time helping young people with complex needs to build positive relationships, be healthy and safe, and achieve more.

Who we help

Our coeducational school will support young people aged 11 to 19 years old with emotional, behavioural and social difficulties and complex needs.

How we help

Integrated approach to education
As a specialist UK children's charity, we will be offering a holistic approach to education, using our wide range of support services and expertise.

Innovative curriculum
Working with young people who may feel that education has no relevance to them, we will create an individual curriculum programme and structured pathway that engages and motivates them.

Better outcomes through a partnership approach
Working together with Local Authorities, carers, parents, colleges, universities, teacher training institutes, local schools, work-based training providers and employers, we will provide young people with opportunities and help them build positive relationships.

Support with transitions to ensure improved life chances
We will help students to live an independent life and to progress to further education, training and employment.

Reintegration into parental home
We will support reintegration into the young person's parental home, where this is in their best interests and it is safe to do so.

Quality leadership and leading-edge professionals including specialist support
Trained in Action for Children's robust accredited behaviour support model, our team will have a positive and productive relationship with young people. We will also be supporting your child with a specialist team, which includes an educational psychologist, counsellor and child health specialist.

Extensive use of information technology and online learning zones
An innovative approach to teaching and learning, we will be using ICT to ensure that our professional staff share best practice and engage students and parents with the curriculum.

The Unicorn School for the Dyslexic Child

(Founded 1991)

20 Marcham Road, Abingdon, Oxfordshire OX14 1AA
Tel: 01235 530222   Email: info@unicorndyslexia.co.uk
Website: www.unicorndyslexia.co.uk

Headteacher: Mrs J Vaux BA(Hons)Oxon, PGCE, OxCertSpLD, BScPsychol
School type: Coeducational Day
Member of: CReSTeD, AMBDA
Age range of pupils: 6–13
No. of pupils enrolled as at 6.9.12: 70
Fees per annum:
Information on application.

An 'outstanding' independent specialist school for dyslexic, dyspraxic and dyscalculic children (Ofsted Feb 2012)

- Aims to provide specialist education for children from both independent and maintained schools to teach strategies and skills to enable them to return to mainstream as soon as possible.

- Structured multisensory, individualised programme with emphasis on synthetic phonic approach.

- Specialist dyslexia teachers, differentiated National Curriculum, daily individual tuition and small classes (maximum ten). Extensive use of computers and encouragement to develop creative talent.

- Speech therapy, occupational therapy, art therapy and instrumental tuition available on site.

- Educational and emotional needs met on an individual basis as well as through friendly atmosphere and community spirit.

The Unicorn School is a registered charity, which exists to provide full-time education for children with specific learning difficulties who require specialist tuition. (Charity no. 1070807 CReSTeD category SP)

Egerton Rothesay School

(Founded 1923)

Durrants Lane, Berkhamsted, Hertfordshire HP4 3UJ
Tel: 01442 877060   Email: admin.dl@eger-roth.co.uk
Fax: 01442 864977   Website: www.eger-roth.co.uk

Headteacher: Mrs N I Boddam-Whetham BA(Hons), PGTC
Appointed: September 1998
School type: Coeducational Day
Age range of pupils: 5–18
No. of pupils enrolled as at 1.1.13: 152
Fees per annum as at 1.1.13: Day: £13,686–£19,485
Average size of class: 10

A Very Different Education

ERS is a school especially for the child who can benefit from additional support. This means delivering the best possible education for each child whilst providing them with a genuinely supportive framework that will help them to achieve their full potential.

We are an inclusive school, welcoming children with a wide range of abilities and from all cultures and faiths. We believe that learning should be enjoyable and holistic – so it is about preparing each child for life after school, as much as academic subjects and exams.

ERS focuses on students who have found, or would find, it difficult to make progress and to succeed within another school. We have a range of specialist support, teachers and therapists who provide for a range of children whose additional needs may include dyslexia, dyspraxia or speech and language issues, Asperger syndrome and high functioning autism. Classes are grouped for individual requirements.

The school has an accepting atmosphere in which children feel understood and in which they do not 'feel different'. This boosts self-confidence and aids in the enrichment of learning.

Our aim is always to see what we can do for your child – and then to work with our resources and your support so that we can help them be successful. Our input can be for the child's whole school career, through to GCSE or simply on an interim basis to help re-focus their progress, depending on their needs.

In September 2012 we launched our new 'Sixth Form' Provision. For students who will continue to mature beyond the age of 16 and require an additional amount of support and time in order to enable them to transfer successfully into a further education establishment or employment. The school is developing both one-year and two-year educational programmes within a high quality, secure and supportive environment in which students are able to continue to mature, develop and learn.

All learning and social activities take place within an environment offering exceptional pastoral care and whole person development that is driven and informed by the school's Christian foundation.

ERS is also more than just a local school – students travel to the school from all directions, many using the comprehensive minibus service that the school runs over a 25 mile radius.

You are most welcome to come to the school to see if you think our approach would be right for your child. To arrange a visit please contact Liz Martin (01442 877060 or liz.martin@eger-roth.co.uk) or see our website: www.eger-roth.co.uk for more information.

I CAN'S Dawn House School

(Founded 1974)

Helmsley Road, Rainworth, Mansfield, Nottinghamshire NG21 0DQ
Tel: 01623 795361   Email: dawnhouse@ican.org.uk
Fax: 01623 491173   Website: www.dawnhouseschool.org.uk or www.ican.org.uk

helps children
communicate
REGISTERED CHARITY 210031

Principal: Angela Child
School type: Coeducational Day & Residential
Member of: NASS
Age range of pupils: 5–19
No. of pupils enrolled as at 1.1.13: 75
Length of school year: 39 weeks
Fees per annum as at 1.1.13:
On request

I CAN's Dawn House School is a specialist speech, language and communication school for children and young people aged 5-19 years. We are committed to the highest quality education, therapy and care for pupils with severe and/or complex speech, language and communication difficulties or Asperger's Syndrome.

At Dawn House School the pupils receive the specialist intensive support that they need. We are able to cater for a number of other difficulties which are commonly associated with communication difficulties, including: learning difficulties, behavioural difficulties, problems with attention and memory, motor dyspraxia, sensory difficulties, autistic spectrum difficulties and emotional problems.

Pupils' individual needs are assessed, and provided for by the schools systems for curriculum planning and

assessment and IEP planning. Speech and language therapists and teachers plan lessons that meet two sets of targets: curriculum learning objectives and specific speech and/or language aims. For pupils who need more specific focused work to develop their speech and language skills, individual or small group sessions are timetabled during the school day.

Our school makes use of Paget Gorman and Signed Speech or Makaton to support children's learning. The school also promotes the use of a range of voice output devices to support individual pupil's communication.

A full-time Occupational Therapist and an OT assistant work within some lessons and with individual pupils on more focused, intensive work where necessary. The Family and Community Liaison Worker supports pupils' families and is a key link between home and school.

Residential Care at Dawn House School aims to ensure the emotional and physical well-being of our boarding pupils through an extended curriculum. The school can provide opportunities for non-residential young people to benefit from extended days and overnight stays. The care staff organise a range of activities out of school hours.

Dawn House was rated as a 'Good School' during the inspection of 2011, many aspects including the care setting, were judged to be outstanding.

The Further Education department caters for students (16-19 years) who have a communication difficulty or Asperger's Syndrome. The provision is based at the Dawn House site but has very close partnerships with Vision West Notts and Portland two local FE colleges, local employers and training providers.

Dawn House School is part of I CAN, the children's communication charity (www.ican.org.uk).

Pield Heath House School

(Founded 1901)

Pield Heath Road, Uxbridge, Middlesex UB8 3NW
Tel: 01895 258507   Email: admin@pieldheathschool.org.uk
Fax: 01895 256497   Website: pieldheathschool.org.uk

Principal: Sister Julie Rose
School type: Coeducational Boarding & Day
Non maintained residential/day. Moderate/severe learning difficulties; language and communication disorders; complex needs; ASD.
Age range of pupils: 7–19
No. of pupils enrolled as at 22.1.13: 64
Fees per annum as at 22.1.13:
On application
Religious denomination: Roman Catholic

Curriculum

The National Curriculum at KS2/KS3 is differentiated to meet the needs of students and programmes include opportunities to develop the foundation for student's independence and social skills.

The KS4/KS5 (14-19) curriculum is an independence programme aimed at allowing students the opportunities to develop their independence skills to their full potential. This is achieved by developing a personalised programme designed to meet the needs of the individual students. The Foundation Learning Programme at 14-19 is divided into three main sections. Firstly, the Functional Skills Programmes of literacy, numeracy and ICT. Secondly, the Vocational Education Programme including work related activities and work experience. Thirdly, the Personal Social Development Programme including community skills and independent living skills. Students also have the opportunity to participate in our Travel Training Programme.

During their final year, students are supported by the Transition Worker to prepare them for the next stage in their life such as college or employment.

Students also have the opportunity to undertake link courses with local colleges.

We have a well-equipped purpose-built centre for the Post-16 students, which also accommodates the Speech and Language Department, Science, Technology, ICT Suite and Drama Studio.

Two full-time speech and language therapists, an occupational therapist and a music therapist liaise closely with teaching/care staff, parents and other professionals who contribute to the Individual Education Programmes for students across all the Key Stages to provide a 24-hour curriculum.

Examinations offered

OCR Functional Skills: Maths, English and ICT (Entry One to Level Two), OCR Entry Level Science, ASDAN Transition Challenge; Bronze Award, NOCN Personal Progress; Independent Living Skills; Step up Award Certificate/ Diploma.

The Trustees of the Sacred Hearts of Jesus and Mary (registered charity no. 287232) aim to prepare students with learning difficulties for life in a challenging and constantly changing world.

Kisimul School

(Founded 1977)

The Old Vicarage, 61 High Street, Swinderby, Lincoln, Lincolnshire LN6 9LU
Tel: 01522 868279   Email: admissions@kisimul.co.uk
Fax: 01522 866000   Website: www.kisimul.co.uk

Director of Education: Mr Danny Carter BA(Hons), MA, MEd
School type: Coeducational Independent Residential Special School
Age range of pupils: 8–19
No. of pupils enrolled as at 1.1.13: 60
Fees per annum as at 1.1.13:
On application

Kisimul School is one of the UK's leading independent residential special schools, offering a homely and safe environment for children who have severe learning difficulties, challenging behaviour, autism and global developmental delay.

Kisimul School offers residential education, care and leisure programmes at both our upper and lower school, for up to 52 weeks of the year, for pupils aged 8 to 19 years. The school is registered with the Department for Education and Ofsted. Limited day placements are also offered at both school sites.

The name Kisimul, pronounced 'kishmul', was taken from Kisimul Castle, which overlooks one of the safest harbours in the British Isles. Like its namesake, Kisimul School offers a safe haven, providing care and protection for its pupils whilst preparing them for the journey ahead into adulthood.

Kisimul School was founded in 1977 in a comfortable Georgian house (known today as the Old Vicarage) set in four acres within the small Lincolnshire village of Swinderby. Facilities at the Old Vicarage include an indoor heated swimming pool, large playground, soft play areas with ball pool and multi-sensory rooms for relaxation and stimulation.

In 2003, our upper school, Acacia Hall opened, offering the same standard of exceptional care and education within grounds adapted and utilised in a way to reflect the older age group. Acacia Hall offers riding stables, an adventure playground, collection of small farm animals and an area dedicated to horticulture.

Kisimul School has opened an additional school, Woodstock House, in Long Ditton, Surrey. Woodstock House received its first pupils in April

2008, and again offers the same quality of care and education for pupils aged 8 to 19 years. Kisimul School has developed this site to be a mirror image of its existing school operations, using the same teaching methods and ethos.

Kisimul School's mission is to continuously strive for excellence in the care and education of its pupils, with a vision to have the best assisted living environment.

The school provides a caring, consistent, safe and supportive environment in which its young people can flourish and develop their skills in order to fully realise their individual potential. Residential and school staff work closely together to enable the pupils to progress in their personal development and learning. The 24-hour approach incorporates a wide range of activities to enrich the learning experiences of all pupils, helping them to learn to communicate and cooperate more effectively with others and enabling them to grow in confidence, self-esteem and independence.

The highly structured school curriculum aims to address the very specific needs of our pupils, by providing every opportunity for them to enjoy their education and develop their skills, knowledge and understanding through practical and functional learning experiences.

Classes are small and staffed at a ratio of at least 1:1. The integrated developmental curriculum incorporates the National Curriculum (lower school) or Adult Pre-Entry Curriculum Framework (Post-16) and a wide range of therapeutic programmes, collectively designed to meet the diverse sensory needs of our pupils. These include speech and language therapy, music therapy, aromatherapy, play development, HANDLE (Holistic Approach to Neuro-Development and Learning Efficiency) and EASIE (Exercise and Sound in Education).

A key priority is to develop our pupils' communication skills and since many are non-verbal we teach the alternative and augmentative systems of Makaton signing and PECS (Picture Exchange Communication System) alongside vocalisations and speech.

External accreditation is gained through a wide variety of ASDAN 'Towards Independence' programmes and the Duke of Edinburgh's Award Scheme.

Kisimul School works closely with the parents, carers and professionals from its placing authorities to ensure the highest possible standards of care and education.

Kisimul School is committed to the view that all people are entitled to equality of opportunity regardless of ability or disability, gender or chosen gender, age, status, religion, belief, nationality, ethnic origins or sexual orientation.

For further information, including exciting job opportunities within Kisimul School, please visit our website at www.kisimul.co.uk or contact us at the address above.

The Centre Academy Schools

(Founded 1974)

Centre Academy London
92 St John's Hill
Battersea, London SW11 1SH
Tel: 020 7738 2344
Fax: 020 7738 9862
info@centreacademy.net

Centre Academy East Anglia
Church Road
Brettenham, Suffolk IP7 7QR
Tel: 01449 736404
Fax: 01449 737881
admin@centreacademy.net

Website: www.centreacademy.net

Principal: Duncan Rollo BA, MA, PhD
Headteacher, CA London: Vikki Langford BA, MA
Head of School, CA East Anglia: Kim Salthouse, BA MEd
CA London: Independent coeducational day school for children ages 9-19 with special needs
CA East Anglia: Independent coeducational day and boarding school for children ages 7-19 with special needs, also pre-prep 4-7 for all abilities.
Members of: ECIS, LISA, BDA, CReSTeD, NASEN ADHD Alliance
Average size of class: 5 or 6
Teacher/pupil ratio: 1:3

'The most successful and unique special needs schools in the UK.'

The Centre Academy Schools enable students with a variety of learning difficulties to reclaim their futures. We do so by teaching the skills and coping strategies that students with Dyslexia, Dyspraxia, AD/HD, ASD and other learning challenges require in order to succeed.

With exceptionally small classes, significant one-on-one instruction and dedicated and experienced faculty members, the Centre Academy Schools make it possible for their students to work to their fullest potential. Following testing and evaluation, we design a programme of instruction tailored to meet the student's individual needs.

We are able to cater to the strengths of the individual student rather than being limited to a 'one size fits all' approach. This is achieved by offering both the British National Curriculum through GCSE and the American High School Diploma. The Diploma, seen as the gateway to university, involves a system of continual assessment, thus reducing the pressure and anxiety that so frequently accompany exams.

English and maths form the core of a student's studies. Other key areas involve history, science, ICT, music, drama, art, PSHE, geography, religious studies and a modern foreign language. Students have a wide variety of choices for GCSE studies, and Centre Academy students frequently earn A*-C in seven or eight subjects (including English and mathematics). The efforts of our teaching staff are complemented by a coterie of specialists: speech and language; occupational therapy; reading; counselling, all offered on site.

At CA London, we are able to use the capital's cultural, artistic and historic possibilities as our own personal classroom. Our choices are as broad as the imagination – and our students are the richer for it. We are well served by all forms of public transportation, and Clapham Junction Railway Station is only a five-minute walk from our front door.

Offering both boarding and day programmes, CA East Anglia is located on the edge of a small, rural village, located 45 minutes from Cambridge by car, and one hour by train from London. Our ten-acre campus comprises a variety of elegant classroom buildings and excellent boarding facilities for both boys and girls. There are excellent activities for sport, art and drama and a range of activities including riding, sailing and karate. All boarding students are supported by highly trained staff members and by an experienced Head of Care.

The Centre Academy Schools have so much emphasis on the individual that we must of necessity remain small. At CA London the coeducational student body is capped at 60; at CA East Anglia it's capped at 45. We view ourselves as a community, and the family atmosphere at both schools reflects our ethos of care and nurturing.

Parents are invited to see our website or ring either school for a prospectus and to arrange a visit.

Parayhouse School

(Founded 1964)

New Kings School Annex, New Kings Road, Fulham, London SW6 4LY
Tel: 020 7751 0914   Email: a:sullivan@parayhouse.com
Fax: 020 7751 0914   Website: www.parayhouse.com

Head: Mrs Sarah Jackson CertEd, DipEd(Complex Learning Handicap)
School type: Coeducational Day
Specialist speech, language & communications needs, learning difficulties
Member of: NASS, NASEN, ICAN, DSA, PWSA, EQUALS, BACD, Afasic, ASDAN, SSAT
Age range of pupils: 7–16
No. of pupils enrolled as at 1.1.13: 46
Boys: 35 Girls: 11
Fees per annum as at 1.1.13: Day: £23,550

Parayhouse is a non-maintained special school for students with speech, language and communication needs, moderate learning disability and associated emotional, social and behavioural difficulties. The school is a registered charity (No. 1090757) and exists to provide its students with the language and learning they need for life.

A major strength of the school is our close-knit multi-professional team, which has grown over the years to include five key teachers and additional specialist teachers, three speech and language therapists, an occupational therapist, a music therapist and a family support manager. Together we have developed a uniquely integrated approach whereby teaching, therapeutic and support staff work side by side to plan and deliver a carefully differentiated curriculum. The aim of our curriculum is to support our students' learning, communication and emotional needs, and ultimately prepare them for life beyond our school.

Families are welcome to book in to one of our monthly Visitors' Mornings, as are LAs and educational professionals. Following a parental visit all prospective students will need to spend at least two days in school for observation, so that we can be sure we can meet that student's complex special educational needs.

Please contact the school for a copy of our prospectus, or visit the website.

I CAN's Meath School

(Founded 1982)

Brox Road, Ottershaw, Surrey KT16 0LF
Tel: 01932 872302   Email: meath@meath-ican.org.uk
Fax: 01932 875180   Website: www.meathschool.org.uk or www.ican.org.uk

i can

helps children
communicate
REGISTERED CHARITY 210031

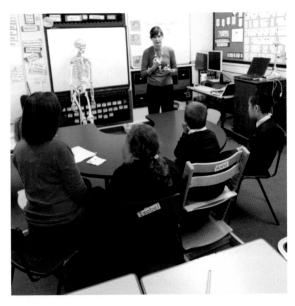

Headteacher: Janet Dunn OBE, MA,
AdvDipSpecEduc
Appointed: September 2003
School type: Coeducational Day & Residential
Age range of pupils:
No. of pupils enrolled as at 1.1.13: 51
Fees per annum as at 1.1.13:
On request

I CAN's Meath School is a residential (weekly) and day school providing teaching, therapy and care to children aged 4-11 years, whose primary difficulty is speech, language and communication, including Asperger's Syndrome learners. Children with associated difficulties including some degree of learning difficulty, attention control, fine and gross motor co-ordination problems, mild visual and/or hearing impairments, medical needs and social interaction problems may also benefit from the provision.

Ofsted Inspectors commented (Jan 2011): "Meath School provides an outstanding education for all its pupils, catering exceptionally well for the mixture of complex needs of the pupils. They make outstanding progress in both their academic and their personal development through the very effective partnership between education, therapy and care staff. The overwhelming majority of parents and carers are right that this is an excellent school."

The school offers many specialist practices, *eg* signing, Cued Articulation, Alternative Augmentative Communication and visual supports, which enable full access to differentiated Early Years, KS1/KS2 National Curriculum teaching. There are high staffing ratios with professionally qualified, highly experienced staff. Each class (average 10 children) has an allocated teacher, speech and language therapist and learning support assistant(s). Occupational therapy staff support individual children and school-wide class based motor-skills groups and sensory integration sessions. There is also a part-time nurse and specialist art, PE and music teaching. An activity and life skills programme is offered in the residential setting by the child care staff.

Strong partnerships with parents/carers are vital to the success of pupils. Families are encouraged to make observation visits to the school, and to contribute to their child's IEP targets. The school has a family liaison worker who can work with the whole family in the home context.

Meath School is housed in fine Victorian buildings and the site includes a modern teaching block, gym, music, art and cookery rooms, ICT suite, small swimming pool, school field, activity play areas and woodland. The school has a programme of after school clubs and a summer holiday club.

Meath School is part of I CAN, the children's communication charity (www.ican.org.uk), and is an integral part of the I CAN Centre in Surrey. The Centre and School offer flexi placements and holistic multi-disciplinary independent two day specialist assessments.

Mark College

Mark, Highbridge, Somerset TA9 4NP
Tel: 01278 641632   Email: markcollege@priorygroup.com
Fax: 01278 641426   Website: www.priorygroup.com/markcollege

Principal: Ms Michelle Whitham-Jones
School type: Coeducational Day & Boarding
Special School for dyslexia, dyspraxia and dyscalculia
Member of: ISA, CReSTeD, BSA
Age range of pupils: 10–19
No. of pupils enrolled as at 1.1.13: 88
Religious denomination: Church of England

Mark College is a specialist residential school for boys and girls aged 10 to 19 with specific learning difficulties including: language disorders, dyslexia, dyscalculia and dyspraxia. Students are offered a flexible curriculum, tailored to meet their needs according to their individual difficulties.

Mark College provides a warm and welcoming environment in which students benefit from being with others who share the same difficulties with language. The level of support and teaching methods are specifically designed to overcome the challenges that students with specific learning difficulties face.

The College is able to provide a wide range of services aimed at each young person and aiding them in their development, including;

- Small classes and personalised programmes of learning geared towards individual success

- Subject specialist staff, trained to teach students with specific learning difficulties and language disorders

- Emphasis on educational achievement

- Voice-output and voice-recognition technology to assist learning

- Focus on self-achievement and becoming independent learners

- Sixth form life skills programs

- A caring environment where students can develop and grow

Therapeutic approaches used at Mark College include:

Speech and language therapies, occupational therapist, art therapy, pets for therapy and key workers and individualised support packages.

Mark College develops a wide range of positive outcomes for each individual young person, with highlights including:

- 100% of young people are engaged in age appropriate independence programmes

- 100% of residential young people are taking part in clubs or social groups within the community

- 100% of pupils are accessing regular key worker sessions

- Consistent success rates when working with young people who have experienced school phobia

A number of former students of Mark College are now developing successful careers that include: film director, plumber, architect, landscape gardener, teacher, computer systems engineer, farmer, marine biologist, car design engineer, retail manager, art and ceramic designer, TV cameraman, web designer and business entrepreneur.

Admissions criteria:

- Girls and boys aged ten to 19 years

- Diagnosed with specific learning difficulties, language disorder, dyslexia, dyspraxia, ASD or dyscalculia

- A desire to learn

- We are unable to accommodate young people with primary behavioural problems

Kisimul School – Woodstock House

(Opened 2008)

Woodstock Lane North, Long Ditton, Surbiton, Surrey KT6 5HN
Tel: 020 8335 2570   Email: admissions@kisimul.co.uk
Fax: 020 8335 2571   Website: www.kisimul.co.uk

Director of Education: Mr Danny Carter BA(Hons), MA, MEd
School type: Coeducational Independent Residential Special School
Age range of pupils: 8–19
No. of pupils enrolled as at 1.1.13: 40
Fees per annum as at 1.1.13:
On application

Kisimul School is one of the UK's leading independent residential special schools, offering a homely and safe environment for children who have severe learning difficulties, challenging behaviour, autism and global developmental delay.

Kisimul School offers residential education, care and leisure programmes at both our upper and lower school, for up to 52 weeks of the year, for pupils aged 8 to 19 years. The school is registered with the Department for Education and Ofsted. Limited day placements are also offered at both school sites.

The name Kisimul, pronounced 'kishmul', was taken from Kisimul Castle, which overlooks one of the safest harbours in the British Isles. Like its namesake, Kisimul School offers a safe haven, providing care

and protection for its pupils whilst preparing them for the journey ahead into adulthood.

The original Kisimul School was founded in 1977 in a comfortable Georgian house (known today as the Old Vicarage) set in four acres within the small Lincolnshire village of Swinderby. Facilities at the Old Vicarage include an indoor heated swimming pool, large playground, soft play areas with ball pool and multi-sensory rooms for relaxation and stimulation.

In 2003, our upper school, Acacia Hall opened, offering the same standard of exceptional care and education within grounds adapted and utilised in a way to reflect the older age group. Acacia Hall offers riding stables, an adventure playground, collection of small farm animals and an area dedicated to horticulture.

Woodstock House received its first pupils in April 2008, and again offers the same quality of care and education for pupils aged 8 to 19 years. Kisimul School has developed this site to be a mirror image of its existing school operations, using the same teaching methods and ethos.

Woodstock House is situated within 8.1 acres of tranquil countryside, offering space to develop in a safe and secure environment. Woodstock House is within easy access from the M25 via the A3.

Kisimul School's mission is to continuously strive for excellence in the care and education of its pupils, with a vision to have the best assisted living environment.

The school provides a caring, consistent, safe and supportive environment in which its young people can flourish and develop their skills in order to fully realise their individual potential. Residential and school staff work closely together to enable the pupils to progress in their personal development and learning. The 24-hour approach incorporates a wide range of activities to enrich the learning experiences of all pupils, helping them to learn to communicate and cooperate more effectively with others and enabling them to grow in confidence, self-esteem and independence.

The highly structured school curriculum aims to address the very specific needs of our pupils, by providing every opportunity for them to enjoy their education and develop their skills, knowledge and understanding through practical and functional learning experiences.

Classes are small and staffed at a ratio of at least 1:1. The integrated developmental curriculum incorporates the National Curriculum (lower school) or Adult Pre-Entry Curriculum Framework (Post-16) and a wide range of therapeutic programmes, collectively designed to meet the diverse sensory needs of our pupils. Our sensory integration programmes include speech and language therapy, music therapy, aromatherapy, occupational therapy, educational psychology input and EASIE (Exercise and Sound in Education).

A key priority is to develop our pupils' communication skills and since many are non-verbal we teach the alternative and augmentative systems of Makaton signing and PECS (Picture Exchange Communication System) alongside vocalisations and speech.

External accreditation is gained through a wide variety of ASDAN 'Towards Independence' programmes and the Duke of Edinburgh's Award Scheme.

Kisimul School works closely with the parents, carers and professionals from its placing authorities to ensure the highest possible standards of care and education.

Kisimul School is committed to the view that all people are entitled to equality of opportunity regardless of ability or disability, gender or chosen gender, age, status, religion, belief, nationality, ethnic origins or sexual orientation.

For further information, including exciting job opportunities within Kisimul School, please visit our website at www.kisimul.co.uk or contact us at the address above.

Portfield School

(Founded 1971)

Parley Lane, Christchurch, Dorset BH23 6BP
Tel: 01202 573808   Email: enquiries@portfieldschool.org.uk
Website: www.portfieldschool.org.uk

Director of Services: Andrew Thomas
Headteacher: Tyler Collins
School type: Non-maintained Special
Residential/Day School
Flexible boarding and respite care also available
Age range of pupils: 3–19
No. of pupils enrolled as at 1.1.13: 57
Boys: 51 Girls: 6
Fees per annum as at 1.1.13:
Available on request
Average size of class: 5

About

Portfield School is managed by Autism Wessex, the regional charity for people with autism. The school supports children and young people with autism and associated difficulties.

Each student's curriculum and care plan is individually designed to reflect their abilities and personal development needs. It is shaped to provide a learning journey to help prepare them for the opportunities, experiences and responsibilities of adult life.

Education

The school is bright, airy and calm, with large spacious rooms and numerous specialist resources. Our curriculum provides a framework for meaningful, age appropriate learning and is designed to ensure the learning that takes place is relevant, engaging and enjoyable.

The primary curriculum has an emphasis on the development of the key skills of literacy, numeracy and ICT as well as a focus on personal and learning skills. The secondary curriculum allows for greater personalisation, it provides a range of vocational, leisure and citizenship opportunities to allow students to make informed choices about their future.

Alongside our highly trained and experienced education and care staff is our specialist support team, which includes a nurse, speech and language therapists, occupational therapists and behaviour therapists.

Residential facilities

Portfield offers flexible boarding opportunities from 30 to 52 weeks. There are four modern purpose-built boarding houses on the school site and an additional house in Christchurch for post-16 students.

Life Skills

Our Life Skills service is designed for students aged 15-19. This full-time curriculum comprises of 'study programmes', which allow for extensive tailoring for each individual. We can adjust the curriculum around students' aspirations and learning needs.

Quotes

"While our initial view of the school was very positive, we totally underestimated the ability of the staff to transform our child's life." (Parent)

"Our son is getting an education in a fantastic, caring school with amazing staff. We cannot imagine life without Portfield." (Parent)

Overley Hall School

(Founded 1979)

Overley, Wellington, Telford, Telford & Wrekin TF6 5HE
Tel: 01952 740262   Email: info@overleyhall.com
Fax: 01952 740262   Website: www.overleyhall.com

Principal: Mrs Anita Brown BA(Hons), CertEd, DipSpEd
Head of School: Ms Gill Flannery
School type: Coeducational Residential
Age range of pupils: 9–19
No. of pupils enrolled as at 1.2.13: 22
Boys: 15 Girls: 7

Overley Hall School is an independent, residential special school and children's home, providing education and care to children and young adults aged from eight to 19 years who have a wide range of complex needs including autism, epilepsy and severe learning disabilities. The school is committed to offering each child a wide range of good quality experiences; this occurs through partnerships with parents/carers, teachers and therapists in the delivery of a waking day curriculum by a dedicated team.

In-house speech and language and occupational therapies are offered regularly to each child.

The school/residential home is set in a quiet, rural location which provides a calm and nurturing learning and living environment for young people in our care. Our school building, alongside the residential house, stands in 13 acres of lawn, walled kitchen garden and woodland.

Other facilities within the campus and grounds include a lifeskills room, indoor sensory hydropool, soft play space, art and craft workshops, sensory rooms, recreational and relaxation areas.

Our registered 'Forest School' operates within the woodland areas, and is led by qualified practitioners from Overley Hall School; this offers pupils opportunities for multi-sensory outdoor learning and recreation experiences throughout the seasons.

Fullerton House School

(Founded 1990)

Tickill Square, Denaby, Doncaster, South Yorkshire DN12 4AR
Tel: 01709 861663   Email: enquiries@hesleygroup.co.uk
Fax: 01709 869635   Website: www.fullertonhouseschool.co.uk

Head: David Whitehead
School type: Coeducational 52-week residential
Age range of pupils: 8–19
No. of pupils enrolled as at 1.1.13: 46
Fees per annum as at 1.1.13:
Available on request

A specialist residential school offering flexible education and care for up to 52-weeks-per-year for young people aged 8-19, all of whom have complex needs including behaviour that may challenge and a learning disability, often in association with autism.

Fullerton House School is situated in the heart of the village of Denaby Main, near Doncaster. Its central location provides easy access by road, rail or air. Our mission is to enhance the lives of the 46 young people entrusted to us by focusing on their specific needs, capabilities and aspirations.

Education: Each young person has a carefully designed Individual Learning Plan based on their specific needs in line with the National Curriculum.

Extended learning: During evenings, weekends and school holidays a wide range of extra-curricular activities are on offer to ensure that young people are fully engaged with stimulating experiences both on and off-site.

Professional services: A dedicated on-site team including carers, teachers, tutors, clinical, communication, behaviour and occupational therapy specialists ensure that young people have ready access to the services they require.

High-quality accommodation: Single person and small group occupancy of high-quality accommodation is the model of living arrangement at Fullerton House School. Every young person has their own bedroom, the majority of which have en-suite bathrooms. We also have a range of on-site facilities to complement and enrich the lives of those who come to live and learn with us.

Keeping in touch: We understand that while we may offer the best service for the young person, we may not be on your doorstep. Keeping in touch with loved ones is essential. Everyone has a plan that will include how they will stay in contact with family/carers and friends whether this be by phone, letter, email or Skype. Whatever works best for the young person we support.

Wilsic Hall School

(Founded 1996)

Wadworth, Doncaster, South Yorkshire DN11 9AG
Tel: 01302 856382   Email: enquiries@hesleygroup.co.uk
Fax: 01302 853608   Website: www.wilsichallschool.co.uk

Head: Geoff Turner
School type: Coeducational 52-week residential
Age range of pupils: 11–19
No. of pupils enrolled as at 1.1.13: 36
Fees per annum as at 1.1.13:
Available on request

A specialist residential school offering flexible education and care for up to 52-weeks-per-year for young people aged 11-19, all of whom have complex needs including behaviour that may challenge and a learning disability, often in association with autism.

Wilsic Hall School is situated in its own 14-acre site approximately five miles south of Doncaster. Its central location provides easy access by road, rail or air. Our mission is to enhance the lives of the 36 young people entrusted to us by focusing on their specific needs, capabilities and aspirations.

Education: Each young person has a carefully designed Individual Education Plan based on their specific needs in line with the National Curriculum.

Extended learning: During evenings, weekends and school holidays a wide range of extra-curricular activities are on offer to ensure that young people are fully engaged with stimulating experiences both on and off-site.

Professional services: A dedicated team including carers, teachers, tutors, clinical, behaviour, communication and occupational therapy specialists ensure that each young person has ready access to the services they require.

High-quality accommodation: Single person and small group occupancy of high-quality accommodation is the model of living arrangement at Wilsic Hall School. Every young person has their own bedroom, the majority of which have en-suite bathrooms. We also have a range of on-site facilities to complement and enrich the lives of those who come to live and learn with us.

Keeping in touch: We understand that while we may offer the best service for the young person, we may not be on your doorstep. Keeping in touch with loved ones is essential. Everyone has a plan that will include how they will stay in contact with family/carers and friends whether this be by phone, letter, email or Skype. Whatever works best for the young person we support.

Action for Children Headlands School

action for children

(Founded 1921)

2 St Augustine's Road, Penarth, Vale of Glamorgan CF64 1YY
Tel: 02920 709771   Email: headlands.school@actionforchildren.org.uk
Fax: 02920 700515   Website: www.actionforchildren.org.uk/headlands

Principal: Matthew Burns
School type: Coeducational Boarding & Day
An independent special needs school that offers day and term time residential placements.
Special needs provision: ADD, ADHD, ASP, ASD, SP, BESD, CD, DYS, MLD, ODD, SP&LD, TOU
Member of: NASEN, NAS
Age range of pupils: 8–19
No. of pupils enrolled as at 1.1.13: 54
Boys: 47 Girls: 7

Action for Children Headlands School provides high-quality education and care to children and young people who have difficulty managing their behaviour, preparing them for a happy and fulfilling adult life.

Who we help

Action for Children Headlands School helps young people who are having difficulty learning as a result of challenging behaviour, including those with behavioural, emotional and social difficulties (BESD), autistic spectrum disorder (ASD) and Asperger syndrome.

How we help

Education, activities and residential care are provided onsite and children may attend as boarders or as day pupils.

At the heart of the school is a pupil support team, a multi-disciplinary group focusing on behaviour management, including regular consultations with local psychiatrists and the school's consultant clinical psychologist.

All our staff are trained in therapeutic crisis intervention (TCI), giving them the skills to respond to crisis behaviour and recognise trigger points.

Education

In addition to the National Curriculum, the school runs a number of innovative initiatives, such as the Award Scheme Development, offering activity-based learning. We also provide a Post-16 provision where students have individualised plans that involve part time placements at a local college, work experience and the facility to study for external and vocational exams, improve on their GCSE grades and access to A levels. In addition, we provide a Key Stage 2 primary centre where we deliver the International Primary Curriculum.

Residential care

Residential care is very high quality, with a strong emphasis on developing relationships and the pupils' wide key skills. Residential care is provided on a term-time basis.

'I have improved my reading and now feel more confident. I have started a college course in construction and go to work one day a week' – a young person at Headlands School.

Plas Dwbl Farm College

Mynachlog-ddu, Clunderwen, Pembrokeshire SA66 7SE
Tel: 01449 419420   Email: info@plasdwbl.rmt.org
Website: www.rmt.org

Principal: Elisabeth Johnson
School type: Coeducational Day & Residential
Age range of pupils: 16–25

Plas Dwbl Farm College offers places to young people with complex learning and behavioural difficulties, mental health issues and autistic spectrum disorders including Asperger's Syndrome.

Practical Skills Therapeutic Education

Plas Dwbl Farm College is set amongst 100 acres of rolling hills with a biodynamic farm and woodlands. It is one of four colleges operated by Ruskin Mill Trust, whose internationally renowned Practical Skills Therapeutic Education method offers young people a unique opportunity to learn and develop through meaningful real-life activities and accredited courses.

The college provides a range of nutritional, therapeutic and medical support. Healthy organic food is grown, harvested and prepared with students. Each core element of the educational cycle is designed to establish active and positive relationships with nature, people and the community through a holistic approach to human development.

Integrated Learning For Living and Work Programme

Plas Dwbl Farm College offers a personalised pre-entry assessment leading to an individualised learning and development programme. A rich and varied curriculum offers exciting opportunities to develop communication, social, work and living skills. Activities include practical land-based and traditional craft activities, animal husbandry, woodland management, horticulture and catering with communication and functional skills embedded throughout the curriculum.

Accreditation and Transition

Courses are accredited through the Qualification and Credit Framework and students will also prepare for work competency through a wide range of internal and external work experience. Qualifications include

NVQs and BTECs; other options are available in partnership with local providers. The curriculum is also supported by additional sessions and activities which help students to understand and explore the culture and history of the area and try their crafts. In their final year, students work with a dedicated and highly skilled transition team to prepare for life after college.

Residential Provision

Students live in family houses or team houses which offer the consistency, warmth and positive role modelling that some young adults need to develop their living skills and reach their full potential. Students can then progress to placements in training flats where they have the opportunity to take greater responsibility for themselves.

Plas Dwbl Farm College takes referrals throughout the year and offers 52-week placements.

Admissions

For all initial enquiries please contact the Admissions Team on 01994 419420 or by email at: admissions@plasdwbl.rmt.org

Ruskin Mill Trust is an educational charity and draws its inspiration from the insights of Rudolf Steiner, John Ruskin and William Morris. Charity No: 1137167

Colleges of further education specialising in learning difficulties (including dyslexia/SPLD)

Ruskin Mill College

The Fisheries, Horsley, Gloucestershire GL6 0PL
Tel: 01453 837500   Email: enquiries@rmc.rmt.org
Fax: 01453 837506   Website: www.rmt.org

Principal: Elisabeth Johnson
School type: Coeducational Day & Residential
Age range of pupils: 16–25

Ruskin Mill College, awarded 'Outstanding' by Ofsted and Beacon status by LSIS, offers over 100 places to young people with complex learning and behavioural difficulties, mental health issues and autistic spectrum disorders including Asperger's Syndrome.

Practical Skills Therapeutic Education

Set in 140 acres including a biodynamic farm, woodlands and a fishery, the college is one of four operated by Ruskin Mill Trust, whose internationally renowned Practical Skills Therapeutic Education method offers young people a unique opportunity to learn and develop through meaningful real-life activities and accredited courses.

The college provides an extensive range of nutritional, therapeutic and medical support. Healthy organic food is grown, harvested and prepared with students. Each core element of the educational cycle is designed to establish active and positive relationships with nature, people and the community through a holistic approach to human development.

Integrated Learning For Living and Work

The college offers a personalised pre-entry assessment leading to an individualised learning and development programme. A rich and varied curriculum offers exciting opportunities to develop communication, social, work and living skills. Activities include practical land-based and traditional craft activities, animal husbandry, fish farming, woodland management, horticulture, catering and hospitality, music, art and drama with communication and functional skills embedded throughout the curriculum.

Accreditation and Transition

Courses are accredited through the Qualification and Credit Framework and students will also prepare for work competency through a wide range of internal and external work experience. Qualifications include OCNs, NVQs and BTECs as well as GCSE and AS levels delivered in partnership with local providers. The college's cultural programme offers students further opportunities to develop their social and work skills. In their final year, students work with a dedicated transition team to prepare for life after college.

Residential Provision

First and second-year students live in family houses or team houses which offer the consistency, warmth and positive role modelling that some young adults need to develop their living skills and reach their full potential. Students can progress to placements in training flats where they have the opportunity to take greater responsibility for themselves.

Ruskin Mill College takes referrals throughout the year and offers 52-week placements.

Admissions

For all initial enquiries please contact the Admissions Team on 01453 837502 or by email: admissions@rmc.rmt.org

Ruskin Mill Trust is an educational charity and draws its inspiration from the insights of Rudolf Steiner, John Ruskin and William Morris. Charity No: 1137167

Glasshouse College

Wollaston Road, Amblecote, Stourbridge, West Midlands DY8 4HF
Tel: 01384 399400   Email: enquiries@ghc.rmt.org
Fax: 01384 399401   Website: www.rmt.org

Principal: Ollie Cheney
School type: Coeducational Day & Residential
Age range of pupils: 16–25

Glasshouse College, awarded 'Good' by Ofsted, offers over 90 places to young people with complex learning and behavioural difficulties, mental health issues and autistic spectrum disorders including Asperger's Syndrome.

Practical Skills Therapeutic Education

Set in the heritage glassmaking district of Stourbridge with a 36-acre farm and woodlands nearby, the college is one of four operated by Ruskin Mill Trust, whose internationally renowned Practical Skills Therapeutic Education method offers young people a unique opportunity to learn and develop through meaningful real-life activities and accredited courses.

The college provides an extensive range of nutritional, therapeutic and medical support. Healthy organic food is grown, harvested and prepared with students. Each core element of the educational cycle is designed to establish active and positive relationships with nature, people and the community through a holistic approach to human development.

Integrated Learning For Living and Work

A personalised pre-entry assessment leads to an individualised learning and development programme.

A rich and varied curriculum offers exciting opportunities to develop communication, social, work and living skills and two newly refurbished state-of-the-art visitor centres, the Glasshouse Arts Centre and the Ruskin Glass Centre, offer students exceptional opportunities to develop social and vocational skills in professional and public environments.

Activities include traditional glassmaking, land-based and traditional craft activities, animal husbandry, woodland management, bow making, archery, mountain biking, catering, narrowboat, music, art, drama and maskmaking with communication and functional skills embedded throughout.

Accreditation and Transition

Courses are accredited through the Qualification and Credit Framework and include OCNs, NVQs, BTECs, and GCSE and AS levels in partnership with local providers. Work competency is gained through a wide range of internal and external work experience. In their final year, students work with a dedicated team to prepare for transition.

Residential Provision

First and second-year students live in family houses or team houses offering the consistency, warmth and positive role modelling that some young adults need to develop living skills and reach their full potential. Students can progress to placements in training flats where they have the opportunity to take greater responsibility for themselves.

Glasshouse College takes referrals throughout the year and offers 52-week placements.

Admissions

For all initial enquiries please contact the Admissions Team on 01384 399434 or by email at:

admissions@ghc.rmt.org

Ruskin Mill Trust is an educational charity and draws its inspiration from the insights of Rudolf Steiner, John Ruskin and William Morris. Charity No: 1137167

Freeman College

Sterling Works, 88 Arundel Street, Sheffield, South Yorkshire S1 2NG
Tel: 0114 252 5940   Email: enquiries@fmc.rmt.org
Fax: 0114 252 5996   Website: www.rmt.org

Principal: Bonny Etchell-Anderson
School type: Coeducational Day & Residential
Age range of pupils: 16–25

Freeman College, awarded 'Good' by Ofsted, offers over 90 places to young people with complex learning and behavioural difficulties, mental health issues and autistic spectrum disorders, including Asperger's Syndrome.

Practical Skills Therapeutic Education

Based in the illustrious metalworking district of Sheffield, the college is one of four operated by Ruskin Mill Trust, whose internationally renowned Practical Skills Therapeutic Education method offers young people a unique opportunity to learn and develop through meaningful real-life activities and accredited courses.

Freeman College provides an extensive range of nutritional, therapeutic and medical support. Healthy organic food is grown, harvested and prepared with students. Each core element of the educational cycle is designed to establish active and positive relationships with nature, people and the community through a holistic approach to human development.

Integrated Learning For Living and Work

A personalised pre-entry assessment leads to an individualised learning and development programme. A rich and varied curriculum offers exciting opportunities to develop communication, social, work and living skills. Activities include traditional metal crafts such as spoon forging, copper and pewter work, gilding and jewellery, as well as land-based and traditional crafts, animal husbandry, horticulture, catering and hospitality, music, art and drama with communication and functional skills embedded throughout the curriculum.

Accreditation and Transition

Courses are accredited through the Qualification and Credit Framework and include OCNs, NVQs, BTECs, as well as GCSE and AS levels delivered in partnership with local providers. Work competency is gained through a wide range of internal and external work experience including through its arts and crafts shop, the Academy of Makers, cultural and events programmes, workshops and award-winning cafŽ. In their final year, students collaborate with a dedicated transition team to prepare for life after college.

Residential Provision

First and second-year students live in family houses or team houses which offer the consistency, warmth and positive role modelling that some young adults need to develop their living skills and reach their full potential. Students can progress to placements in training flats where they have the opportunity to take greater responsibility for themselves.

Freeman College takes referrals throughout the year and offers 52-week placements.

Admissions

For all initial enquiries please contact the Admissions Team on 0114 252 5953 or by email: admissions@fmc.rmt.org

Ruskin Mill Trust is an educational charity and draws its inspiration from the insights of Rudolf Steiner, John Ruskin and William Morris. Charity No: 1137167

Schools and colleges specialising in emotional, behavioural and/or social difficulties (EBSD)

Wings School, Nottinghamshire

(Founded 2010)

Kirklington Hall, Kirklington, Newark, Nottinghamshire NG22 8NB
Tel: 01636 817430   Email: info@wingsnottsschool.co.uk
Fax: 01636 817435   Website: www.wingsschool.co.uk

Director of Education & Care: Mrs Pam Redican
School type: Coeducational Independent Residential Special School
Member of: NASS
Age range of pupils: 9–17
DfE and Ofsted full registration–for 54 pupils
No. of pupils enrolled as at 1.1.13: 45
Boys: 25 Girls: 20
Fees per annum as at 1.1.13:
Available on application

Aims and philosophy

Wings School was established to replicate the excellent work of its sister school Wings in Cumbria.

We place particular emphasis on progress in schoolwork, success in national examinations and mainstream standards of behaviour, which are expected for all our young people. We help them to recognise the ways in which they approach everyday difficulties and to develop ways of dealing with them that make them happier and more successful, using emotional intelligence and effective thinking skills. We stress the importance of developing *self*-awareness and *self*-management rather than relying on external controls. We pay attention to everything that can make a difference in teaching, management or the physical environment and aim to develop the best practice in everything we do. We are committed to becoming a centre of excellence.

Staffing

(Total 80, including Teaching x 18, Care x 42, Learning Support Assistants x 8)

Pam Redican received a National Teaching Award for outstanding School Leadership in 2000 and the Pride of Britain Best Teacher Award 2007. We have a caring, enthusiastic and committed staff already highly experienced in working with children with emotional and behavioural difficulties. All teachers are fully qualified.

Support services provided

We have a school nurse and access to medical, mental health, careers and counselling services.

Specialist facilities

Our school building is a restored 16th century hall with excellent state-of-the-art classroom facilities, including specialist rooms for science, art, ICT and design and technology. We have an extensive sports hall on site to accommodate our PE and activity programmes. The residential accommodation for our children is purpose-built and furnished to a high standard of comfort and safety.

General environment

The school and accommodation are set in 20 acres of beautiful grounds in a pleasant rural location. There are excellent sports and recreational areas on the site and easy access to motorways and rail systems.

Home/school links

Emphasis is placed on excellent levels of consultation and communication with parents and carers at all times. Young people can be in daily contact with their parents/carers if they wish. Parents/carers are most welcome to visit at any time by appointment and assistance can be given to arrange overnight accommodation.

Wings School, Cumbria

(Founded 2003)

Whassett, Milnthorpe, Cumbria LA7 7DN
Tel: 01539 562006   Email: info@wingsschool.co.uk
Fax: 01539 564811   Website: www.wingsschool.co.uk

Director of Education & Care: Mrs Pam Redican
School type: Coeducational Independent Residential Special School
DfE and Ofsted - Full registration and approval for 59 pupils
Member of: NASS
Age range of pupils: 11–17
No. of pupils enrolled as at 1.1.13: 56
Boys: 28 Girls: 28
Fees per annum as at 1.1.13:
Available on application

Aims and philosophy

We place particular emphasis on progress in schoolwork, success in national examinations and mainstream standards of behaviour, which are expected for all our young people. We help them to recognise the ways in which they approach everyday difficulties and to develop ways of dealing with them that make them happier and more successful, using emotional intelligence and effective thinking skills. We stress the importance of developing *self*-awareness and *self*-management rather than relying on external controls. We pay attention to everything that can make a difference in teaching, management or the physical environment and aim to develop the best practice in everything we do. We are committed to becoming a centre of excellence.

Staffing

(Total 109, including Teaching x 14, Care x 59, Learning Support Assistants x 9)

Pam Redican received a National Teaching Award for outstanding School Leadership in 2000 and the Pride of Britain Best Teacher Award 2007. We have a caring, enthusiastic and committed staff highly experienced in working with children with emotional and behavioural difficulties. All teachers are fully qualified.

Support services provided

We have the services of a part-time consultant chartered educational psychologist and a school nurse and access to medical, mental health, careers and counselling services.

Specialist facilities

We have purpose-built, modern classrooms, technology and science facilities and award-winning residential accommodation, all furnished to a high standard of safety and comfort. We have an ICT suite to the most up-to-date specification and a new state-of-the-art sports hall, which accommodates the coaching of trampolining to national competition level.

General environment

We have 24 acres of beautiful grounds in a very pleasant rural location in south Cumbria with easy access to motorways and rail systems. There are excellent sports and recreational areas that include football pitches, a tennis/basketball court and safe fishing.

Home/school links

Emphasis is placed on excellent levels of consultation and communication with parents and carers at all times. Young people can be in daily contact with their parents/carers if they wish. Parents/carers are most welcome to visit at any time by appointment and assistance can be given to arrange overnight accommodation.

Philpots Manor School

(Founded 1959)

West Hoathly, East Grinstead, West Sussex RH19 4PR
Tel: 01342 810268   Email: jill.roberts@philpotsmanorschool.co.uk
Website: www.philpotsmanorschool.co.uk

Education Co-ordinator: Ms Linda Churnside BEd
School type: Coeducational Boarding
Member of: SWSF
Age range of pupils: 7–19
No. of pupils enrolled as at 9.1.13: 34
Boys: 22 Girls: 12
Fees per annum as at 1.1.13: Day: £55,116
Boarding: £55,116

Founded in 1959 and set in the heart of the Sussex countryside, Philpots Manor School is an independent residential school and training centre offering an academic and social education to children and young adults from 7 to 19 years of age.

The emotional, behavioural, social and communication problems that most of our students display may stem from a learning difficulty, social deprivation, abuse or from a recognised clinical condition, such as epilepsy, a development disorder or a mild autistic tendency. Students need to have the potential to function in a social situation. Because of this we do not admit students with severe learning difficulties, severe psychological problems, or with extreme behavioural problems.

Classes usually contain a maximum of six students with one class teacher and at least one class assistant. Our residential units can accommodate either up to six or ten residential students, depending on the size of the unit. We also cater for day students. We offer a 36 week curriculum with residential children returning home at weekends. As well as offering a wide range of academic subjects we also offer horse-riding, pottery, gardening, weaving, art and music. Most pupils are entered for examination at GCSE or Entry Level in English, maths, science and art at a time that is appropriate for each. Up to six GCSE subjects are offered.

OCN courses for Post-16 pupils accredit a wide range of subjects that most pupils study. Continuous assessment by the teachers avoids examinations for those pupils who least benefit from additional stress in their lives. Current courses include stable management, weaving, pottery and handwork.

We have play therapy, counselling, speech, music, Eurythmy and Bothmer Gym as well as a visiting osteopath. Therapies are included in the basic fee.

For further information, please visit our website at:

www.philpotsmanorschool.co.uk

or telephone 01342 810268

The New School at West Heath

(Founded 1998)

Ashgrove Road, Sevenoaks, Kent TN13 1SR
Tel: 01732 460553   Email: principal@westheathschool.com
Fax: 01732 456734   Website: www.westheathschool.com

Principal: Mrs Christina Wells
Appointed: September 2008
School type: Coeducational Day & Boarding
Age range of pupils: 10–19
No. of pupils enrolled as at 1.1.13:
Boys: 80 Girls: 31 Sixth Form: 40
No. of boarders: 28
Fees per annum as at 1.1.13: Day: £18,781
Weekly Boarding Supplement: £30,936
Average size of class: 9
Teacher/pupil ratio: 1:9

'Rebuilding Lives through education'

The New School at West Heath is a registered charity and is governed by a board of Trustees. We are an independent (residential) special school for boys and girls of secondary age and have high expectations of achievement for each and every one of our students. We provide for a wide range of accomplishment and academic success, with some of our ex-students progressing to university.

The strap line beneath our school logo is 'Rebuilding Lives through education' and this conveys the essence of what our school seeks to achieve. We provide for the needs of a constituency of students whose education has broken down because other

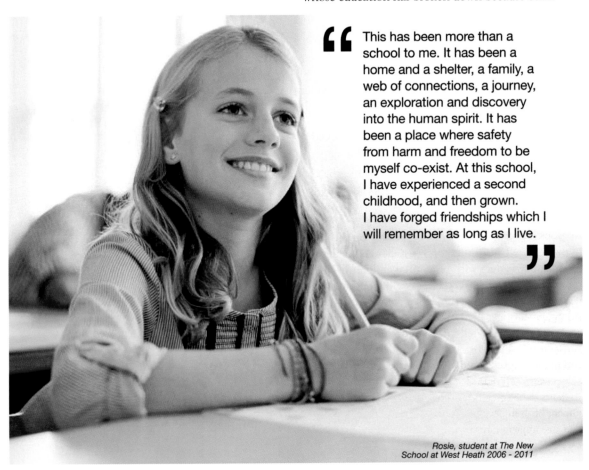

“ This has been more than a school to me. It has been a home and a shelter, a family, a web of connections, a journey, an exploration and discovery into the human spirit. It has been a place where safety from harm and freedom to be myself co-exist. At this school, I have experienced a second childhood, and then grown. I have forged friendships which I will remember as long as I live. ”

Rosie, student at The New School at West Heath 2006 - 2011

(mostly mainstream) schools have not been able to provide for their special educational needs.

We believe ...

- In our youngsters until they can believe in themselves.
- Happy people make good learners.
- Change is possible, success is mandatory.
- Qualifications are a good armour in life.
- Shadows of the past must not be allowed to shade the future.

We aim to develop mutually respectful and meaningful relationships amongst staff and students within a framework of sound values rooted in an absolute 'child centred' approach. Our staff are selected for their capacity to build warm, caring, nurturing and thoroughly professional relationships. We espouse the values of dignity, privacy, independence, self-fulfilment, choice and rights in preparing our youngsters both for their learning pathway within our school and for their future as potentially wise and responsible parents and active citizens.

This approach is reflected not only in the warm and accepting emotional atmosphere that we foster, which features high expectations of all, but also in the value and unique qualities of each individual student. This is reflected in the sense of pride we have in our history, the facilities we offer and the excellent physical environment in which we live and work.

We have achieved a unique blend of high academic achievement with students having emotional, social and behavioural difficulties. Our individual approach is reflected in the curriculum we offer, which features emotional literacy (including self science and anger management). Equally importantly our sound systems for tracking and monitoring achievement provide tangible evidence to students that they are all capable of success.

The major driver for change in our students' lives is the success achieved through their engagement with the curriculum. At the heart of our school's work is the challenging academic, practical, and social/emotional curriculum within the context of a holistic approach and in collaboration with other agencies. The social-emotional-behavioural curriculum is designed to help students develop self-awareness, an appreciation of the impact of their actions on others and the ability to take age appropriate responsibility.

The Key Stage 3 curriculum is based on the National

Curriculum, which features a strong academic core as well as physical education, performing arts and practical subjects. In Key Stage 4, all students follow a compulsory curriculum comprising the core subjects, careers and citizenship, physical education and self science. In addition students can choose from at least 17 subject options to study for GCSE. Our work is supported by in-house communication, speech and language programmes and an emotional literacy curriculum. Our language and communication department run regular conversation groups in response to the needs of students with social communication difficulties. Other focus groups are held from time-to-time on specific issues such as memory techniques.

All Post-16 students have as one component on their placement a further education course leading to a recognised Post-16 qualification. They also benefit from supported study at school and an independent living skills programme, the relative proportions of which are determined by individual need.

We provide excellent residential facilities for students that choose to board with us. They are encouraged to learn from one another as well as benefit from supportive staff from both during and beyond the school day, who are dedicated to ensuring a healthy pre-disposition for learning whilst developing their independent living skills. For the second year in a row we are proud to receive an 'Outstanding' grade across all areas from Ofsted for our Boarding facility.

We are proud of our school and the quality of the service we provide. Reports from our inspections, available from the school office or the internet are highly complimentary. Please contact our school administrator, Sara Henderson, for more information:

Telephone: 01732 460553

Email: principal@westheathschool.com

The Marchant-Holliday School

BUILDING ON A TRADITION
OF EXCELLENCE

(Founded 1951)

North Cheriton, Templecombe, Somerset BA8 0AH
Tel: 01963 33234   Email: office@marchant-holliday.co.uk
Fax: 01963 33432   Website: www.marchantholliday.co.uk

Head Teacher: Mr T J Kitts MEd, BEd(Hons),
DPSE(SEN)
School type: Boys' Boarding, Flexible Boarding & Day
Age range of pupils:
Boys: 5–13
Fees per annum as at 1.1.13:
Available upon application

Special needs catered for

Behavioural, emotional & social difficulties (BESD), aspects of ASD, Asperger syndrome, dyslexia, dyspraxia, ADHD, ADD and other challenging behaviours and complex needs.

Environment

The school is situated in beautiful countryside surroundings near Wincanton in Somerset and consists of a large country house in 17 acres of woodland, field and gardens. It is close to the A303 trunk road and is readily accessible from London, Bristol, Southampton, the South and West and from all areas of the home counties. There are mainline train stations nearby at Castle Cary and Templecombe. We provide a caring, secure and structured environment, which promotes self-esteem and the enjoyment of school life. A wide range of facilities including sports hall, heated outdoor swimming pool, sports field, adventure play equipment, science and technology rooms. Homely living accommodation with single and double rooms, the majority with en suite facilities.

Aims and philosophy

The school aims to offer positive learning experiences within a secure and caring environment that will enable each child to develop his full potential for social, emotional, physical and intellectual growth. We consider the children's happiness to be important and place emphasis on developing feelings of self worth and achievement. The curriculum is carefully planned to promote success and employs positive reinforcement to develop the children's potential. All National Curriculum subjects are taught and children receive a high level of individual support to facilitate the acquisition of skills and knowledge. The school encourages children to examine and take responsibility for their behaviour and promotes acceptable behaviour patterns with the use of praise and rewards. Many children make a successful transition back to mainstream schooling and find acceptance within their homes and communities. The school retains the services of a qualified child counsellor and a social worker. Speech therapy, OT or other services can be arranged.

Home school links

The school is warm and welcoming, open to visits and phone communication is encouraged. A weekly pupil report is sent home and staff contact parents and carers weekly by telephone. We offer flexible boarding opportunities short term, weekly or fortnightly, as well as day or part-time placements that can be tailored to the needs of individual pupils and referring authorities.

Staff qualification and selection

The school's governing body is committed to safeguarding and promoting the welfare of children and young people and expects all staff and volunteers to share this commitment. Staff members are rigorously screened before they are appointed in order to ensure the continuing quality of service provided. All staff have professional and safeguarding qualifications, work to clear guidelines as noted in our most recent Ofsted report (June 2012): "an outstanding residential experience and teaching that successfully improves pupils' personal development, particularly their behaviour and attitudes to learning, leading to good outcomes."

Young Options College

Options Group
making a difference

Lamledge Lane, Shifnal, Shropshire TF11 8SD
Tel: 01952 468220   Email: info@youngoptions.co.uk
Fax: 01952 468221   Website: www.optionsgroup.co.uk

Headteacher: Louise De-Hayes
School type: Coeducational Residential & Day
DfE approved (Reg No 893/6017).
Age range of pupils: 7–19
Fees per annum as at 1.1.13:
On application

Young Options College is a specialist service providing care and education for children and young people aged 7 to 19 with behavioural, emotional and social difficulties (BESD).

Ofsted 'Outstanding' rated Young Options College is a highly successful DfE-registered independent day special school offering both day and residential placements. Up to 52-week residential care is provided within small group homes, which are rated as either "Good" or "Outstanding" by Ofsted and located in the communities surrounding the school.

Attendance at Young Options College is often the first step of a longer journey through the Young Options Pathway, which includes Transitions, Fostering and Supported Housing Services. The Young Options Pathway prepares students for leaving care and the transition to independent living.

Set in 28 acres of beautiful Shropshire countryside, Young Options College is a purpose-built school offering access to high quality education and dedicated facilities for specialist subjects including science, art, design and technology, food technology and music. As well as offering nationally accredited Level 1, 2 and 3 courses such as GCSE, AS/A2 Level, OCR Nationals and BTEC, practical activities are provided on-site promoting the development of key life skills.

Young Options College provides:

- individually tailored programmes that integrate care, education and therapy;
- Ofsted "Outstanding" care and education;
- safe, homely environments within small group homes;
- a comprehensive evaluation and assessment service;
- access to the Young Options First Steps programme to independent living;
- an on-site Professional and Clinical Multi-disciplinary Team;
- a focus on community living.

Young Options College takes a multi-disciplinary and person-centred approach to the delivery of care, education and therapy that enables students to develop their life skills as well as progress academically. Priority is given to ensuring that students are well-equipped to make the transition to young adult life.

Young Options Pathway College Stoke

Options Group
making a difference

Phoenix House, Marlborough Road, Longton, Stoke-on-Trent ST3 1EJ
Tel: 01782 377270   Email: info@pathwaystoke.co.uk
Fax: 01782 313667   Website: www.optionsgroup.co.uk

Headteacher: Mel Callaghan
School type: Coeducational Day & Boarding
Age range of pupils: 11–19
Fees per annum as at 1.1.13:
On application

Young Options Pathway College Stoke provides integrated programmes of care, education and therapy for young people with complex behavioural, emotional and social difficulties (BESD).

Young Options Pathway College Stoke is a purpose-built DfE-registered independent special school for young people aged 11 to 19. Both day and residential placements are available, with up to 52-week residential care provided within small group homes located in the communities surrounding the school.

At Young Options Pathway College Stoke, education is delivered in ways that are the most appropriate and the most conducive to the student's learning needs. As many students arrive having experienced multiple placement breakdowns and with little experience of formal education, both intensive and small group teaching are available.

Young Options Pathway College Stoke provides access to nationally accredited courses such as GCSE, diplomas, AQA entry level certificates, ASDAN, CLAIT and BTEC vocational skills qualifications. Vocational courses include diploma options in art and media, hair and beauty, hospitality, ICT, public services and food technology.

Students are also supported to identify and access work placements in their local communities, promoting the development of life skills, and increased confidence and wellbeing. Young Options Pathway College Stoke is part of the Young Options Pathway, which includes Transitions, Fostering and Supported Housing Services. The Young Options Pathway prepares students for leaving care and the transition to independent living.

Young Options Pathway College Stoke provides:

- person-centred programmes that integrate care, education and therapy;
- access to the National Curriculum and vocational courses, and work related learning;
- a focus on community living and life skills development;
- safe, homely environments in registered homes located in the surrounding communities;
- a comprehensive evaluation and assessment service;
- an on-site Professional and Clinical Multi-disciplinary Team;
- access to the Young Options First Steps programme to independent living.

Brantwood Specialist School

1 Kenwood Bank, Nether Edge, Sheffield, South Yorkshire S7 1NU
Tel: 0114 258 9062   Email: admin@brantwood.rmt.org
Website: www.rmt.org

Headteacher: Constantin Court
School type: Coeducational Day & Residential
Age range of pupils: 7–19

Brantwood is an independent specialist school for children and young people aged 7-19 with complex behavioural, emotional and social difficulties (BESD), Autistic Spectrum Disorder including Asperger's Syndrome, attachment disorder, ADHD and those deemed 'hard to engage'. The school offers daytime and residential provision up to 52 weeks and respite care subject to availability. Graded as 'Good' by Ofsted (2012), Brantwood is set in a quiet neighbourhood with secure grounds.

Curriculum

The curriculum at Brantwood has four distinct strands:

Steiner Waldorf Education: A holistic and inclusive approach to the development of the young person which emphasises the importance of the distinct ways in which humans relate to the world through their intellectual, emotional and physical activity.

Practical Skills Therapeutic Education (PSTE): PSTE enables people to develop skills through real-life purposeful activities, gain confidence through achievement in school, engage in the wider community and achieve a wide range of qualifications according to their interests and skills.

The National Curriculum: Students can achieve appropriate nationally recognised qualifications from NOCNs and BTECs to GCSEs.

Individual Therapies: Speech and Language, Movement (Eurythmy), Massage, Art and Occupational Therapies are incorporated into each young person's education plan as appropriate. The school doctor and therapists work closely with staff and parents/carers at all times.

Brantwood Specialist School provides:

- Small class sizes and house groups of five students or fewer according to a student's needs and levels of skill and independence
- Healthy organic food and nutritional education
- Engagement with the local community and help in planning leisure time and outdoor activities
- Involvement in festivals, other celebrations and social and cultural events
- Opportunities to develop and improve living skills for both day and residential students

Residential

Brantwood has residential provision within its central school location and the local community providing consistency, warmth and positive role modelling that young people need to develop their living skills and full potential. Students are actively engaged in developing their leisure activities and community participation and planning and cooking a healthy organic diet.

Admissions

For enquiries contact Admissions on 01142 589 062 or email admissions@brantwood.rmt.org

Referrals are taken throughout the year.

Brantwood Specialist School Registered No: 373/6002. Children's Home Registered No: SC423753. Ruskin Mill Trust is an educational charity No: 1137167.

Breckenbrough School

(Founded 1934)

Sandhutton, Thirsk, North Yorkshire YO7 4EN
Tel: 01845 587238   Email: office@breckenbrough.org.uk
Fax: 01845 587385   Website: www.breckenbrough.org.uk

Headmaster: Geoffrey Brookes BEd
School type: Boys' Boarding & Day
A residential non-maintained special school for boys
Member of: NASS, ISBA
Age range of pupils:
Boys: 9–19
No. of pupils enrolled as at 1.1.13: 49
Fees per annum as at 1.1.13:
Available on request
Average size of class: 6

Special Needs catered for include primarily ASD BESD ADHD

Breckenbrough in brief

- Over 70 years of experience in educating boys with complex needs.
  * A unique special school with a Quaker ethos.
  * Educates boys aged 9 to 19 with academic potential.
  * Accommodates both day and boarding pupils on a 38 week basis.
  * Has expertise and success with boys with Asperger Syndrome and ADHD.
  * Has high educational expectations and offers a wide range of GCSEs, vocational programmes and A levels.
  * Provides individualised learning and programmes of study.
  * Offers a relaxed atmosphere, within an holistic and therapeutic environment.
  * Operates an effective ethos of conflict resolution.
  * Encourages pupils to understand and take responsibility for their own actions.
  * Employs a full-time registered psychologist and counsellor.
  * Enjoys and encourages strong partnerships with families.
  * Offers a wide range of activities and opportunities.
  * Provides post-16 provision for working in partnership with other local providers.
  * Operates a unique After Care service to provide contact and support for pupils once they have left school and in later life.
  * The vast majority of boys go on to full-time further education, training and work.

- Has good access from the motorway and rail networks.

The school is a non-profit-making charity, whose governors are appointed by Quakers in Yorkshire.

Housed in a Victorian country house with 10 acres of land in the heart of North Yorkshire, Breckenbrough is located a few miles from Thirsk, close to the Yorkshire Dales and North York Moors National Parks.

Outdoor Education and PHSE programmes are integral to the work of the school. Life skills are developed and pupils are offered a wide and varied range of activities which provide emotional, physical and social challenge. The experiences include motorbike riding and maintenance on site, kayaking, climbing and mountain biking. Work experience and regular opportunities to integrate with the local community are a vital part of our provision.

The school has an experienced staff skilled in conflict resolution, who understand Asperger Syndrome and young people experiencing emotional problems. Students are continually encouraged through the powerful ethos of the school where external pressure is reduced and individuality encouraged.

Spring Hill School

(Founded 1950)

Palace Road, Ripon, North Yorkshire HG4 3HN
Tel: 01765 603320   Email: springhill.school@barnardos.org.uk
Fax: 01765 692073   Website: www.barnardos.org.uk/springhillschool

Principal: Linda Nelson
School type: Coeducational Day & Boarding
Age range of pupils: 9–19
No. of pupils enrolled as at 1.1.13: 31
Registered residential places: 40
Fees per annum as at 1.1.13:
On request to: springhill.school@barnardos.org.uk

General information

Spring Hill School is a non-maintained residential special school, situated on the outskirts of the beautiful cathedral city of Ripon on the edge of the North Yorkshire Dales, providing quality education and care for children and young people who have a wide range of learning difficulties and challenging behaviour.

The school works with children and young people aged 9 to 19 and offers placement options of 52 week provision, 38 week provision, or day placements. Spring Hill has six residential houses that have accommodation for 40 young people. The school also offers day placements.

Within the school there is a wide range of skill and expertise to meet the needs of the young people and it provides therapy within the school setting and works closely with the local Child and Adolescent Mental Health Team. The school is caring and flexible, and recognises and meets the needs of each individual young person.

Spring Hill is an inclusive school whose mission is to equip its young people with the skills, knowledge and experiences that will help them to accomplish their ambitions as adults.

Education

Spring Hill School provides a curriculum that is designed to meet the needs of all young people while fostering an environment that stimulates, supports and challenges them to achieve their potential. The curriculum embraces a wide range of academic, vocational, therapeutic and leisure activities, as well as focusing on the personal and social development of young people.

Spring Hill offers a wide range of externally accredited courses as appropriate to the needs of each individual young person. Classrooms are well resourced and have a high staff-pupil ratio.

Personal development

Spring Hill School believes that all young people deserve the chance to realise their potential in a safe and caring environment. We have high expectations for all our pupils, which is evidenced in the achievements and progress young people make while they are at the school.

As part of the 24 hour curriculum in both the academic and care settings, we aim to prepare pupils for the time when they leave the school. The development of a young person's self-esteem and self awareness is central to all we do.

Barnardo's is a registered charity (nos. 216250 & SCO37605).

DIRECTORY

Schools and colleges specialising in sensory or physical impairment

Abbreviations

ACLD	Autism, Communication and Associated Learning Difficulties
ADD	Attention Deficit Disorder
ADHD	Attention Deficit and Hyperactive Disorder (Hyperkinetic Disorder)
ASD	Autistic Spectrum Disorder
ASP	Asperger Syndrome
AUT	Autism
BESD	Behavioural, Emotional and Social Difficulties
CCD	Complex Communication Difficulties
CLD	Complex Learning Difficulties
CP	Cerebral Palsy
D	Deaf
DEL	Delicate
DYS	Dyslexia
DYSP	Dyspraxia
EBD	Emotional and Behavioural Difficulties
EBSD	Emotional, Behavioural and/or Social Difficulties
EPI	Epilepsy
GLD	General Learning Difficulties
HA	High Ability
HI	Hearing Impairment
HS	Hospital School
LD	Learning Difficulties
MLD	Moderate Learning Difficulties
MSI	Multi-sensory Impairment
OCD	Obsessive Compulsive Disorder
PD	Physical Difficulties
PH	Physical Impairment
Phe	Partially Hearing
PMLD	Profound and Multiple Learning Difficulties
PNI	Physical Neurological Impairment
PRU	Pupil Referral Unit
SCD	Social and Communication Difficulties
SCLD	Severe and Complex Learning Difficulties
SEBD	Severe Emotional and Behavioural Disorders
SEBN	Social, Emotional and Behavioural Needs
SLD	Severe Learning Difficulties
SLI	Specific Language Impairment
SPLD	Specific Learning Difficulties
SP&LD	Speech and Language Difficulties
SLCN	Speech Language & Communication Needs
VIS	Visually Impaired

Key to symbols

Type of school:

(�) Boys' school

(♀) Girls' school

(🌐) International school

School offers:

(A) A levels

(♨) Boarding accommodation

(16+) Entrance at 16+

(🎓) Vocational qualifications

(✎) Learning support

(✔) This is a DfE approved independent or non-maintained school under section 342 or 347(1) of the 1996 Education Act

Please note: Unless otherwise indicated, all schools are coeducational day schools. Single-sex and boarding schools will be indicated by the relevant icon.

CENTRAL AND WEST

BUCKINGHAMSHIRE

Penn School
Church Road, Penn, High Wycombe,
Buckinghamshire HP10 8LZ
Tel: 01494 812139
Headteacher: Mary-Nest Richardson
Type: Coeducational Boarding
Age range: 11–18
No. of pupils: 29 B18 G11
Special needs catered for: HI SP&LD

The PACE Centre
Philip Green House, Coventon Road,
Aylesbury, Buckinghamshire HP19 9JL
Tel: 01296 392739
Head Teacher: Mrs A Richardson
Type: Coeducational Day
Age range: 0–12
Special needs catered for: CLD CP DYSP
HI LD MLD MSI PD PNI SCLD SLD SP&LD
VIS

GLOUCESTERSHIRE

National Star College
Ullenwood Manor, Cheltenham,
Gloucestershire GL53 9QU
Tel: 01242 527631
Principal & Chief Executive Officer: Mrs H
Sexton
Type: Coeducational Boarding & Day
Age range: 16–25
No. of pupils: 161 B81 G80
Special needs catered for: ASP CP DEL
MLD PH PNI SCD SCLD SP&LD

St Rose's School
Stratford Lawn, Stroud,
Gloucestershire GL5 4AP
Tel: 01453 763793
Headteacher: Mr Jan Daines
Type: Coeducational Residential & Day
Age range: 2–25
No. of pupils: 54 B33 G21
Special needs catered for: CLD CP D DEL
DYS DYSP EPI GLD HI LD MLD MSI PD PH
Phe PMLD PNI SCD SCLD SLD SLI SP&LD
VIS

WEST BERKSHIRE

Mary Hare Primary School for the Deaf
Mill Hall, Pigeons Farm Road, Thatcham,
Newbury, West Berkshire RG19 8XA
Tel: 01635 573800
Head of Centre: Mrs K D Smith
Type: Coeducational Boarding & Day
Age range: 5–12
No. of pupils: B12 G11
Special needs catered for: HI

Mary Hare School
Arlington Manor, Snelsmore Common,
Newbury, West Berkshire RG14 3BQ
Tel: 01635 244200
Principal: Mr D A J Shaw BTech,
MEd(Aud), NPQH
Type: Coeducational Boarding & Day
Age range: 11–19
No. of pupils: 205 B118 G87 VIth68
Special needs catered for: D HI

EAST

HERTFORDSHIRE

Meldreth Manor School
Fenny Lane, Meldreth, Royston,
Hertfordshire SG8 6LG
Tel: 01763 268000
Principal: Roger Gale MSc(Ed)
Type: Coeducational Boarding & Day
Age range: 9–19+
No. of pupils: 30
Special needs catered for: CP D EPI GLD
HI LD MLD MSI PD PH Phe PMLD SP&LD
VIS

St Elizabeth's School
South End, Much Hadham,
Hertfordshire SG10 6EW
Tel: 01279 844270
Principal: Mr Philip Poulton BA(Hons),
PGCE
Type: Coeducational Boarding & Day
Age range: 9–19
Special needs catered for: AUT CP DYS
DYSP EBD EPI MLD SLD SPLD SP&LD

EAST MIDLANDS

DERBY

ROYAL SCHOOL FOR THE DEAF DERBY
For further details see p.57
Ashbourne Road, Derby DE22 3BH
Tel: 01332 362512
Email: principal@rsdd.org.uk
Website: www.rsd-derby.org
Principal: Cheryll Ford BA, BPhil, NPQH
Type: Coeducational Day & Boarding
Age range: 3–19
No. of pupils: 140 B97 G43
Special needs catered for: D

LEICESTERSHIRE

Homefield College
42 St Mary's Road, Sileby,
Loughborough, Leicestershire LE12 7TL
Tel: 01509 815696
Principal: Mr Chris Berry
Type: Coeducational Day
Special needs catered for: ASD BESD LD
SCD

RNIB College Loughborough
Radmoor Road, Loughborough,
Leicestershire LE11 3BS
Tel: 01509 611077
Principal: Tony Warren MA(Cantab), MBA,
PGCE
Type: Specialist coeducational
Age range: 16
No. of pupils: 67
Special needs catered for: ASP AUT MLD
VIS

NORTHAMPTONSHIRE

**Hinwick Hall College of Further
Education**
Hinwick, Wellingborough,
Northamptonshire NN29 7JD
Tel: 01933 312470
Principal: Mr Martyn Hays
Type: Coeducational Boarding & Day
Age range: 19–25
No. of pupils: 58 B32 G26
Special needs catered for: CP DYSP EPI
PH SCD SLD SP&LD

NOTTINGHAM

Portland College
Nottingham Road, Mansfield,
Nottingham NG18 4TJ
Tel: 01623 499111
Head: M E A Syms OBE
Type: Coeducational Boarding & Day
Age range: 16–59
No. of pupils: 230
Special needs catered for: CP DYS DYSP
EPI HI MLD PH SPLD SP&LD

RUTLAND

The Shires School
Great North Road, Stretton,
Rutland LE15 7QT
Tel: 01780 411944
Director of Care & Education: Gail Pilling
Type: Coeducational Boarding
Age range: 11–19
Special needs catered for: AUT SLD

GREATER LONDON

KENT

Nash College
Croydon Road, Hayes, Bromley,
Kent BR2 7AG
Tel: 020 8462 7419
Principal: Andrew Giles CertEd,
DipTeacher of the Deaf
Type: Coeducational Boarding & Day
Age range: 19–25
No. of pupils: 60
Special needs catered for: CP EPI MLD PH
PMLD PNI SCD SCLD SLD SPLD SP&LD

MIDDLESEX

**RNIB SUNSHINE HOUSE SCHOOL AND
CHILDREN'S HOME**
For further details see p.58
33 Dene Road, Northwood,
Middlesex HA6 2DD
Tel: 01923 822538
Email: shsadmin@rnib.org.uk
Website:
www.rnib.org.uk/sunshinehouse
Head: John Ayres
Type: Coeducational
Age range: 2–11
Special needs catered for: VIS

LONDON

LONDON

Conductive Education Centre: Hornsey
54 Muswell Hill, London N10 3ST
Tel: 020 8444 7242
Head of Education Services: Donna
Billington BA, PGCE(SEN)
Type: Coeducational Day
Age range: 0–11
No. of pupils: 16 B10 G6
Special needs catered for: CP PD

**The London School for Children with
Cerebral Palsy**
54 Muswell Hill, London N10 3ST
Tel: 020 84447242
Headteacher: Ms Donna Billington
Type: Coeducational Day
Age range: 3–11
Special needs catered for: PD

NORTH-EAST

TYNE & WEAR

Northern Counties School
Great North Road, Newcastle upon Tyne,
Tyne & Wear NE2 3BB
Tel: 0191 281 5821
Headteacher: Mrs Frances Taylor
Type: Coeducational Boarding & Day
Age range: 3–19
No. of pupils: B54 G31
Special needs catered for: HI PMLD SLD
VIS

Percy Hedley School
Station Road, Forest Hall, Newcastle
upon Tyne, Tyne & Wear NE12 8YY
Tel: 0191 266 5491
Headteacher: Mr N O Stromsoy MA,
DipSE
Type: Coeducational Boarding & Day
Age range: 3–18
No. of pupils: 170 B120 G50
Special needs catered for: HI

NORTH-WEST

GREATER MANCHESTER

Seashell Trust
Stanley Road, Cheadle Hulme, Cheadle,
Greater Manchester SK8 6RQ
Tel: 0161 610 0100
Head
Type: Coeducational Boarding & Day
Age range: 2–22
No. of pupils: 83 B58 G25
Special needs catered for: ASD AUT CLD
CP D HI MSI PD PH PMLD PNI SCD SCLD
SLD SP&LD VIS

LANCASHIRE

Beaumont College
Slyne Road, Lancaster,
Lancashire LA2 6AP
Tel: 01524 541400
Principal: Mr Graeme Pyle
Type: Coeducational Boarding
Age range: 16–25
No. of pupils: 77
Special needs catered for: ASD AUT
BESD CLD CP DYS DYSP EBD EPI GLD HI
MSI PD PH PMLD PNI SCD SCLD SEBD
SLD SLI SP&LD VIS

MERSEYSIDE

Royal School for the Blind
Church Road North, Wavertree, Liverpool,
Merseyside L15 6TQ
Tel: 0151 733 1012
Principal: J Byrne
Type: Coeducational Boarding & Day
Age range: 2–19
No. of pupils: B28 G20
Special needs catered for: BESD CLD CP
EBD EPI HI MLD MSI PD PH PMLD PNI
SCLD SLD SLI SPLD VIS

**St Vincent's School for the Visually
Handicapped**
Yew Tree Lane, West Derby, Liverpool,
Merseyside L12 9HN
Tel: 0151 228 9968
Headmaster: Mr A Macquarrie
Type: Coeducational Boarding & Day
Age range: 3–17
No. of pupils: B49 G36
Special needs catered for: MLD VIS

SOUTH-EAST

BRIGHTON & HOVE

Hamilton Lodge School
9 Walpole Road, Brighton,
Brighton & Hove BN2 2ET
Tel: 01273 682362
Principal: Mrs A K Duffy MEd
Type: Coeducational Boarding & Day
Age range: 5–18
No. of pupils: 72 B42 G30
Special needs catered for: HI

EAST SUSSEX

CHAILEY HERITAGE SCHOOL
For further details see p.59
Haywards Heath Road, North Chailey,
Lewes, East Sussex BN8 4EF
Tel: 01825 724444
Email: schooloffice@chs.org.uk
Website: www.chs.org.uk
Principal: Sylvia Lamb
Type: Coeducational Boarding & Day
Age range: 3–19
No. of pupils: 73
Special needs catered for: ASD AUT CLD
CP D EBD EPI HI MLD MSI PD PH PMLD
PNI SCLD SLD SP&LD VIS

St Mary's School & College
Wrestwood Road, Bexhill-on-Sea,
East Sussex TN40 2LU
Tel: 01424 730740
Chief Executive: Ms Gail Pilling BA(Hons),
MA(Ed Mng), PGCE, C(Ed) Psychol,
AFBPsS, LCSLT (MRCSLT)
Type: Coeducational Boarding & Day
Age range: 7–19
No. of pupils: 137
Special needs catered for: ASD ASP AUT
CLD CP D DEL DYS DYSP EPI GLD HI LD
MLD MSI PD PH Phe SCD SLI SPLD
SP&LD VIS

HAMPSHIRE

Treloar School
Holybourne, Alton, Hampshire GU34 4GL
Tel: 01420 547400
Head: Melissa Farnham
Type: Coeducational Boarding & Day
Age range: 7–19
No. of pupils: 72
Special needs catered for: CP DEL DYSP
EPI HI MLD PH SPLD SP&LD VIS

ISLE OF WIGHT

St Catherine's School
Grove Road, Ventnor,
Isle of Wight PO38 1TT
Tel: 01983 852722
Principal: G E Shipley BA(Hons), MEd,
PGCE
Type: Coeducational Boarding
Age range: 9–19
No. of pupils: 58 B36 G22
Special needs catered for: SCD SLI
SP&LD

KENT

Dorton College of Further Education
Seal Drive, Seal, Sevenoaks,
Kent TN15 0AH
Tel: 01732 592600
Director of Education: Dorothea
Hackman
Type: Coeducational Day & Boarding
Age range: 16–19
No. of pupils: 60 B28 G32
Special needs catered for: VIS

Royal London Society for the Blind, Dorton House School
Seal, Sevenoaks, Kent TN15 0ED
Tel: 01732 592650
Headteacher: Ms Jude Thompson
Type: Coeducational Boarding & Day
Age range: 5–16
No. of pupils: 78 B50 G28
Special needs catered for: ADHD ASP
AUT CP DYS EBD EPI HI PH SLD SP&LD
VIS

The Royal School for Deaf Children Margate and Westgate College
Victoria Road, Margate, Kent CT9 1NB
Tel: 01843 227561
Headteacher: Mr C Owen BA(Hons),
MA(Ed), ToD
Type: Coeducational Boarding & Day
Age range: 4–16
No. of pupils: 82 B48 G33
Special needs catered for: ADD ADHD
ASD ASP AUT BESD CP D DEL EBD EPI HI
LD MLD PMLD SCD SCLD SLD SPLD VIS

SURREY

Moor House School
Hurst Green, Oxted, Surrey RH8 9AQ
Tel: 01883 712271
Principal: A A Robertson BA(Hons),
CertEd
Type: Coeducational Boarding
Age range: 7–16
No. of pupils: B64 G26
Special needs catered for: ADD ASP DYS
DYSP SP&LD

QEF Neuro Rehabilitation Services Brain Injury Centre
Banstead Place, Park Road, Banstead,
Surrey SM7 3EE
Tel: 01737 356222
Principal: Eileen Jackman MA, BSc
Type: Coeducational Boarding & Day
Age range: 16–35
No. of pupils: 28
Special needs catered for: EBD SP&LD

Queen Elizabeth's Training College
Leatherhead Court, Leatherhead,
Surrey KT22 0BN
Tel: 01372 841100
Principal: Garry Billing
Type: Coeducational Residential
Age range: 18–63
No. of pupils: 171 B154 G17
Special needs catered for: ADD ADHD
ASD ASP AUT CP DYS DYSP EPI GLD LD
MLD PD PH

St Piers School and College
St Piers Lane, Lingfield, Surrey RH7 6PW
Tel: 01342 832243
Chief Executive: Mr D Ford BSc,
MSc(Econ), MBA, CQSW
Type: Coeducational Boarding & Day
Age range: 5–25
No. of pupils: 181
Special needs catered for: ADD ADHD
ASP AUT CP EPI MLD PMLD PNI SCD
SCLD SLD SP&LD

Stepping Stones School
Tower Road, Hindhead, Surrey GU26 6SU
Tel: 01428 609083
Headteacher: Mr Neil Clark BA(Oxon),
PGCE, DipSpEd
Type: Coeducational Day
Age range: 7–16
No. of pupils: 20
Special needs catered for: MLD PD

THE SCHOOL FOR PROFOUND EDUCATION (FORMERLY ST MARGARET'S SCHOOL)

For further details see p.60

The Children's Trust, Tadworth,
Surrey KT20 5RU
Tel: 01737 365810
Email: profoundeducation@
thechildrenstrust.org.uk
Website: www.thechildrenstrust.org.uk/
profoundeducation
Head: Mrs Sylvia Kerambrum
Type: Coeducational Boarding
Age range: 5–25
No. of pupils: B25 G17
Special needs catered for: CLD CP EPI HI
MSI PD PH PMLD PNI SLD SP&LD VIS

WEST SUSSEX

Ingfield Manor School

Five Oaks, Billingshurst,
West Sussex RH14 9AX
Tel: 01403 782294/784241
Type: Coeducational Boarding & Day
Age range: 3–16
Special needs catered for: CP

SOUTH-WEST

DEVON

Dame Hannah Rogers School

Woodland Road, Ivybridge,
Devon PL21 9HQ
Tel: 01752 892461
Head: Mr Brian Carlyon
Type: Coeducational Boarding & Day
Age range: 5–19
No. of pupils: B15 G15
Special needs catered for: CP PH PMLD

Exeter Royal Academy for Deaf Education

50 Topsham Road, Exeter,
Devon EX2 4NF
Tel: 01392 267023
Chief Executive: Jonathan Farnhill
Type: Coeducational Boarding & Day
Age range: 5–25
No. of pupils: B58 G39 VIth68
Special needs catered for: AUT CP D EPI
HI MLD MSI Phe SP&LD VIS

On Track Training Centre

Unit 8, Paragon Buildings, Ford Road,
Totnes, Devon TQ9 5LQ
Tel: 01803 866462
Head Teacher: Mrs J Cox
Type: Coeducational Day
Age range: 11–18
No. of pupils: 24
Special needs catered for: ASP EBD MSI
SPLD

Vranch House

Pinhoe Road, Exeter, Devon EX4 8AD
Tel: 01392 468333
Headteacher: Miss M R C Boon BA, MSc,
MPhil
Type: Coeducational Day
Age range: 2–12
No. of pupils: B15 G15
Special needs catered for: CP EPI MLD PH
PMLD SP&LD

WESC FOUNDATION – THE SPECIALIST COLLEGE FOR VISUAL IMPAIRMENT

For further details see p.69

Countess Wear, Exeter, Devon EX2 6HA
Tel: 01392 454200
Principal: Mrs Tracy de Bernhardt-Dunkin
Type: Non-maintained Special School
and College
Age range: 16
Special needs catered for: EPI PH PMLD
VIS

WESC FOUNDATION - THE SPECIALIST SCHOOL FOR VISUAL IMPAIRMENT

For further details see p.61

Countess Wear, Exeter, Devon EX2 6HA
Tel: 01392 454200
Email: info@wescfoundation.ac.uk
Website: www.wescfoundation.ac.uk
Chief Executive: Mrs Tracy de Bernhardt-
Dunkin
Type: Non-maintained Special School
and College
Age range: 5–16
Special needs catered for: EPI PH PMLD
VIS

DORSET

The Fortune Centre of Riding Therapy

Avon Tyrrell, Bransgore, Christchurch,
Dorset BH23 8EE
Tel: 01425 673297
Director: Mrs J Dixon-Clegg SRN
Type: Coeducational Boarding
Age range: 16–25
No. of pupils: 47
Special needs catered for: AUT CP DEL
DYS EBD EPI HI MLD PH PMLD SLD SPLD
SP&LD VIS

POOLE

Langside School

Langside Avenue, Parkstone,
Poole BH12 5BN
Tel: 01202 518635
Principal: V. Seaward BEd (Hons) Oxon
NPQH
Type: Coeducational Day
Age range: 2–19
No. of pupils: 27 B13 G14
Special needs catered for: CLD CP EPI
MSI PD PMLD SCD SCLD SLD

Victoria Education Centre

12 Lindsay Road, Branksome Park,
Poole BH13 6AS
Tel: 01202 763697
Head: Mrs Christina Davies
Type: Coeducational Boarding & Day
Age range: 3–19
No. of pupils: 90
Special needs catered for: DEL EPI PH
SP&LD

WEST MIDLANDS

HEREFORDSHIRE

The Royal National College for the Blind (RNC)

College Road, Hereford,
Herefordshire HR1 1EB
Tel: 01432 265725
Principal: Mr Geoff Draper
Type: Coeducational Boarding & Day
Age range: 16–65
Special needs catered for: ASP AUT DYS
HA MLD PD Phe VIS

SHROPSHIRE

Derwen College
Oswestry, Shropshire SY11 3JA
Tel: 01691 661234
Director: D J Kendall BEng, FCA, MEd
Type: Coeducational Boarding
Age range: 16–25
No. of pupils: 160 B80 G80
Special needs catered for: CP DEL DYS
EPI HI MLD PH PMLD SLD SPLD SP&LD
VIS

WEST MIDLANDS

Hereward College of Further Education
Bramston Crescent, Tile Hill Lane,
Coventry, West Midlands CV4 9SW
Tel: 024 7646 1231
Headmistress: Mrs Cath Cole BA, RGN,
CertEd
Type: Coeducational Boarding & Day
Age range: 16
No. of pupils: 400 B200 G200
Special needs catered for: ASP AUT CP
DEL DYS DYSP EBD EPI HA HI MLD PH
SPLD VIS

National Institute for Conductive Education
Cannon Hill House, Russell Road,
Birmingham, West Midlands B13 8RD
Tel: 0121 449 1569
Director of Children's Services: Mrs
Wendy Baker
Type: Coeducational Day
Age range: 0–11
No. of pupils: 19 B13 G6
Special needs catered for: CP DYSP PNI

Queen Alexandra College, Birmingham (QAC)
Court Oak Road, Harborne, Birmingham,
West Midlands B17 9TG
Tel: 0121 428 5050
Principal: Hugh J Williams
Type: Coeducational Boarding & Day
Age range: 16
No. of pupils: 150
Special needs catered for: VIS

RNIB PEARS CENTRE FOR SPECIALIST LEARNING
For further details see p. 62
Wheelwright Lane, Ash Green, Coventry,
West Midlands CV7 9RA
Tel: 024 7636 9500
Email: pearscentre@rnib.org.uk
Website: www.rnib.org.uk/pearscentre
Head of Education: Andy Moran
Type: Coeducational Boarding & Day
Age range: 4–19
No. of pupils: 20
Special needs catered for: ASD AUT CLD
CP D EPI HI LD MSI PD PH PMLD SCLD
SLD SPLD VIS

WORCESTERSHIRE

New College Worcester
Whittington Road, Worcester,
Worcestershire WR5 2JX
Tel: 01905 763933
Principal: Mardy Smith
Type: Coeducational Boarding
Age range: 11–19
No. of pupils: 81 B40 G41
Special needs catered for: VIS

YORKSHIRE & HUMBERSIDE

NORTH YORKSHIRE

HENSHAWS COLLEGE
For further details see p. 70
Bogs Lane, Harrogate,
North Yorkshire HG1 4ED
Tel: 01423 886451
Principal: Nicki Eyre (acting)
Type: Coeducational Independent
Specialist College
Age range: 16
No. of pupils: 74 B42 G32
Special needs catered for: CLD CP D EPI
HI LD MLD MSI PD Phe SCD SLD SP&LD
VIS

SOUTH YORKSHIRE

Doncaster College for the Deaf
Leger Way, Doncaster,
South Yorkshire DN2 6AY
Tel: 01302 386720
Executive Principal: Alan W Robinson
Type: Coeducational Boarding & Day
Age range: 16–59
No. of pupils: 185
Special needs catered for: HI

DONCASTER SCHOOL FOR THE DEAF
For further details see p. 63
Leger Way, Doncaster,
South Yorkshire DN2 6AY
Tel: 01302 386733
Email: principal@ddt-deaf.org.uk or
secretary@ddt-deaf.org.uk
Website: www.deaf-trust.co.uk
Executive Principal: Mr Alan W Robinson
Type: Non-maintained (Special)
Coeducational Boarding and Day
Age range: 5–19
No. of pupils: 27 B18 G9
Special needs catered for: BESD CP DYS
HI MLD PH PMLD SLD SPLD SP&LD VIS

Paces High Green School for Conductive Education
Paces High Green Centre, Pack Horse
Lane, High Green, Sheffield,
South Yorkshire S35 3HY
Tel: 0114 284 5298
Headteacher: Gabor Fellner
Type: Coeducational Day
Age range: 0–18
No. of pupils: 24 B15 G9
Special needs catered for: CP PD

WEST YORKSHIRE

Holly Bank School
Roe Head, Far Common Road, Mirfield,
West Yorkshire WF14 0DQ
Tel: 01924 490833
Headteacher: Pam King CertEd
Type: Coeducational Boarding & Day
Age range: 5–19
No. of pupils: 40 B20 G20
Special needs catered for: CLD CP MSI
PD PH PMLD PNI SCLD SLD

ST JOHN'S CATHOLIC SCHOOL FOR THE DEAF
For further details see p. 64
Church Street, Boston Spa, Wetherby,
West Yorkshire LS23 6DF
Tel: 01937 842144
Email: info@stjohns.org.uk
Website: www.stjohns.org.uk
Headteacher: Mrs A Bradbury BA(Hons),
MSc
Type: Coeducational Boarding & Day
Age range: 4–19
No. of pupils: 80
Special needs catered for: ASD ASP CP D
DYS DYSP EPI HI MSI Phe SLI SP&LD VIS

NORTHERN IRELAND

COUNTY ANTRIM

Jordanstown Schools
85 Jordanstown Road, Newtownabbey,
County Antrim BT37 0QE
Tel: 028 9086 3541
Principal: Mrs A P Magee MEd,
DipSpEd(VI), PQH(NI)
Type: Coeducational Boarding & Day
Age range: 4–19
No. of pupils: 124
Special needs catered for: D HI MSI PD
SP&LD VIS

COUNTY TYRONE

**Buddy Bear Trust Conductive Education
School**
Killyman Road, Dungannon,
County Tyrone BT71 6DE
Tel: 02887 752 025
Type: Coeducational Day
Special needs catered for: CP

SCOTLAND

ABERDEEN

Camphill School Aberdeen
Murtle House, Bieldside,
Aberdeen AB15 9EP
Tel: 01224 867935
Administrator: Mr Piet Hogenboom
Type: Coeducational Boarding & Day
Age range: 3–19
No. of pupils: B60 G26
Special needs catered for: ADD ADHD
ASD ASP AUT BESD CLD CP D DEL DYS
DYSP EBD EPI GLD HA HI LD MLD MSI PD
PH Phe PMLD PNI SCD SCLD SEBD SLD
SLI SPLD SP&LD VIS

EDINBURGH

Royal Blind School
2B Craigmillar Park, Edinburgh EH16 5NA
Tel: 0131 667 1100
Principal: Julie Fardell
Type: Coeducational Boarding & Day
Age range: 5–19
No. of pupils: 68 B41 G27 VIth9
Special needs catered for: AUT CP DEL
EPI MLD PH PMLD SLD SPLD SP&LD VIS

RENFREWSHIRE

Corseford School
Milliken Park, Johnstone,
Renfrewshire PA10 2NT
Tel: 01505 702141
Headteacher: Mrs M Boyle
Type: Coeducational Boarding & Day
Age range: 3–18
No. of pupils: 50
Special needs catered for: CP DEL DYSP
EPI HI MLD PH SPLD SP&LD VIS

SOUTH LANARKSHIRE

Stanmore House School
Lanark, South Lanarkshire ML11 7RR
Tel: 01555 665041
Head Teacher: Hazel Aitken
Type: Coeducational Boarding & Day
Age range: 0–18
No. of pupils: 47 B27 G20
Special needs catered for: CP PH SCLD
SP&LD VIS

WEST LOTHIAN

Donaldson's School
Preston Road, Linlithgow,
West Lothian EH49 6HZ
Tel: 01506 841900
Principal: Mrs Janice MacNeill
Type: Coeducational Boarding & Day
Age range: 2–19
No. of pupils: 54 B37 G17
Special needs catered for: ASP AUT D HI
Phe PMLD SCD SLD SLI SP&LD

WALES

CARDIFF

Craig-y-Parc School
Pentyrch, Cardiff CF15 9NB
Tel: 029 2089 0397/2089 0361
Principal: Anthony Mulcamy
Type: Coeducational Boarding & Day
Age range: 3–19
No. of pupils: B21 G17
Special needs catered for: CP EPI HI LD
MLD MSI PD PH Phe PMLD SCLD SLD
SP&LD VIS

Schools and colleges specialising in social interaction difficulties (Autism, ASD & ASP)

Abbreviations

ACLD	Autism, Communication and Associated Learning Difficulties
ADD	Attention Deficit Disorder
ADHD	Attention Deficit and Hyperactive Disorder (Hyperkinetic Disorder)
ASD	Autistic Spectrum Disorder
ASP	Asperger Syndrome
AUT	Autism
BESD	Behavioural, Emotional and Social Difficulties
CCD	Complex Communication Difficulties
CLD	Complex Learning Difficulties
CP	Cerebral Palsy
D	Deaf
DEL	Delicate
DYS	Dyslexia
DYSP	Dyspraxia
EBD	Emotional and Behavioural Difficulties
EBSD	Emotional, Behavioural and/or Social Difficulties
EPI	Epilepsy
GLD	General Learning Difficulties
HA	High Ability
HI	Hearing Impairment
HS	Hospital School
LD	Learning Difficulties
MLD	Moderate Learning Difficulties
MSI	Multi-sensory Impairment
OCD	Obsessive Compulsive Disorder
PD	Physical Difficulties
PH	Physical Impairment
Phe	Partially Hearing
PMLD	Profound and Multiple Learning Difficulties
PNI	Physical Neurological Impairment
PRU	Pupil Referral Unit
SCD	Social and Communication Difficulties
SCLD	Severe and Complex Learning Difficulties
SEBD	Severe Emotional and Behavioural Disorders
SEBN	Social, Emotional and Behavioural Needs
SLD	Severe Learning Difficulties
SLI	Specific Language Impairment
SPLD	Specific Learning Difficulties
SP&LD	Speech and Language Difficulties
SLCN	Speech Language & Communication Needs
VIS	Visually Impaired

Key to symbols

Type of school:

(♦) Boys' school

(♦) Girls' school

(🌐) International school

School offers:

(A) A levels

(⚓) Boarding accommodation

(16) Entrance at 16+

(⚽) Vocational qualifications

(✎) Learning support

(✔) This is a DfE approved independent or non-maintained school under section 342 or 347(1) of the 1996 Education Act

Please note: Unless otherwise indicated, all schools are coeducational day schools. Single-sex and boarding schools will be indicated by the relevant icon.

CENTRAL AND WEST

BATH & NORTH-EAST SOMERSET

Rookery Radstock
Wells Road, Radstock, Bath,
Bath & North-East Somerset BA3 3RS
Tel: 01761 438611
Principal/Manager: Ms Doreen Paisley
Type: Coeducational Residential
Age range: 18–25
No. of pupils: 27
Special needs catered for: ASD ASP

BRISTOL

NAS ANDERSON SCHOOL
For further details see p. 73
Rookery Lane, Pilning, Bristol BS35 4JN
Tel: 01454 632532
Email: nasanderson@nas.org.uk
Website:
www.autism.org.uk/andersonschool
Head of Education: Simon Cartwright
Type: Coeducational Day & Residential
Age range: 10–19
No. of pupils: 20
Special needs catered for: ASD ASP AUT

OXFORDSHIRE

SWALCLIFFE PARK SCHOOL TRUST
For further details see p. 75
Swalcliffe, Banbury,
Oxfordshire OX15 5EP
Tel: 01295 780302
Email: admin@swalcliffepark.co.uk
Website: www.swalcliffepark.co.uk
Principal: Mr Kiran Hingorani
Type: Boys' Boarding & Day
Age range: B11–19
No. of pupils: 45
Special needs catered for: ADHD ASD
BESD DYS DYSP MLD SP&LD

SWINDON

Farleigh Further Education College Swindon
Fairview House, 43 Bath Road, Old Town,
Swindon SN1 4AS
Tel: 01793 719500
Principal/Manager: Mr Martin Bentham
Type: Coeducational Day & Residential
Age range: 16–25
No. of pupils: 63
Special needs catered for: ASP LD

WEST BERKSHIRE

PRIOR'S COURT SCHOOL
For further details see p. 74
Hermitage, Thatcham,
West Berkshire RG18 9NU
Tel: 01635 247202
Email: mail@priorscourt.org.uk
Website: www.priorscourt.org.uk
Director of Education and Learning: Sue
Piper
Type: Coeducational Boarding & Day
Age range: 5–19
No. of pupils: 56 B42 G14 VIth22
Special needs catered for: AUT CLD EPI
MLD SCLD

WILTSHIRE

Stratford Lodge
4 Park Lane, Castle Road, Salisbury,
Wiltshire SP1 3NP
Tel: 0800 288 9779
Head: Sue King BA(Hons), PGCE Dip in
Adv Ed Studies SEN, NPQH
Type: Coeducational Boarding
Age range: 16–19
Special needs catered for: ADHD ASD
ASP

EAST

CAMBRIDGESHIRE

Gretton School
High Street, Girton, Cambridge,
Cambridgeshire CB3 0QL
Tel: 01223 277438
Headteacher: Lyndsey Stone
Type: Coeducational Day
Age range: 5–19
Special needs catered for: ASD AUT LD

On Track Training Centre
Enterprise House, Old Field Lane,
Wisbech, Cambridgeshire PE13 2RJ
Tel: 01945 580898
Headteacher: Mrs Sharon Claydon
Type: Coeducational Day
Age range: 11–18
Special needs catered for: ADHD ASP
EBD

ESSEX

The Yellow House School
1 Alderford Street, Sible Hedingham,
Halstead, Essex CO9 3HX
Tel: 01787 462504
Type: Coeducational Day
Age range: 13–17
No. of pupils: 11
Special needs catered for: ADHD ASP
EBD

HERTFORDSHIRE

NAS RADLETT LODGE SCHOOL
For further details see p. 76
Harper Lane, Radlett,
Hertfordshire WD7 9HW
Tel: 01923 854922
Email: radlett.lodge@nas.org.uk
Website: www.autism.org.uk/radlett
Principal: Jo Galloway
Type: Coeducational Day & Residential
Age range: 4–19
No. of pupils: 55
Special needs catered for: ASD ASP AUT

NORFOLK

Acorn Park School
Mill Road, Banham, Norwich,
Norfolk NR16 2HU
Tel: 01953 888656
Head Teacher: Mr John Shaw BEd(Hons),
DipEdMan
Type: Coeducational Day & Boarding
Age range: 4–19
Special needs catered for: ASD AUT CLD
EPI LD MLD SCD SCLD SLD SPLD

PETERBOROUGH

Park House
Wisbech Road, Thorney,
Peterborough PE6 0SA
Tel: 01733 271187
Head: Mr Alan Crossland
Type: Coeducational Day
Age range: 4–16
Special needs catered for: AUT

EAST MIDLANDS

DERBY

High Grange School
Hospital Lane, Mickleover,
Derby DE3 0DR
Tel: 01332 412777
Headteacher: Marisa Kelsall
Type: Coeducational Day
Age range: 8–19
Special needs catered for: ASD ASP AUT

LEICESTERSHIRE

Sketchley Horizon
Manor Way, Sketchley, Burbage,
Leicestershire LE10 3HT
Tel: 01455 890023
Principal: Ms Sarah-Jane Astbury
Type: Coeducational Day & Extended Day
Age range: 8–19
No. of pupils: 30
Special needs catered for: ASD ASP AUT

NORTHAMPTONSHIRE

Alderwood
302 Wellingborough Road, Rushden,
Northamptonshire NN10 6BB
Tel: 01933 359861
Head: Mrs Jacqueline Wadlow
Type: Coeducational Boarding
Special needs catered for: ASD AUT

Hill Farm College
c/o The Manor House, Squires Hill,
Rothwell, Northamptonshire NN14 6BQ
Tel: 01536 711111
Principal: Jo Morris
Type: Coeducational Day & Residential
Age range: 14–19
No. of pupils: 12
Special needs catered for: ADHD ASD ASP

POTTERSPURY LODGE SCHOOL
For further details see p.77
Towcester, Northamptonshire NN12 7LL
Tel: 01908 542912
Email: mail@potterspurylodge.co.uk
Website: www.potterspurylodge.co.uk
Principal: Mr John W D Brown
Type: Boys' Termly Boarding, Weekly
Boarding and Day
Age range: B8–18
No. of pupils: 44 VIth6
Special needs catered for: ADD ADHD
ASD ASP AUT DYS DYSP EBD SCD SP&LD

GREATER LONDON

KENT

Baston House School
Baston Road, Hayes, Bromley,
Kent BR2 7AB
Tel: 020 8462 1010
Principal: Steve Vincent
Type: Coeducational Day
Age range: 3–19
Special needs catered for: ASD

MIDDLESEX

NAS SYBIL ELGAR SCHOOL
For further details see p.78
Havelock Road, Southall,
Middlesex UB2 4NR
Tel: 020 8813 9168
Email: sybil.elgar@nas.org.uk
Website: www.autism.org.uk/sybilelgar
Principal: Chloe Phillips
Type: Coeducational Day & Residential
Age range: 4–19
No. of pupils: 99
Special needs catered for: ASD ASP AUT

SURREY

'the little group'
c/o St Josephs Catholic Primary School,
Rosebank, Epsom, Surrey KT18 7RT
Tel: 01372 720218
Head Teacher: Judy Gilham
Type: Coeducational Day
Age range: 2–5+
Special needs catered for: ASD AUT

LONDON

LONDON

Kestrel House School
104 Crouch Hill, London N8 9EA
Tel: 020 8348 8500
Headteacher: Kerry Harris
Type: Coeducational Day
Age range: 4–16
Special needs catered for: ASP AUT

**Rainbow School for Children and Young
People with Autism**
The Tram House, 520 Garratt Lane,
London SW17 0NY
Tel: 020 8879 7700
Head of School: Mrs Sally Anne Palmer
Type: Coeducational Day
Age range: 4–17
No. of pupils: 30 B25 G5
Special needs catered for: ASD ASP AUT
SCD

RIVERSTON SCHOOL
For further details see p.79
63-69 Eltham Road, Lee Green,
London SE12 8UF
Tel: 020 8318 4327
Email: office@riverstonschool.co.uk
Website: www.riverstonschool.co.uk
Headmistress: Mrs S E Salathiel
Type: Independent Non-Selective Day
School
Age range: 1–19
No. of pupils: 215 B155 G60
Special needs catered for: ASD ASP AUT
LD

The Chelsea Group of Children
The Gate House, Magdalen Road,
London SW18 3NP
Tel: 020 8946 8330
Director: Libby Hartman
Type: Coeducational Day
Age range: 4–8
Special needs catered for: ADHD ASP
AUT LD MLD SPLD SP&LD

THE HOLMEWOOD SCHOOL
For further details see p. 80
88 Woodside Park Road, London N12 8SH
Tel: 020 8920 0660
Email: enquiries@thsl.org.uk
Website: www.thsl.org.uk
Head of School: Lucia Santi
Type: Coeducational Day
Age range: 7–18
Special needs catered for: ASP AUT DYS DYSP SP&LD

The Priory Lodge School
Priory Lane, London SW15 5JJ
Tel: 020 8392 4410
Principal: Pancho Martinez
Type: Coeducational Day & Extended Day
Age range: 7–19
No. of pupils: 40
Special needs catered for: ASD ASP AUT LD

TreeHouse School
Woodside Avenue, London N10 3JA
Tel: 020 8815 5424
Head: Julie O'Sullivan
Type: Coeducational Day
Age range: 3–19
No. of pupils: 67
Special needs catered for: ASD AUT

NORTH-EAST

DARLINGTON

Priory Hurworth House
38 The Green, Hurworth-on-Tees, Darlington DL2 2AD
Tel: 01325 720424
Principal: Mr John Anderson
Type: Coeducational Day
Age range: 7–19
No. of pupils: 30
Special needs catered for: AUT BESD EBD

TYNE & WEAR

ESPA College
6-7 The Cloisters, Ashbrooke, Sunderland, Tyne & Wear SR2 7BD
Tel: 0191 510 2600
Principal (Acting): Mrs C Pickup
Type: Coeducational Day & Boarding
Age range: 16–25
No. of pupils: 100
Special needs catered for: ASD ASP AUT

Thornhill Park School
21 Thornhill Park, Sunderland, Tyne & Wear SR2 7LA
Tel: 0191 514 0659
Head Teacher: Margaret Burton
Type: Coeducational Boarding & Day
Age range: 4–19
No. of pupils: 74 B59 G15
Special needs catered for: ASD ASP AUT

NORTH-WEST

CUMBRIA

Lindeth College
The Oaks, Lindeth, Bowness on Windermere, Cumbria LA23 3NH
Tel: 01539 446265
Principal/Manager: Ms Shirley Harrison
Type: Coeducational Day & Residential
Age range: 16–25
No. of pupils: 30
Special needs catered for: ASP LD

GREATER MANCHESTER

Fairfield House School
59 Warburton Lane, Partington, Manchester,
Greater Manchester M31 4NL
Tel: 0161 7762827
Headteacher: Ms Melanie Sproston
Type: Coeducational Day
Age range: 8–19
Special needs catered for: ASD

Inscape House Cheadle
Schools Hill, Cheadle, Greater Manchester SK8 1JE
Tel: 0161 283 4750
Headteacher: Liz Loftus
Type: Coeducational Day
Age range: 5–16
No. of pupils: 55
Special needs catered for: AUT

LANCASHIRE

Bracken School
1 Harbour Lane, Warton, Preston, Lancashire PR4 1YA
Tel: 01772 631531
Headteacher: Paul Addison
Type: Girls' Day
Age range: G11–16
No. of pupils: 5
Special needs catered for: ADHD DYS MLD

Oliver House
Hall Gate, Astley Village, Chorley, Lancashire PR7 1XA
Tel: 01257 220011
Principal: Ms Wendy Sparling
Type: Coeducational Day & Residential
Age range: 6–19
No. of pupils: 28
Special needs catered for: ASD ASP

Rossendale School
Bamford Road, Ramsbottom, Bury, Lancashire BL0 0RT
Tel: 01706 822779
Principal: Mr David Duncan
Type: Coeducational Day & Residential
Age range: 8–16
No. of pupils: 68
Special needs catered for: ADD ADHD ASD ASP AUT BESD CLD DYS DYSP EBD EPI HA SEBD SLD

Trax Academy
Riverside Park, Wallend Road, Preston, Lancashire PR2 2HW
Tel: 01772 731832
Head: Mr Rodger Davies
Type: Coeducational Day
Age range: 11–18
No. of pupils: 12
Special needs catered for: ADHD EBD

MERSEYSIDE

Arden College
40 Derby Road, Southport, Merseyside PR9 0TZ
Tel: 01704 534433
Principal/Manager: Mr Mark Musselle
Type: Coeducational Day & Residential
Age range: 16–25
No. of pupils: 53
Special needs catered for: ASP LD

Peterhouse School for Pupils with Autism & Asperger's Syndrome
Preston New Road, Southport, Merseyside PR9 8PA
Tel: 01704 506682
Principal: Janet Allan
Type: Coeducational Boarding & Day
Age range: 5–19
No. of pupils: 57 B44 G13 VIth20
Special needs catered for: ASD ASP AUT

SOUTH-EAST

BRIGHTON & HOVE

Rookery Hove
22-24 Sackville Gardens, Hove, Brighton & Hove BN3 4GH
Tel: 01273 202 520
Principal/Manager: Mr Loz Blume
Type: Coeducational Residential
Age range: 18–35
No. of pupils: 13
Special needs catered for: ASD ASP

EAST SUSSEX

Step by Step School for Autistic Children
Neylands Farm, Grinstead Lane, Sharpethorne, East Sussex RH19 4HP
Tel: 01342 811852
Headteacher: Miss Faye Rapley
Type: Coeducational Day
Age range: 4–11
No. of pupils: 12
Special needs catered for: AUT

HAMPSHIRE

Grateley House School
Pond Lane, Grateley, Andover, Hampshire SP11 8TA
Tel: 0800 288 9779
Head: Mrs Sue King BA(Hons), PGCE, DAE (SEN) NPQH
Type: Coeducational Boarding & Day
Age range: 9–19
Special needs catered for: ASD ASP

Hill House School
Rope Hill, Boldre, Lymington, Hampshire SO41 8NE
Tel: 0800 288 9779
Head: Ms Kate Landells BSc (open), CertSocSci(open) NVQ3 HSC, PTLLS(Level 4)
Type: Coeducational Boarding
Age range: 11–19
Special needs catered for: ASD AUT SCD SCLD SLD

Southlands School
Vicars Hill, Boldre, Lymington, Hampshire SO41 5QB
Tel: 0800 288 9779
Head: Ms Naomi Clarke BEd DipEd, SEN, AMBDA
Type: Boys' Boarding & Day
Age range: B7–16
Special needs catered for: ASD ASP

Tadley Horizon
Tadley Common Road, Tadley, Basingstoke, Hampshire RG26 3TB
Tel: 01189 817720
Principal: Phil Jonas
Type: Coeducational Residential & Day
Age range: 5–19
No. of pupils: 67
Special needs catered for: ASD ASP AUT

KENT

Blue Skies School
Fort Pitt House Annexe, New Road, Rochester, Kent ME1 1DX
Tel: 01634 817770
Headteacher: Mrs Fran Higgins
Type: Coeducational Day
Age range: 11–19
Special needs catered for: AUT EBD

NAS HELEN ALLISON SCHOOL
For further details see p. 81
Longfield Road, Meopham, Kent DA13 0EW
Tel: 01474 814878
Email: helen.allison@nas.org.uk
Website: www.autism.org.uk/helenallison
Executive Principal: Dr Jacqui Ashton Smith
Type: Coeducational Day & Residential
Age range: 5–19
No. of pupils: 70
Special needs catered for: ASD ASP AUT

The Quest School
Church Farm, Church Road, The Old Stables, Offham, Kent ME19 5NX
Tel: 01732 522700
Headteacher: Mrs Anne Martin
Type: Coeducational Day
Age range: 4–14
No. of pupils: 8
Special needs catered for: AUT EBD

READING

NAS THAMES VALLEY FREE SCHOOL
For further details see p. 82
Conwy Close, Tilehurst, Reading RG30 4BZ
Tel: 0117 9748 430
Email: naseducationgroup@nas.org.uk
Website: www.thamesvalleyfreeschool.co.uk
Principal Designate: Fiona Veitch
Type: Coeducational Day
Age range: 5–16
Special needs catered for: ASP AUT

SURREY

Eagle House School (Mitcham)
224 London Road, Mitcham, Surrey CR4 3HD
Tel: 020 8687 7050
Head Teacher: Alan Simons
Type: Coeducational Day
Age range: 4–11
Special needs catered for: ASD ASP AUT MLD SCD SLD

Eagle House School (Sutton)
95 Brighton Road, Sutton, Surrey SM2 5SJ
Tel: 020 8661 1419
Head Teacher: Mr Tom Coulter
Type: Coeducational Day
Age range: 11–19
Special needs catered for: AUT

Papillon House
Pebble Close, Tadworth, Surrey KT20 7PA
Tel: 01372 363663
Headteacher and Director: Mrs Gillian Hutton
Type: Coeducational Day
Age range: 4–16
No. of pupils: B22 G2
Special needs catered for: ASD AUT

Unsted Park School
Munstead Heath Road, Godalming,
Surrey GU7 1UW
Tel: 01483 892061
Principal: Mr Steve Dempsey
Type: Coeducational Day & Residential
Age range: 7–19
No. of pupils: 55
Special needs catered for: ASD ASP AUT

WEST SUSSEX

LVS Hassocks
London Road, Sayers Common,
Hassocks, West Sussex BN6 9HT
Tel: 01273 832901
Head Teacher: Sarah Sherwood
Type: Coeducational Day
Age range: 8–19
Special needs catered for: ASD ASP AUT

WINDSOR & MAIDENHEAD

Heathermount, The Learning Centre
Devenish Road, Ascot,
Windsor & Maidenhead SL5 9PG
Tel: 01344 875101
Consultant Principal: Christine Edden
Type: Coeducational Day & Residential
Age range: 5–19
No. of pupils: 38 B34 G4
Special needs catered for: ASD ASP AUT

SOUTH-WEST

CORNWALL

Three Bridges Education Centre
East Hill, Blackwater, Truro,
Cornwall TR4 8EG
Tel: 01872 561010
Headteacher: Rebecca Edwards
Type: Coeducational Day
Age range: 11–19
No. of pupils: 8
Special needs catered for: ASD ASP AUT

DEVON

Chelfham Senior School
Bere Alston, Yelverton, Devon PL20 7EX
Tel: 01822 840379
Principal: Mr John Steward
Type: Coeducational Day & Residential
Age range: 7–19
No. of pupils: 63
Special needs catered for: ADHD ASD
ASP AUT BESD CLD EBD GLD MLD SCD
SCLD

Coombe House
Coleford, Crediton, Devon EX17 5BY
Tel: 01363 85910
Principal: Pat Dingle
Type: Coeducational Residential
Age range: 16–30
No. of pupils: 16
Special needs catered for: ASD

**NAS Broomhayes School & Children's
Centre**
Kingsley House, Alverdiscott Road,
Bideford, Devon EX39 4PL
Tel: 01237 473830
Principal: Ben Higgins
Type: Coeducational Day & Residential
Age range: 10–23
No. of pupils: 31
Special needs catered for: ASD ASP AUT

DORSET

Purbeck View School
Northbrook Road, Swanage,
Dorset BH19 1PR
Tel: 0800 288 9779
Head: Susan Harvey CQSW Ex Dip in
Management
Type: Coeducational Boarding
Age range: 7–19
Special needs catered for: ASD AUT

The Forum School
Shillingstone, Blandford Forum,
Dorset DT11 0QS
Tel: 0800 288 9779
Head: Mr Adrian J A Wylie BED PG DIP
(Autism) NPQH
Type: Coeducational Boarding
Age range: 7–19
Special needs catered for: ASD AUT

The Wing Centre
126 Richmond Park Road, Bournemouth,
Dorset BH8 8TH
Tel: 0800 288 9779
Head: Janette Morgan MA, BA, NPQH,
PGCert in AS, CM CIPD
Type: Boys' Boarding & Day
Age range: B16–19
Special needs catered for: ASD ASP

SOMERSET

3 Dimensions
Chardleigh House, Chardleigh Green,
Wadeford, Chard, Somerset TA20 3AJ
Tel: 01460 68055
Education Manager: Ms Nita Ellul
Type: Boys' Boarding & Day
Age range: B11–16
No. of pupils: 5
Special needs catered for: ADHD AUT
EBD

Farleigh College Mells
Newbury, Nr Mells, Frome,
Somerset BA11 3RG
Tel: 01373 814980
Principal: Ms Sharon Edney
Type: Coeducational Day & Boarding
Age range: 11–19
No. of pupils: 52
Special needs catered for: ADD ADHD
ASD ASP AUT DYS DYSP

**Farleigh Further Education College
Frome**
North Parade, Frome, Somerset BA11 2AB
Tel: 01373 475470
Principal/Manager: Mr Alun Maddocks
Type: Coeducational Day & Residential
Age range: 16–25
No. of pupils: 87
Special needs catered for: ASP LD

North Hill House
Fromefield, Frome, Somerset BA11 2HB
Tel: 01373 466222
Principal: Ms Sharon Edney
Type: Boys' Boarding & Day
Age range: B7–18
No. of pupils: 62
Special needs catered for: ADD ADHD
ASD ASP AUT

WEST MIDLANDS

SHROPSHIRE

CRUCKTON HALL

For further details see p. 84
Cruckton, Shrewsbury,
Shropshire SY5 8PR
Tel: 01743 860206
Email: pdm@cruckton.com
Website: www.cruckton.com
Head Teacher: P D Mayhew
Type: Boys' Residential
Age range: B8–19
No. of pupils: 80
Special needs catered for: ADD ADHD
ASP AUT DYS EBD PMLD SPLD

HIGFORD SCHOOL

For further details see p. 83
Higford Hall, Higford, Shifnal,
Shropshire TF11 9ET
Tel: 01952 630600
Email: info@higfordschool.co.uk
Website: www.optionsgroup.co.uk
Headteacher: Anne Adams
Type: Coeducational Residential & Day
Age range: 8–19
Special needs catered for: ASD

STAFFORDSHIRE

Priory Highfields

9 & 11 Highfields Road, Chasetown,
Burntwood, Staffordshire WS7 4QR
Tel: 01543 672 173
Principal: Ms Joan Pearson
Type: Coeducational Residential
Age range: 18–25
No. of pupils: 10
Special needs catered for: ASD

Rugeley Horizon

Blithbury Road, Blithbury, Rugeley,
Staffordshire WS15 3JQ
Tel: 01889 504400
Principal: Ms Joan Pearson
Type: Coeducational Day & Boarding
Age range: 5–19
No. of pupils: 48
Special needs catered for: ASD ASP AUT

STOKE-ON-TRENT

Strathmore College

38/40 Dimsdale Parade East,
Wolstanton, Stoke-on-Trent ST5 8BU
Tel: 01782 740864
Principal/Manager: Ms Kate Ward
Type: Coeducational Day & Residential
Age range: 16–25
No. of pupils: 37
Special needs catered for: ASP LD

WEST MIDLANDS

The Island Project School

Diddington Hall, Diddington Lane,
Meriden, West Midlands CV7 7HQ
Tel: 01675 442588
Principal: Jacqui Walters-Hutton
Type: Coeducational Day
Age range: 6–19
Special needs catered for: ASD AUT

WORCESTERSHIRE

AALPS Midlands

The Rhydd, Hanley Castle,
Worcestershire WR8 0AD
Tel: 01684 312 610
Registered Manager: Darren Goodwin
Type: Coeducational Residential
Age range: 16–25
Special needs catered for: ASD

YORKSHIRE & HUMBERSIDE

LINCOLNSHIRE

BARTON SCHOOL

For further details see p. 86
Barrow Road, Barton-upon-Humber,
Lincolnshire DN18 6DA
Tel: 01652 631280
Email: info@bartonschool.co.uk
Website: www.optionsgroup.co.uk
Headteacher: Mark Eames
Type: Coeducational Residential & Day
Age range: 8–19
Special needs catered for: ASD

NORTH LINCOLNSHIRE

AALPS North

Winterton Road, Roxby, Scunthorpe,
North Lincolnshire DN15 0BJ
Tel: 01724 733777
Centre Head: Mr Russell Leese
Type: Coeducational Day & Boarding
Age range: 16–30
Special needs catered for: ASD

Demeter House

98-100 Oswald Road, Scunthorpe,
North Lincolnshire DN15 7PA
Tel: 01724 277877
Headteacher: Mrs L Wardlaw
Type: Boys' Boarding
Age range: B5–14
No. of pupils: 5
Special needs catered for: ADD EBD

SOUTH YORKSHIRE

NAS ROBERT OGDEN SCHOOL

For further details see p. 87
Clayton Lane, Thurnscoe, Rotherham,
South Yorkshire S63 0BG
Tel: 01709 874443
Email: robert.ogden@nas.org.uk
Website:
www.autism.org.uk/robertogden
Executive Principal: Dr Jacqui Ashton-
Smith
Type: Coeducational Day & Residential
Age range: 5–19
No. of pupils: 80
Special needs catered for: ASD ASP AUT

SCOTLAND

EAST AYRSHIRE

NAS DALDORCH HOUSE SCHOOL

For further details see p. 88
Sorn Road, Catrine,
East Ayrshire KA5 6NA
Tel: 01290 551666
Email: daldorch@nas.org.uk
Website: www.autism.org.uk/daldorch
Principal: Shona Pinkerton DCE,
DPSE(SEN), MEdSEN
Type: Coeducational Day & Residential
Age range: 5–21
No. of pupils: 64
Special needs catered for: ASD ASP AUT

MORAY

Troup House School
Gamrie, Banff, Moray AB45 3JN
Tel: 01261 851 584
Principal: Mr David McNally
Type: Coeducational Day & Residential
Age range: 8–16
No. of pupils: 12
Special needs catered for: AUT BESD

SOUTH LANARKSHIRE

NAS DALDORCH SATELLITE SCHOOL
For further details see p. 89
St Leonards, East Kilbride,
South Lanarkshire G74
Tel: 01355 246242
Email: daldorch@nas.org.uk
Website: www.autism.org.uk/daldorch
Principal: Shona Pinkerton
Type: Coeducational Residential
Age range: 5–19
No. of pupils: 5
Special needs catered for: ASD ASP AUT

WALES

CARMARTHENSHIRE

Coleg Elidyr
Rhandirmwyn, Llandovery,
Carmarthenshire SA20 ONL
Tel: 01550 760400
Contact: The College Manager
Type: Coeducational Boarding
Age range: 18–25
No. of pupils: 43 B31 G12
Special needs catered for: ADD ADHD
ASD ASP AUT BESD CLD DEL DYSP EBD
EPI GLD LD MLD Phe SCD SLD

FLINTSHIRE

AALPS Cymru
Llanerach-y-mor, Holywell,
Flintshire CH8 9DX
Tel: 01745 562570
Registered Manager: Shian Thomas
Type: Coeducational Residential
Age range: 18
Special needs catered for: ASD

KINSALE SCHOOL
For further details see p. 90
Kinsale Hall, Llanerch-y-Mor, Holywell,
Flintshire CH8 9DX
Tel: 01745 562500
Email: info@kinsaleschool.co.uk
Website: www.optionsgroup.co.uk
Headteacher: Emma Keyworth
Type: Coeducational Residential & Day
Age range: 8–19
Special needs catered for: ASD AUT

TORFAEN

Priory Coleg Wales
Coleg Gwent, Pontypool Campus,
Blaendare Road, Pontypool,
Torfaen NP4 5YE
Tel: 01495 762609
Principal/Manager: Mr Simon Coles
Type: Coeducational Day
Age range: 16–25
No. of pupils: 11
Special needs catered for: ASP LD

VALE OF GLAMORGAN

Beechwood College
Hayes Road, Penarth,
Vale of Glamorgan CF64 5SE
Tel: 029 2053 2210
Principal: Mr Darren Jackson
Type: Coeducational Boarding & Day
Age range: 16
No. of pupils: 66
Special needs catered for: ASD ASP SLD

WREXHAM

Priory Coleg North Wales
Yale College, Grove Park Road,
Wrexham LL2 7AB
Tel: 01978 366 006
Principal/Manager: Mr Simon Coles
Type: Coeducational Day
Age range: 16–25
No. of pupils: 5
Special needs catered for: ASP LD

Schools and colleges specialising in learning difficulties (including dyslexia/SPLD)

Abbreviations

ACLD	Autism, Communication and Associated Learning Difficulties
ADD	Attention Deficit Disorder
ADHD	Attention Deficit and Hyperactive Disorder (Hyperkinetic Disorder)
ASD	Autistic Spectrum Disorder
ASP	Asperger Syndrome
AUT	Autism
BESD	Behavioural, Emotional and Social Difficulties
CCD	Complex Communication Difficulties
CLD	Complex Learning Difficulties
CP	Cerebral Palsy
D	Deaf
DEL	Delicate
DYS	Dyslexia
DYSP	Dyspraxia
EBD	Emotional and Behavioural Difficulties
EBSD	Emotional, Behavioural and/or Social Difficulties
EPI	Epilepsy
GLD	General Learning Difficulties
HA	High Ability
HI	Hearing Impairment
HS	Hospital School
LD	Learning Difficulties
MLD	Moderate Learning Difficulties
MSI	Multi-sensory Impairment
OCD	Obsessive Compulsive Disorder
PD	Physical Difficulties
PH	Physical Impairment
Phe	Partially Hearing
PMLD	Profound and Multiple Learning Difficulties
PNI	Physical Neurological Impairment
PRU	Pupil Referral Unit
SCD	Social and Communication Difficulties
SCLD	Severe and Complex Learning Difficulties
SEBD	Severe Emotional and Behavioural Disorders
SEBN	Social, Emotional and Behavioural Needs
SLD	Severe Learning Difficulties
SLI	Specific Language Impairment
SPLD	Specific Learning Difficulties
SP&LD	Speech and Language Difficulties
SLCN	Speech Language & Communication Needs
VIS	Visually Impaired

Key to symbols

Type of school:

(†) Boys' school

(‡) Girls' school

(🌍) International school

School offers:

(A) A levels

(🏫) Boarding accommodation

(16+) Entrance at 16+

(🎓) Vocational qualifications

(✎) Learning support

(✔) This is a DfE approved independent or non-maintained school under section 342 or 347(1) of the 1996 Education Act

Please note: Unless otherwise indicated, all schools are coeducational day schools. Single-sex and boarding schools will be indicated by the relevant icon.

CENTRAL AND WEST

BRISTOL

Belgrave School
10 Upper Belgrave Road, Clifton,
Bristol BS8 2XH
Tel: 0117 974 3133
Head Teacher: Pat Jones
Type: Coeducational Day
Age range: 5–13
No. of pupils: B14 G10
Special needs catered for: ADD ASD ASP
DEL DYS DYSP HA MLD SLI SPLD SP&LD

Bristol Dyslexia Centre
10 Upper Belgrave Road, Clifton,
Bristol BS8 2XH
Tel: 0117 973 9405
Headmistress: Mrs Pat Jones BEd(Hons),
SEN, SpLD, CertEd, IrSc, CMBDA
Type: Coeducational Day
No. of pupils: B120 G80
Special needs catered for: DYS DYSP SLD

Sheiling School, Thornbury
Thornbury Park, Thornbury,
Bristol BS35 1HP
Tel: 01454 412194
Type: Coeducational Day & Boarding
Age range: 6–19
No. of pupils: 17 B12 G5
Special needs catered for: ADD ADHD
ASD ASP AUT BESD CLD CP DEL DYS
DYSP EBD EPI GLD HA HI LD MLD MSI PD
Phe PMLD SCD SCLD SEBD SLD SLI SPLD
SP&LD

St Christopher's School
Carisbrooke Lodge, Westbury Park,
Bristol BS6 7JE
Tel: 0117 973 3301/973 6875
Head of Education: Ms Orna Matz BEd,
MEd(Autism)
Type: Coeducational Boarding
Age range: 5–19
No. of pupils: 49 B36 G13
Special needs catered for: ASD AUT CLD
CP EPI PD PH PMLD SCLD SLD SP&LD

BUCKINGHAMSHIRE

MacIntyre Wingrave School
Leighton Road, Wingrave,
Buckinghamshire HP22 4PA
Tel: 01296 681274
Principal: Ms Annemari Ottridge
Type: Coeducational Boarding & Day
Age range: 10–19
No. of pupils: 38 B35 G3
Special needs catered for: ASD SCD SLD

GLOUCESTERSHIRE

Cambian Southwick Park School
Gloucester Road, Tewkesbury,
Gloucestershire GL20 7DG
Tel: 0800 288 9779
Head: Mr Jason Goddard
Type: Coeducational Boarding
Age range: 11–19
Special needs catered for: AUT LD SCD
SCLD SEBD SLD

RUSKIN MILL COLLEGE
For further details see p. 115
The Fisheries, Horsley,
Gloucestershire GL6 0PL
Tel: 01453 837500
Principal: Elisabeth Johnson
Type: Coeducational Day & Residential
Age range: 16–25
Special needs catered for: ADHD ASD
ASP BESD CLD EBD GLD LD MLD PMLD
SCD SCLD SEBD SPLD

William Morris House
William Morris Camphill Community,
Eastington, Stonehouse,
Gloucestershire GL10 3SH
Tel: 01453 824025
Contact: Admissions Group
Type: Coeducational Day & Boarding
Age range: 16–25
No. of pupils: 30
Special needs catered for: ASP AUT DYSP
EBD EPI MLD

OXFORDSHIRE

ACTION FOR CHILDREN PARKLANDS CAMPUS
For further details see p. 93
Action for Children Parklands Campus,
Near Appleton, Abingdon,
Oxfordshire OX13 5QB
Tel: 01865 390436
Email: parklands.campus@
actionforchildren.org.uk
Website:
www.actionforchildren.org.uk/parklands
Principal: Raymond Wilson
Type: Coeducational Day & Boarding
Age range: 11–19
Special needs catered for: ASD BESD
DYS MLD SPLD

Action for Children Penhurst School
New Street, Chipping Norton,
Oxfordshire OX7 5LN
Tel: 01608 642559
Principal: Derek Lyseight-Jones
Type: Coeducational Boarding & Day
Age range: 5–19
No. of pupils: 21 B17 G4
Special needs catered for: CP EPI HI PH
PMLD SLD SP&LD VIS

Bruern Abbey School
Chesterton, Bicester,
Oxfordshire OX26 1UY
Tel: 01869 242448
Principal: Mr P Fawkes MBA, CertEd
Type: Boys' Boarding & Day
Age range: B7–13
No. of pupils: 44
Special needs catered for: DYS DYSP

THE UNICORN SCHOOL FOR THE DYSLEXIC CHILD
For further details see p. 94
20 Marcham Road, Abingdon,
Oxfordshire OX14 1AA
Tel: 01235 530222
Email: info@unicorndyslexia.co.uk
Website: www.unicorndyslexia.co.uk
Headteacher: Mrs J Vaux BA(Hons)Oxon,
PGCE, OxCertSpLD, BScPsychol
Type: Coeducational Day
Age range: 6–13
No. of pupils: 70
Special needs catered for: DYS DYSP

WILTSHIRE

Appleford School
Shrewton, Salisbury, Wiltshire SP3 4HL
Tel: 01980 621020
Head: Mrs Lesley Nell
Type: Coeducational Day & Boarding
Age range: 7–14
No. of pupils: 79 B62 G17
Special needs catered for: ADD ADHD ASP DYS DYSP HA MLD SPLD SP&LD

Calder House School
Thickwood Lane, Colerne,
Wiltshire SN14 8BN
Tel: 01225 742329
Head: Mr Andrew Day BEd(Hons)
Type: Coeducational Day
Age range: 6–13
No. of pupils: 48 B30 G18
Special needs catered for: DEL DYS DYSP SLI SPLD SP&LD

Fairfield Farm College
Dilton Marsh, Westbury,
Wiltshire BA13 4DL
Tel: 01373 866066
Principal: Ms Janet Kenward
Type: Coeducational Day & Residential
Age range: 16–23
No. of pupils: B21 G8
Special needs catered for: MLD

Tumblewood Project School
The Laurels, 4 Hawkeridge Road,
Heywood, Westbury, Wiltshire BA13 4LF
Tel: 01373 824 466
Head: Mr John Kearney
Type: Girls' Boarding & Day
Age range: G11–18
No. of pupils: 12
Special needs catered for: ADHD DYS DYSP LD

EAST

BEDFORDSHIRE

Holme Court School
Great North Road, Biggleswade,
Bedfordshire SG18 9ST
Tel: 01767 312766
Headteacher: Mrs Julia Hewerdine
Type: Coeducational Day
Age range: 5–16
No. of pupils: 27
Special needs catered for: ADD ADHD ASP CLD DYS DYSP GLD HA LD MLD SCD SPLD SP&LD VIS

ESSEX

Doucecroft School
Abbots Lane, Eight Ash Green,
Colchester, Essex CO6 3QL
Tel: 01206 771234
Head Teacher: Miss Kathy Cranmer BEd
Type: Coeducational Boarding & Day
Age range: 3–19
No. of pupils: 46 B45 G1
Special needs catered for: ASD ASP AUT

Woodcroft School
Whitakers Way, Loughton,
Essex IG10 1SQ
Tel: 020 8508 1369
Headteacher: Mrs Margaret Newton
Type: Coeducational Day
Age range: 2–11
No. of pupils: 36
Special needs catered for: ADD ADHD ASD ASP AUT CLD CP DEL DYSP EBD EPI LD MLD MSI PH PMLD SCLD SLD SLI SPLD SP&LD VIS

HERTFORDSHIRE

EGERTON ROTHESAY SCHOOL
For further details see p. 95
Durrants Lane, Berkhamsted,
Hertfordshire HP4 3UJ
Tel: 01442 877060
Email: admin.dl@eger-roth.co.uk
Website: www.eger-roth.co.uk
Headteacher: Mrs N I Boddam-Whetham BA(Hons), PGTC
Type: Coeducational Day
Age range: 5–18
No. of pupils: 152
Special needs catered for: DYS DYSP MLD SP&LD

NORFOLK

St Andrews School
Lower Common, East Runton, Cromer,
Norfolk NR27 9PG
Tel: 01263 511727
Headteacher: Ms Gillian Baker BSc(Hons), BA, CertEd, PGCE
Type: Coeducational Day
Age range: 6–12
No. of pupils: 4 B1 G3
Special needs catered for: ADD ADHD ASD ASP AUT DYS DYSP SCD SLD SLI SP&LD

The Beehive
Stubbs House, Stubbs Green, Loddon,
Norfolk NR14 6EA
Tel: 01508 521190
Headteacher: Mrs Valerie Freear
Type: Coeducational Day
Age range: 5–14
No. of pupils: 4
Special needs catered for: ASD BESD MLD SPLD

SUFFOLK

CENTRE ACADEMY EAST ANGLIA
For further details see p. 100
Church Road, Brettenham, Ipswich,
Suffolk IP7 7QR
Tel: 01449 736404
Principal: Duncan Rollo BA, MA, PhD
Type: Coeducational Day & Boarding School
Age range: 4–19
No. of pupils: 40 B33 G7
Special needs catered for: ADHD ASP CLD DYS DYSP GLD HA LD SPLD SP&LD

EAST MIDLANDS

DERBYSHIRE

Alderwasley Hall School & Callow Park College
Alderwasley, Belper,
Derbyshire DE56 2SR
Tel: 01629 822586
Head Teacher: Ms Angela Findlay MEd, NPQH, CertEd
Type: Coeducational Boarding & Day
Age range: 5–19
Special needs catered for: ASP DYS DYSP HA SP&LD

Pegasus School

Caldwell Hall, Main Street, Caldwell,
Derbyshire DE12 6RS
Tel: 01283 761352
Head Teacher: Mr Hugh Rodger
BEd(Hons), MBA(Educ), CertEd(Hearing
Imp)
Type: Coeducational Boarding & Day
Age range: 8–19
Special needs catered for: ADHD ASD
AUT EPI SLD SPLD SP&LD

The Trust Centre

Alderwasley Hall School, Alderwasley,
Belper, Derbyshire DE56 2SR
Tel: 01629 821480
Head of Centre: Mrs Janette Ashworth
BA(Hons), PGCE, PDGEM
Type: Coeducational Day & Boarding
Age range: 9–19
Special needs catered for: EBD LD
SP&LD

LINCOLNSHIRE

KISIMUL SCHOOL

For further details see p. 98
The Old Vicarage, 61 High Street,
Swinderby, Lincoln, Lincolnshire LN6 9LU
Tel: 01522 868279
Email: admissions@kisimul.co.uk
Website: www.kisimul.co.uk
Director of Education: Mr Danny Carter
BA(Hons), MA, MEd
Type: Coeducational Independent
Residential Special School
Age range: 8–19
No. of pupils: 60
Special needs catered for: ASD AUT CLD
EPI LD MSI PMLD SCLD SLD SPLD SP&LD

Linkage College - Toynton Campus

Toynton All Saints, Spilsby,
Lincolnshire PE23 5AE
Tel: 01790 752499
Type: Coeducational Residential & Day
Age range: 16–25
Special needs catered for: ADD ADHD
ASD ASP AUT CLD CP D DEL DYS DYSP
EPI GLD HI LD MLD PD PH Phe SCD SCLD
SLD SPLD SP&LD VIS

NOTTINGHAM

Sutherland House - Continuing Education Centre

8 Clinton Avenue, Nottingham NG5 1AW
Tel: 0115 9693373
Principal: Maria Allen
Type: Coeducational Day
Age range: 11–19
Special needs catered for: ASD AUT

Sutherland House School

Sutherland Road, Nottingham NG3 7AP
Tel: 0115 9873375
Principal: Maria Allen BEd
Type: Coeducational Day
Age range: 3–19
No. of pupils: 84 B80 G4
Special needs catered for: ASD ASP AUT

NOTTINGHAMSHIRE

I CAN'S DAWN HOUSE SCHOOL

For further details see p. 96
Helmsley Road, Rainworth, Mansfield,
Nottinghamshire NG21 0DQ
Tel: 01623 795361
Email: dawnhouse@ican.org.uk
Website: www.dawnhouseschool.org.uk
or www.ican.org.uk
Principal: Angela Child
Type: Coeducational Day & Residential
Age range: 5–19
No. of pupils: 75
Special needs catered for: CLD DYS DYSP
SCD SLD SPLD SP&LD

Landmarks

Upper Mill Farm Sheffield Road, Creswell,
Worksop, Nottinghamshire S80 4HP
Tel: 01909 724724
Principal: Mr Vic Hartwell
Type: Coeducational Day
Special needs catered for: LD

GREATER LONDON

ESSEX

St John's RC Special School

Turpins Lane, Woodford Bridge,
Essex IG8 8AX
Tel: 020 8504 1818
Principal: Jacqueline Sheehy
Type: Coeducational Day
Age range: 5–19
Special needs catered for: MLD SLD

MIDDLESEX

Hillingdon Manor School

Moorcroft Complex, Harlington Road,
Hillingdon, Middlesex UB8 3HD
Tel: 01895 813679
Principal: Ms Angela Austin
Type: Coeducational Day
Age range: 3–19
No. of pupils: 70 B58 G12
Special needs catered for: ASD CLD

PIELD HEATH HOUSE SCHOOL

For further details see p. 97
Pield Heath Road, Uxbridge,
Middlesex UB8 3NW
Tel: 01895 258507
Email: admin@pieldheathschool.org.uk
Website: pieldheathschool.org.uk
Principal: Sister Julie Rose
Type: Coeducational Boarding & Day
Age range: 7–19
No. of pupils: 64
Special needs catered for: MLD SLD
SP&LD

SURREY

Link Primary Day School

138 Croydon Road, Beddington, Croydon,
Surrey CR0 4PG
Tel: 020 8688 5239
Head Teacher: Mrs Beverley Dixon
CertEd, ASE, NPQH
Type: Coeducational Day
Age range: 5–12
No. of pupils: 40 B32 G8
Special needs catered for: ASD ASP DYSP
GLD LD MLD SCD SLI SP&LD

Link Secondary Day School
82-86 Croydon Road, Beddington,
Croydon, Surrey CR0 4PD
Tel: 020 8688 7691
Headteacher: Mr J Pearson CertEd, BEd,
AdvDipSEN, NPQH
Type: Coeducational Day
Age range: 11–19
No. of pupils: 48
Special needs catered for: ASD ASP DYS
SCD SLI SPLD SP&LD

Rutherford School
1A Melville Avenue, South Croydon,
Surrey CR2 7HZ
Tel: 0208 406 8222
Head of School: Sylvia Kerambrum
Type: Coeducational Day
Age range: 3–19
No. of pupils: 26 B17 G9
Special needs catered for: CP D EPI HI
MSI PD PH Phe PMLD PNI SLD SP&LD VIS

The Anchor School
Sutton Junior Tennis Centre, Rose Hill,
Sutton, Surrey SM1 3HH
Tel: 077 34110054
Headteacher: Mrs Wendy Holmes
Type: Coeducational Day
Age range: 4–11
Special needs catered for: SPLD

LONDON

Abingdon House School
Broadley Terrace, London NW1 6LG
Tel: 0845 2300426
Headmaster: Nick Rees
Type: Coeducational Day
Age range: 5–13
No. of pupils: 50 B40 G10
Special needs catered for: ADD ADHD
ASP ASP DYS DYSP SPLD SP&LD

Blossom House School
8a The Drive, Wimbledon,
London SW20 8TG
Tel: 020 8946 7348
Principal: Joanna Burgess DipCST,
MRCSLT, DipRSA SpLD, PGCE
Type: Coeducational Day
Age range: 3–16
No. of pupils: 149 B110 G39
Special needs catered for: ADD ADHD
ASP DYS DYSP SCD SPLD SP&LD

CENTRE ACADEMY LONDON
For further details see p. 100
92 St John's Hill, Battersea,
London SW11 1SH
Tel: 020 7738 2344
Email: info@centreacademy.net
Website: www.centreacademy.net
Principal: Duncan Rollo BA, MA, PhD
Type: Independent coeducational day
Age range: 9–19
No. of pupils: 60 B45 G15 VIth13
Special needs catered for: ADD ADHD
ASD ASP AUT CLD DYS DYSP HA SP&LD

Fairley House School
30 Causton Street, London SW1P 4AU
Tel: 020 7976 5456
Principal & Educational Psychologist:
Jacqueline Murray BA(Hons), MEd, MSc,
DipPsychol, DipRSA(SpLD)
Type: Coeducational Day
Age range: 5–14
No. of pupils: B164 G34
Special needs catered for: DYS DYSP HA
SPLD

Frederick Hugh House
48 Old Church Street, London SW3 5BY
Tel: 020 73498833
Headteacher: Miss Tanya Jamil
Type: Coeducational Day
Age range: 4–16
Special needs catered for: MLD PD
SP&LD

Kisharon School
1011 Finchley Road, London NW11 7HB
Tel: 020 8455 7483
Headteacher: Mrs L Amdurer
Type: Coeducational Day
Age range: 4–19
No. of pupils: 17 B12 G5
Special needs catered for: ADD ADHD
ASD ASP AUT BESD CLD CP D DEL DYS
DYSP EBD EPI GLD HA HI LD MLD MSI PD
PH Phe PMLD PNI SCD SCLD SEBD SLD
SLI SPLD SP&LD VIS

Limespring School
Park House, 16 High Road, East Finchley,
London N2 9PJ
Tel: 020 8444 1387
Principal: Denise Drinkwater
Type: Coeducational Day
Age range: 7–11
Special needs catered for: DYS DYSP

PARAYHOUSE SCHOOL
For further details see p. 101
New Kings School Annex, New Kings
Road, Fulham, London SW6 4LY
Tel: 020 7751 0914
Email: a.sullivan@parayhouse.com
Website: www.parayhouse.com
Head: Mrs Sarah Jackson CertEd,
DipEd(Complex Learning Handicap)
Type: Coeducational Day
Age range: 7–16
No. of pupils: 46 B35 G11
Special needs catered for: BESD CLD CP
DEL EBD MLD SCD SP&LD

Side by Side Kids School
9 Big Hill, London E5 9HH
Tel: 020 88808300
Headteacher: Ms R Atkins
Type: Coeducational Day
Age range: 2–16
No. of pupils: 60
Special needs catered for: MLD SLD
SP&LD

The Dominie
55 Warriner Gardens, Battersea,
London SW11 4DX
Tel: 020 7720 8783
Principal: Miss Anne O'Doherty
Type: Coeducational Day
Age range: 6–13
No. of pupils: 30 B15 G15
Special needs catered for: DYS DYSP
SP&LD

The Moat School
Bishops Avenue, Fulham,
London SW6 6EG
Tel: 020 7610 9018
Head: Abigail Gray
Type: Coeducational Day
Age range: 11–16
No. of pupils: B62 G18
Special needs catered for: SPLD

NORTH-EAST

NORTHUMBERLAND

Mencap Dilston College
Dilston Hall, Corbridge,
Northumberland NE45 5RJ
Tel: 01434 632692
Principal: Mr John A Jameson BA, PGCE
Type: Coeducational Day & Boarding
Age range: 16–25
No. of pupils: B42 G29
Special needs catered for: ASP AUT CP
EPI HI MLD SCD SLD SPLD VIS

Nunnykirk Centre for Dyslexia
Netherwitton, Morpeth,
Northumberland NE61 4PB
Tel: 01670 772685
Headteacher: C Hodgson BA(Hons),
PGCE, NPQH, ACFPS (SpLD/Dys), BDA
Approved Teacher
Type: Coeducational Boarding & Day
Age range: 9–18
No. of pupils: 39 B35 G4
Special needs catered for: DYS DYSP
SPLD

NORTH-WEST

CHESHIRE

The David Lewis School
Mill Lane, Warford, Alderley Edge,
Cheshire SK9 7UD
Tel: 01565 640066
Headteacher: Mrs Pauline Greenall BA,
MEd
Type: Coeducational Boarding & Day
Age range: 14–19
No. of pupils: 20 B14 G6
Special needs catered for: AUT CP EPI HI
PD PMLD SCD SLD SPLD SP&LD VIS

GREATER MANCHESTER

Birtenshaw Hall School
Bromley Cross, Bolton,
Greater Manchester BL7 9AB
Tel: 01204 306043
Head Teacher: Mr Paul Carolan
Type: Coeducational Day
Age range: 3–19
No. of pupils: 12 B10 G2
Special needs catered for: ADD ADHD
ASD ASP AUT CLD CP DEL EPI GLD HI LD
MLD MSI PD PH Phe PMLD PNI SCD SCLD
SLD SLI SP&LD VIS

Bridge College
Curzon Road, Offerton, Stockport,
Greater Manchester SK2 5DG
Tel: 0161 487 4293
Principal: Maggie Thompson
Type: Independent Specialist Day FE
College
Age range: 16–23
No. of pupils: 75
Special needs catered for: AUT CLD PH

Inscape Centre for Autism (INCA)
Schools Hill, Cheadle,
Greater Manchester SK8 1JE
Tel: 0161 283 4761
Head: Susan Allison
Type: Coeducational Day
Special needs catered for: AUT

Inscape House Salford
Walkden Road, Worsley, Manchester,
Greater Manchester M28 7FG
Tel: 0161 975 2340
Headteacher: Keith Cox
Type: Coeducational Day
Age range: 5–19
No. of pupils: 65
Special needs catered for: AUT

Langdon College
9 Leicester Avenue, Salford,
Greater Manchester M7 4HA
Tel: 0161 740 5900
Principal: Mr Christopher Mayho
Type: Coeducational Residential & Day
Age range: 16–25
Special needs catered for: ASD ASP AUT
BESD DYS DYSP EBD GLD HI LD MLD PH
Phe SCD SLI SPLD SP&LD VIS

LANCASHIRE

Pontville
Black Moss Lane, Ormskirk,
Lancashire L39 4TW
Tel: 01695 578734
Head Teacher: Iain E Sim MEd, BSc, ToD
Type: Coeducational Day and 38 week
Residential School.
Age range: 5–19
No. of pupils: 69
Special needs catered for: ASD ASP CLD
MLD SCD SLI SPLD SP&LD

Progress School
Gough Lane, Bamber Bridge, Preston,
Lancashire PR26 7TZ
Tel: 01772 334832
Principal: Mrs Lyn Lewis
Type: Coeducational Residential Special
Age range: 7–19
No. of pupils: 17
Special needs catered for: AUT PMLD
SCLD SLD

Red Rose School
28-30 North Promenade, St Annes on
Sea, Lytham St Annes,
Lancashire FY8 2NQ
Tel: 01253 720570
Principal: Colin Lannen
Type: Coeducational Day
Age range: 5–16
Special needs catered for: DYS

Springvale Independent School
Springfield House, 71 Todmorden Road,
Burnley, Lancashire BB11 3ES
Tel: 01282 458891
Head Teacher: Mrs Elaine Kruse
Type: Coeducational Day
Age range: 7–16
No. of pupils: 6
Special needs catered for: ADHD DYS
DYSP

Westmorland School
Weldbank Lane, Chorley,
Lancashire PR7 3NQ
Tel: 01257 278899
Head Teacher: Mrs S M Asher
Type: Coeducational Day
Age range: 5–11
No. of pupils: 25
Special needs catered for: ADHD ASD
BESD MLD SPLD

MERSEYSIDE

Lakeside School
Naylors Road, Huyton, Liverpool,
Merseyside L27 2YA
Tel: 0151 4877211
Head Teacher: Mrs V I Size BEd(Hons),
MEd(Autism)
Type: Coeducational Day
Age range: 5–13
No. of pupils: 20
Special needs catered for: ADD ADHD
ASD ASP AUT BESD CLD DEL DYS DYSP
EPI HA HI LD MLD PH SCD SLI SPLD
SP&LD VIS

Walton Progressive School
Progressive Lifestyles Education
Services, Rice Lane, Liverpool,
Merseyside L9 1NR
Tel: 0151 5254004
Headteacher: Ms Diane Jones
Type: Coeducational Day
Age range: 8–19
No. of pupils: 20 B14 G6
Special needs catered for: SP&LD

Wargrave House School
449 Wargrave Road, Newton-le-Willows,
Merseyside WA12 8RS
Tel: 01925 224899
Principal: Mrs Wendy Mann BSc, PGCE,
DipSpLD, NPQH
Type: Coeducational Boarding & Day
Age range: 5–19
No. of pupils: 70
Special needs catered for: ASP AUT

SOUTH-EAST

BRIGHTON & HOVE

St John's School & College
Business Centre, Walpole Road,
Brighton, Brighton & Hove BN2 0AF
Tel: 01273 244000
Principal & Chief Executive: Mr Mark
Hughes
Type: Coeducational Boarding & Day
Age range: 7–19
No. of pupils: 43 B34 G9
Special needs catered for: ADD ADHD
ASD ASP AUT BESD CLD CP D DEL DYS
DYSP EBD EPI GLD HA HI LD MLD MSI
Phe PNI SCD SCLD SEBD SLD SLI SPLD
SP&LD VIS

EAST SUSSEX

Frewen College
Brickwall,, Rye Road, Northiam, Rye,
East Sussex TN31 6NL
Tel: 01797 252494
Principal: Mrs Linda Smith BA(Hons),
PGCE
Type: Coeducational Boarding & Day
Age range: 7–19
No. of pupils: 103 B72 G31
Special needs catered for: ASP DYS DYSP
SPLD SP&LD

Northease Manor School
Rodmell, Lewes, East Sussex BN7 3EY
Tel: 01273 472915
Headteacher: Carmen Harvey-Browne
BA(Hons), PGCE, NPQH
Type: Coeducational Boarding & Day
Age range: 10–17
No. of pupils: 95 B76 G19
Special needs catered for: ADD ADHD
ASD ASP DYS DYSP SCD SPLD SP&LD

Owlswick School
Newhaven Road, Kingston, Lewes,
East Sussex BN7 3NF
Tel: 01273 473078
Headteacher: Michael Mayne
Type: Coeducational Boarding
Age range: 10–17
No. of pupils: B7
Special needs catered for: ADD ADHD
ASD ASP BESD DYS DYSP EBD GLD LD
MLD SCD

St John's School
Firle Road, Seaford,
East Sussex BN25 2HU
Tel: 01323 872940
Principal: Don Kent
Type: Coeducational Boarding
Age range: 7–16
No. of pupils: 115 B96 G19
Special needs catered for: MLD SLD

HAMPSHIRE

Chiltern Tutorial School
Otterbourne New Hall, Cranbourne Drive,
Otterbourne, Winchester,
Hampshire SO21 2ET
Tel: 01962 717696
Headmistress: Mrs Jane Gaudie BA,
CertEd, AMBDA
Type: Coeducational Day
Age range: 7–11
No. of pupils: 24 B20 G4
Special needs catered for: DYS DYSP

Minstead Training Project
Minstead Lodge, Minstead, Lyndhurst,
Hampshire SO43 7FT
Tel: 023 80812254
Principal: Mr Martin Lenaerts
Type: Coeducational Boarding & Day
Age range: 18
No. of pupils: 14
Special needs catered for: GLD LD MLD

Sheiling School, Ringwood
Horton Road, Ashley, Ringwood,
Hampshire BH24 2EB
Tel: 01425 477488
Principal: Ms Corine van Barneveld
Type: Coeducational Boarding & Day
Age range: 6–19
No. of pupils: 38
Special needs catered for: ASD AUT CLD
EBD EPI GLD LD MLD SCD SCLD SLD
SPLD SP&LD

The Loddon School
Wildmoor Lane, Sherfield-on-Loddon,
Hook, Hampshire RG27 0JD
Tel: 01256 884600
Principal: Lynn Young BEd, MEd(SLD)
Type: Coeducational Boarding
Age range: 8–19
No. of pupils: 29 B25 G4
Special needs catered for: ADD ADHD
ASD AUT CLD EPI SCLD SLD SP&LD

KENT

Great Oaks Small School
Ebbsfleet Farmhouse, Ebbsfleet Lane,
Minster, Ramsgate, Kent CT12 5DL
Tel: 01843 822 022
Head of School: Mrs Liz Baker
Type: Coeducational Day
Age range: 10–18
No. of pupils: 18 B13 G5 VIth3
Special needs catered for: SPLD

MEDWAY

Trinity School
13 New Road, Rochester,
Medway ME1 1BG
Tel: 01634 812233
Principal: Mrs C Dunn BA(Hons),
RSA(Dip), SpLD(NHCSS)
Type: Coeducational Day
Age range: 6–16
No. of pupils: 43 B28 G15
Special needs catered for: ASD ASP DYS
DYSP SLD SP&LD

SOUTHAMPTON

Hope Lodge School
22 Midanbury Lane, Bitterne Park,
Southampton SO18 4HP
Tel: 023 8063 4346
Headteacher: Mike Robinson
Type: Coeducational Boarding & Day
Age range: 4–19
No. of pupils: 60 B51 G9
Special needs catered for: ASP AUT MLD SLD

SURREY

I CAN'S MEATH SCHOOL
For further details see p.102
Brox Road, Ottershaw, Surrey KT16 0LF
Tel: 01932 872302
Email: meath@meath-ican.org.uk
Website: www.meathschool.org.uk or www.ican.org.uk
Headteacher: Janet Dunn OBE, MA, AdvDipSpecEduc
Type: Coeducational Day & Residential
No. of pupils: 51
Special needs catered for: SP&LD

KISIMUL SCHOOL - WOODSTOCK HOUSE
For further details see p.104
Woodstock Lane North, Long Ditton,
Surbiton, Surrey KT6 5HN
Tel: 020 8335 2570
Email: admissions@kisimul.co.uk
Website: www.kisimul.co.uk
Director of Education: Mr Danny Carter BA(Hons), MA, MEd
Type: Coeducational Independent Residential Special School
Age range: 8–19
No. of pupils: 40
Special needs catered for: ASD AUT CLD EPI LD MSI PMLD SCLD SLD SPLD SP&LD

Moon Hall College
Burys Court, Flanchford Road, Leigh,
Reigate, Surrey RH2 8RE
Tel: 01306 611372
Principal: Mrs Berry Baker BA(Hons)History, PGCE, BSc(Hons)Psych, BDA Diploma, AMBDA
Type: Coeducational Day
Age range: 3–16
No. of pupils: B57 G28
Special needs catered for: DYS LD SPLD

Moon Hall School
Pasturewood Road, Holmbury St Mary,
Dorking, Surrey RH5 6LQ
Tel: 01306 731464
Head: Mrs Pamela Lore BA(Hons)
(Psych), MA(Ed), Dip RSA SpLD, PGCE
Type: Coeducational Boarding & Day
Age range: 7–13
No. of pupils: B84 G12
Special needs catered for: DYS SPLD

More House School
Moons Hill, Frensham, Farnham,
Surrey GU10 3AP
Tel: 01252 792303
Headmaster: Barry Huggett BA(Hons), QTS, MIBiol
Type: Boys' Boarding & Day
Age range: B8–18
No. of pupils: 330
Special needs catered for: SPLD

Orchard Hill College of Further Education
6 Elm Avenue, Foutain Drive, Carshalton,
Surrey SM5 4NR
Tel: 020 8770 8126
Principal: Ms Caroline Allen OBE, BEd(Hons), MBA(Ed)
Type: Coeducational Day
Age range: 16
Special needs catered for: ADD ADHD ASD ASP AUT BESD CLD CP DEL DYS DYSP EBD EPI GLD HA HI LD MLD MSI PD PH Phe PMLD PNI SCD SCLD SEBD SLD SLI SPLD SP&LD VIS

St Dominic's School
Hambledon, Godalming, Surrey GU8 4DX
Tel: 01428 684693/682741
Principal: Mrs Angela Drayton
Type: Coeducational Boarding & Day
Age range: 8–19
No. of pupils: 77 B72 G5 VIth19
Special needs catered for: ADD ADHD ASD ASP CLD DEL DYS DYSP EPI HA HI SCD SPLD SP&LD

St Joseph's School
Amlets Lane, Cranleigh, Surrey GU6 7DH
Tel: 01483 272449
Headteacher: Mrs Mary Fawcett
Type: Coeducational Boarding & Day
Age range: 5–19
No. of pupils: 78 B58 G20 VIth31
Special needs catered for: ADHD ASD CLD DYS DYSP EPI LD MLD SCLD SLD SP&LD

The Jigsaw School
Building 21, Dunsfold Park, Stovolds Hill,
Cranleigh, Surrey GU6 8TB
Tel: 01483 273874
Executive Head: Kate Grant
Type: Coeducational Day
Age range: 4–19
Special needs catered for: AUT

The Knowl Hill School
School Lane, Pirbright, Woking,
Surrey GU24 0JN
Tel: 01483 797032
Head: James Dow-Grant MA Ed, Dip IEP, CertSpld, DipPD
Type: Coeducational Day
Age range: 7–16
No. of pupils: 57 B42 G15
Special needs catered for: DYS

SOUTH-WEST

DEVON

Kingsley School
Northdown Road, Bideford,
Devon EX39 3LY
Tel: 01237 426200
Headmaster: Mr Andy Waters BEd, MA
Type: Coeducational Boarding & Day
Age range: 3–18 years
No. of pupils: 400 VIth80
Special needs catered for: DYS DYSP

DORSET

Boveridge House School (formerly Philip Green Memorial School)
Boveridge House, Cranborne, Wimborne,
Dorset BH21 5RU
Tel: 01725 517218
Headmistress: Mrs L Water
Type: Coeducational Boarding
Age range: 8–19
No. of pupils: 38
Special needs catered for: MLD SCD SLD

PORTFIELD SCHOOL
For further details see p. 106
Parley Lane, Christchurch,
Dorset BH23 6BP
Tel: 01202 573808
Email: enquiries@portfieldschool.org.uk
Website: www.portfieldschool.org.uk
Director of Services: Andrew Thomas
Type: Non-maintained Special
Residential/Day School
Age range: 3–19
No. of pupils: 57 B51 G6
Special needs catered for: ASD AUT

SOMERSET

Foxes Academy
The Esplanade, Minehead,
Somerset TA24 5QP
Tel: 01643 708529
Principal: Mrs Vanessa Cleere
Type: Coeducational Residential
Age range: 18–25
No. of pupils: 73 B28 G45
Special needs catered for: MLD SCD

Inaura School
Manor Farm Cottage, Wells,
Somerset BA5 1RZ
Tel: 0145 8830434
Headteacher: Dr Adam Abdelnoor
Type: Coeducational Day
Age range: 10–18
Special needs catered for: ADHD EBD
MLD

MARK COLLEGE
For further details see p. 103
Mark, Highbridge, Somerset TA9 4NP
Tel: 01278 641632
Email: markcollege@priorygroup.com
Website:
www.priorygroup.com/markcollege
Principal: Ms Michelle Whitham-Jones
Type: Coeducational Day & Boarding
Age range: 10–19
No. of pupils: 88
Special needs catered for: DYS DYSP SLD
SPLD

Mencap Lufton College
Lufton, Yeovil, Somerset BA22 8ST
Tel: 01935 403120
Principal: Mr Rupert Elliott DipM, IPD
Type: Coeducational Boarding
Age range: 16–25
No. of pupils: 72
Special needs catered for: HI MLD PH
PMLD SLD

Shapwick Prep
Mark Road, Burtle, Bridgwater,
Somerset TA7 8NJ
Tel: 01278 722012
Joint Headmasters: D C Walker BA(Hons)
& J P Whittock CertEd
Type: Coeducational Day & Boarding
Age range: 8–18
No. of pupils: 142 B105 G37
Special needs catered for: DYS

WEST MIDLANDS

HEREFORDSHIRE

Rowden House School
Rowden, Bromyard,
Herefordshire HR7 4LS
Tel: 01885 488096
Head Teacher: Mr Ian Gateley BMET, BA,
PGCE
Type: Coeducational Boarding
Age range: 11–19
No. of pupils: 44 B34 G10
Special needs catered for: AUT EPI SCLD
SLD

SHROPSHIRE

Access School
Holbrook Villa Farm, Harmer Hill,
Broughton, Shrewsbury,
Shropshire SY4 3EW
Tel: 01939 220797
Headteacher: Miss Verity White
Type: Coeducational Day
Age range: 5–16
No. of pupils: 10
Special needs catered for: EBD GLD MLD

Jigsaw School
Queensway, Hadley, Telford,
Shropshire TF1 6AJ
Tel: 01952 388555
Headteacher: Nigel Griffiths
Type: Coeducational Day
Age range: 11–16
Special needs catered for: EBD SPLD

STAFFORDSHIRE

Bladon House School
Newton Solney, Burton upon Trent,
Staffordshire DE15 0TA
Tel: 01283 563787
Head Teacher: Mrs Kate Britt CEd,
MA(Educ Management)
Type: Coeducational Day & Boarding
Age range: 5–19
Special needs catered for: ADD ADHD
AUT CLD MLD SLD SP&LD

Maple Hayes Dyslexia School
Abnalls Lane, Lichfield,
Staffordshire WS13 8BL
Tel: 01543 264387
Principal: Dr E N Brown MSc, BA, MINS,
MSCMe, AFBPsS, CPsychol
Type: Independent Day School
Age range: 7–17
No. of pupils: 118 B97 G23
Special needs catered for: DYS DYSP
SPLD

STOKE-ON-TRENT

Regent College
77 Shelton New Road, Shelton, Stoke-on-
Trent ST4 7AA
Tel: 01782 263326
Principal: Wendy Williams
Type: Coeducational Day
Age range: 16–25
No. of pupils: 30
Special needs catered for: CLD EPI PD
SLD SP&LD

TELFORD & WREKIN

OVERLEY HALL SCHOOL
For further details see p. 107
Overley, Wellington, Telford,
Telford & Wrekin TF6 5HE
Tel: 01952 740262
Email: info@overleyhall.com
Website: www.overleyhall.com
Principal: Mrs Anita Brown BA(Hons),
CertEd, DipSpEd
Type: Coeducational Residential
Age range: 9–19
No. of pupils: 22 B15 G7
Special needs catered for: ADHD AUT EPI
HI PMLD SLD SP&LD

WEST MIDLANDS

GLASSHOUSE COLLEGE

For further details see p. 116

Wollaston Road, Amblecote, Stourbridge,
West Midlands DY8 4HF
Tel: 01384 399400
Principal: Ollie Cheney
Type: Coeducational Day & Residential
Age range: 16–25
Special needs catered for: ADHD ASD
ASP BESD CLD EBD GLD LD PMLD SCD
SCLD SEBD SLD SPLD

Sunfield School

Woodman Lane, Clent, Stourbridge,
West Midlands DY9 9PB
Tel: 01562 882253
Chief Executive: Professor Barry
Carpenter OBE
Type: Coeducational Boarding
Age range: 6–19
No. of pupils: 72 B58 G14
Special needs catered for: AUT EBD EPI
MLD SLD SP&LD

YORKSHIRE & HUMBERSIDE

NORTH-EAST LINCOLNSHIRE

Linkage College - Weelsby Campus

Weelsby Road, Grimsby, North-
East Lincolnshire DN32 9RU
Tel: 01472 241044
Director of Education: Hugh Williams
Type: Coeducational Boarding & Day
Age range: 16–25
No. of pupils: 220
Special needs catered for: ADD ADHD
ASD ASP AUT CLD CP D DEL DYS DYSP
EPI GLD HI LD MLD PH Phe SCD SCLD
SLD SPLD SP&LD VIS

SOUTH YORKSHIRE

49 King Street

Thorne, Doncaster,
South Yorkshire DN8 5AU
Tel: 01405 818580
Registered Care Manager: Eileen
Champion
Type: Coeducational 52-week residential
Age range: 19
No. of pupils: 12
Special needs catered for: AUT CLD SLD

FREEMAN COLLEGE

For further details see p. 117

Sterling Works, 88 Arundel Street,
Sheffield, South Yorkshire S1 2NG
Tel: 0114 252 5940
Principal: Bonny Etchell-Anderson
Type: Coeducational Day & Residential
Age range: 16–25
Special needs catered for: ADHD ASD
ASP BESD CLD EBD GLD LD MLD PMLD
SCD SCLD SEBD SLD

FULLERTON HOUSE SCHOOL

For further details see p. 108

Tickill Square, Denaby, Doncaster,
South Yorkshire DN12 4AR
Tel: 01709 861663
Email: enquiries@hesleygroup.co.uk
Website:
www.fullertonhouseschool.co.uk
Head: David Whitehead
Type: Coeducational 52-week residential
Age range: 8–19
No. of pupils: 46
Special needs catered for: AUT CLD SLD

Hesley Village

Tickhill, Doncaster,
South Yorkshire DN11 9HH
Tel: 01302 866906
Principal: David O'Connor
Type: Coeducational 52-week residential
Age range: 18
No. of pupils: 68
Special needs catered for: AUT CLD SLD

Low Laithes Village

Old Farm Lane, Wombwell, Barnsley,
South Yorkshire S73 8SU
Tel: 01226 272050
General Manager: David Little
Type: Coeducational 52-week residential
Age range: 18
No. of pupils: 30
Special needs catered for: AUT CLD SLD

WILSIC HALL SCHOOL

For further details see p. 109

Wadworth, Doncaster,
South Yorkshire DN11 9AG
Tel: 01302 856382
Email: enquiries@hesleygroup.co.uk
Website: www.wilsichallschool.co.uk
Head: Geoff Turner
Type: Coeducational 52-week residential
Age range: 11–19
No. of pupils: 36
Special needs catered for: AUT CLD SLD

WEST YORKSHIRE

Pennine Camphill Community

Wood Lane, Chapelthorpe, Wakefield,
West Yorkshire WF4 3JL
Tel: 01924 255281
Principal: S Hopewell
Type: Coeducational Day & Boarding
Age range: 16–25
No. of pupils: 46 B26 G20
Special needs catered for: ADHD ASP
AUT DYSP EBD EPI MLD SLD SPLD

SCOTLAND

ABERDEEN

Linn Moor Residential School

Peterculter, Aberdeen AB14 0PJ
Tel: 01224 732246
Principal: John M Davidson PGDipCC,
DipSW, DipHE, CRCCYP
Type: Coeducational Boarding & Day
Age range: 5–18
No. of pupils: 25 B21 G4
Special needs catered for: ASD ASP AUT
BESD CLD EBD GLD LD MLD SCD SCLD
SEBD SPLD

CLACKMANNANSHIRE

Struan House

Bradbury Campus, 100 Smithfield Loan,
Alloa, Clackmannanshire FK10 1NP
Tel: 01259 222000
*Director of Education & Support
Services:* Jim Taylor
Type: Coeducational Boarding & Day
Age range: 5–17
No. of pupils: B25 G5
Special needs catered for: ASD AUT

GLASGOW

East Park

1092 Maryhill Road, Glasgow G20 9TD
Tel: 0141 946 2050
Principal: Mrs L Gray
Type: Coeducational Boarding & Day
Age range: 0–25
No. of pupils: B17 G22
Special needs catered for: AUT CP DEL
EPI HI MLD PH PMLD SLD SP&LD VIS

Springboig St John's
1190 Edinburgh Road, Glasgow G32 4EH
Tel: 0141 774 9791
Principal: Mr W Fitzgerald
Type: Boys' Boarding
Age range: B14–17
No. of pupils: 37
Special needs catered for: DYS EBD MLD SPLD

PERTH & KINROSS

Ochil Tower
140 High Street, Auchterarder, Perth,
Perth & Kinross PH3 1AD
Tel: 01764 662416
Co-ordinators: Mr Ueli Ruprecht BA CEd,
DASE(SpecialEd), Administration & Mrs
Hilary Ruprecht DipSW, Admissions and
Reviews Child Protection
Type: Independent Coeducational Day
and Boarding
Age range: 5–18
No. of pupils: 35
Special needs catered for: ADD ADHD
ASD BESD CLD EBD EPI LD MLD MSI
PMLD SCD SCLD SP&LD

The New School
Butterstone, Dunkeld,
Perth & Kinross PH8 0HA
Tel: 01350 724216
Head Teacher: Ms Anne Cadden
Type: Coeducational Day & Boarding
Age range: 12–20
No. of pupils: 35
Special needs catered for: ASD

WALES

DENBIGHSHIRE

Mencap Pengwern College
Sarn Lane, Rhuddlan, Rhyl,
Denbighshire LL18 5UH
Tel: 01745 590300
Principal: Tina Ruane
Type: Coeducational Day & Boarding
Age range: 16–25
Special needs catered for: ADD ADHD
ASD ASP AUT BESD CLD CP DYSP EBD
EPI GLD HI LD MLD MSI PD PH Phe PMLD
SCD SCLD SEBD SLD SLI SP&LD VIS

GWYNEDD

Aran Hall School
Rhydymain, Dolgellau,
Gwynedd LL40 2AR
Tel: 01341 450641
Head Teacher: Mr Duncan Pritchard
CertEd, DipAppSS, BSc(Hons),
MSc(psych)
Type: Coeducational Boarding & Day
Age range: 11–19
Special needs catered for: ADHD ASP
AUT EPI MLD SLD SPLD

PEMBROKESHIRE

PLAS DWBL FARM COLLEGE
For further details see p. 111
Mynachlog-ddu, Clunderwen,
Pembrokeshire, SA66 7SE
Tel: 01994 419420
Principal: Elisabeth Johnson
Type: Coeducational Day & Residential
Age range: 16–25
Special needs catered for: ASD ASP CLD
EBD

POWYS

MacIntyre Womaston School
Womaston, Walton, Presteigne,
Powys LD8 2PT
Tel: 01544 230308
Principal: Mr Martin Carter
Type: Coeducational Boarding & Day
Age range: 11–19
No. of pupils: 16 B10 G6
Special needs catered for: ADD ADHD
ASD ASP AUT LD PMLD SCLD SEBD

VALE OF GLAMORGAN

ACTION FOR CHILDREN HEADLANDS SCHOOL
For further details see p. 110
2 St Augustine's Road, Penarth,
Vale of Glamorgan CF64 1YY
Tel: 02920 709771
Email:
headlands.school@actionforchildren.org.uk
Website:
www.actionforchildren.org.uk/headlands
Principal: Matthew Burns
Type: Coeducational Boarding & Day
Age range: 8–19
No. of pupils: 54 B47 G7
Special needs catered for: ADD ADHD
ASD ASP AUT BESD DYS EBD MLD SPLD
SP&LD

WREXHAM

Prospects for Young People
12 Grosvenor Road, Wrexham LL11 1BU
Tel: 01978 313777
Head Teacher: Tony Clifford
Type: Coeducational Day & Boarding
Age range: 11–16
No. of pupils: 21 B12 G9
Special needs catered for: MLD SPLD

Schools and colleges specialising in emotional, behavioural and/or social difficulties (EBSD)

Abbreviations

ACLD	Autism, Communication and Associated Learning Difficulties
ADD	Attention Deficit Disorder
ADHD	Attention Deficit and Hyperactive Disorder (Hyperkinetic Disorder)
ASD	Autistic Spectrum Disorder
ASP	Asperger Syndrome
AUT	Autism
BESD	Behavioural, Emotional and Social Difficulties
CCD	Complex Communication Difficulties
CLD	Complex Learning Difficulties
CP	Cerebral Palsy
D	Deaf
DEL	Delicate
DYS	Dyslexia
DYSP	Dyspraxia
EBD	Emotional and Behavioural Difficulties
EBSD	Emotional, Behavioural and/or Social Difficulties
EPI	Epilepsy
GLD	General Learning Difficulties
HA	High Ability
HI	Hearing Impairment
HS	Hospital School
LD	Learning Difficulties
MLD	Moderate Learning Difficulties
MSI	Multi-sensory Impairment
OCD	Obsessive Compulsive Disorder
PD	Physical Difficulties
PH	Physical Impairment
Phe	Partially Hearing
PMLD	Profound and Multiple Learning Difficulties
PNI	Physical Neurological Impairment
PRU	Pupil Referral Unit
SCD	Social and Communication Difficulties
SCLD	Severe and Complex Learning Difficulties
SEBD	Severe Emotional and Behavioural Disorders
SEBN	Social, Emotional and Behavioural Needs
SLD	Severe Learning Difficulties
SLI	Specific Language Impairment
SPLD	Specific Learning Difficulties
SP&LD	Speech and Language Difficulties
SLCN	Speech Language & Communication Needs
VIS	Visually Impaired

Key to symbols

Type of school:

(†) Boys' school

(‡) Girls' school

(🌐) International school

School offers:

(A) A levels

(🏫) Boarding accommodation

(16) Entrance at 16+

(🎓) Vocational qualifications

(✎) Learning support

(✔) This is a DfE approved independent or non-maintained school under section 342 or 347(1) of the 1996 Education Act

Please note: Unless otherwise indicated, all schools are coeducational day schools. Single-sex and boarding schools will be indicated by the relevant icon.

CENTRAL AND WEST

BUCKINGHAMSHIRE

Benjamin College
4 Wren Path, Fairford Leys, Aylesbury,
Buckinghamshire HP19 7AR
Tel: 01296 483584
Principal: Mr Jeremy Yelland
Type: Coeducational Day
Age range: 12–18
Special needs catered for: BESD

GLOUCESTERSHIRE

Cotswold Chine School
Box, Stroud, Gloucestershire GL6 9AG
Tel: 01453 837550
Headteacher: Maureen Smith MA(Ed),
PGCertSpLd, PGCE, BA(Hons)
Type: Coeducational Boarding
Age range: 9–19
No. of pupils: 48 B30 G18
Special needs catered for: ADD ADHD
ASP AUT DYS DYSP EBD EPI MLD SP&LD

OXFORDSHIRE

Chilworth House School
Thames Road, Wheatley, Oxford,
Oxfordshire OX33 1JP
Tel: 01844 339077
Headteacher: Sophie Garner BEd,
MEd(Oxon), NPQH
Type: Coeducational Day
Age range: 5–12
No. of pupils: 23
Special needs catered for: EBD SLD

Chilworth House Upper School
Grooms Farm, Thame Road, Wheatley,
Oxfordshire OX33 1JP
Tel: 01844 337720
Headteacher: Kevin Larsen BEd(SpEd),
MA(SpEd)
Type: Coeducational Day
No. of pupils: 36
Special needs catered for: EBD SP&LD

Hillcrest Park School
Southcombe, Chipping Norton, Oxford,
Oxfordshire OX7 5QH
Tel: 01608 644621
Headteacher: David Davidson MA(Hons),
PGCE
Type: Coeducational Boarding
Age range: 7–16
Special needs catered for: ADD ADHD
ASD ASP BESD DYS DYSP EBD GLD MLD
SCD SEBD

Mulberry Bush School
Standlake, Witney,
Oxfordshire OX29 7RW
Tel: 01865 300202
Director: John Turberville BSc, MA
Type: Coeducational Boarding
Age range: 5–12
No. of pupils: 36
Special needs catered for: EBD

EAST

BEDFORDSHIRE

**Advanced Education - Walnut Tree Lodge
School**
Avenue Farm, Renhold Road, Wilden,
Bedford, Bedfordshire MK44 2PY
Tel: 01234 772081
Headteacher: Mr John Boslem
Type: Coeducational Day
Age range: 11–16
Special needs catered for: EBD

CAMBRIDGESHIRE

**Advanced Education - Wisbech School &
Vocational Centre**
Old Session House, 32 Somers Road,
Wisbech, Cambridgeshire PE13 1JF
Tel: 01945 427276
Headteacher: Mr Mick Coleman
Type: Coeducational Day
Age range: 9–16
Special needs catered for: EBD SEBD

Chartwell House School
Goodens Lane, Newton, Wisbech,
Cambridgeshire PE13 5HQ
Tel: 01945 870793
Head: Mrs D A Wright
Type: Boys' Boarding
No. of pupils: 8
Special needs catered for: DYS EBD

The Old School House
March Road, Friday Bridge, Wisbech,
Cambridgeshire PE14 0HA
Tel: 01945 861114
Manager: Rick Ogle-Welbourn
Type: Boys' Boarding
Age range: B7–13
Special needs catered for: EBD

ESSEX

Advanced Education - Essex School
Unit 7 Woodgates Farm, Broxted,
Dunmow, Essex CM6 2BN
Tel: 01279 850474
Headteacher: Julie Barnes
Type: Coeducational Day
Age range: 11–16
Special needs catered for: BESD

Continuum School Whitewebbs
Whitewebbs, Molehill Green, Takely,
Stansted, Essex CM22 6PQ
Tel: 01279 850474/07966 543931
Headteacher: Mr David Flack
Type: Coeducational Day
Age range: 11–18
Special needs catered for: EBD

Donyland Lodge School
Fingringhoe Road, Rowhedge,
Colchester, Essex CO5 7JL
Tel: 01206 728869
Director: Lesley Woodhouse
Type: Coeducational Day
Age range: 11–18
Special needs catered for: EBD

Hopewell School
Harmony House, Baden Powell Close,
Dagenham, Essex RM9 6XN
Tel: 020 8593 6610
Headteacher: Ms Sharina Klaasens
Type: Day School, Junior & Senior
Age range: 5–18
Special needs catered for: EBD MLD
SEBD

Jacques Hall
Harwich Road, Bradfield, Manningtree,
Essex CO11 2XW
Tel: 01255 870311
Principal: Mr Paul Emmerson
Type: Coeducational Boarding & Day
Age range: 11–18
No. of pupils: 21
Special needs catered for: ADHD BESD
EBD MLD SEBD

NORFOLK

Avocet House
The Old Vicarage, School Lane,
Heckingham, Norfolk NR14 6QP
Tel: 01508 549320
Principal: Mr Jonathan Lees
Type: Boys' Boarding
Age range: B8–16
No. of pupils: 8
Special needs catered for: EBD SEBD
SPLD

Copperfield School
22 Euston Road, Great Yarmouth,
Norfolk NR30 1DX
Tel: 07825130014
Headteacher:
Type: Coeducational Day
Age range: 11–16
Special needs catered for: BESD

Future Education
168b Motum Road, Norwich,
Norfolk NR5 8EG
Tel: 01603 250505
Headteacher: Mr Dennis Freeman
Type: Coeducational Day
Age range: 14–16
Special needs catered for: BESD

Kadesh Education
DC3 Vinces Road, Diss, Norfolk IP22 4HG
Tel: 01379 644223
Headteacher: Ms Andi Roy
Type: Coeducational Day
Age range: 11–16
Special needs catered for: BESD

Sheridan School
Thetford Road, Northwold, Thetford,
Norfolk IP26 5LQ
Tel: 01366 726040
Principal: Mr Andy Clark
Type: Coeducational Day & Residential
Age range: 10–19
No. of pupils: 35
Special needs catered for: ADD ADHD
BESD EBD SEBD

SUFFOLK

Bramfield House
Walpole Road, Bramfield, Halesworth,
Suffolk IP19 9AB
Tel: 01986 784235
Head: Mrs D Jennings
Type: Boys' Boarding & Day
Age range: B10–18
No. of pupils: 51 B51
Special needs catered for: ADD ADHD
BESD DEL EBD

Greenfield School
Four Elms, Norwich Road, Stonham
Parva, Stowmarket, Suffolk IP14 5LB
Tel: 01449 711105
Head: Raymond Saunders
Type: Boys' Day & Boarding
Age range: B11–16
No. of pupils: 11
Special needs catered for: EBD MLD

On Track Education Centre (Mildenhall)
82E & F Fred Dannatt Road, Mildenhall,
Suffolk IP28 7RD
Tel: 01638 715555
Headteacher: Mrs Ruth Durrant
Type: Coeducational Day
Age range: 11–18
Special needs catered for: EBD

The Ryes College & Community
New Road, Aldham, Colchester,
Suffolk CO6 3PN
Tel: 01206 243473
Headteacher: Miss Jackies Shanks
Type: Coeducational Boarding
Age range: 7–24
No. of pupils: B21 G7
Special needs catered for: ADD ADHD
ASD ASP AUT BESD EBD SCD SEBD

EAST MIDLANDS

DERBYSHIRE

Eastwood Grange School
Milken Lane, Ashover, Chesterfield,
Derbyshire S45 0BA
Tel: 01246 590255
Principal: Mr Ray Scales
Type: Boys' Residential & Day
Age range: B9–16
No. of pupils: 34
Special needs catered for: ADD ADHD
BESD DYS EBD HA SCD

Ravenswood School
Ilkeston Road, Heanor,
Derbyshire DE75 7DT
Tel: 01733 719208
Head Teacher: Tree Price
Type: Coeducational Day
Age range: 11–16
Special needs catered for: SEBD

The Linnet Independent Learning Centre
107 Mount Pleasant Road, Castle Gresley,
Swadlincote, Derbyshire DE11 9JE
Tel: 01283 213989
Head Teacher: Jan Sullivan
Type: Coeducational Day
Age range: 5–16
No. of pupils: 13
Special needs catered for: ADD ADHD
ASD ASP BESD CLD DEL DYS DYSP EBD
GLD LD MLD SCD SEBD SPLD SP&LD

The Meadows
Beech Lane, Dove Holes,
Derbyshire SK17 8DJ
Tel: 01298 814000
Headteacher: Ms Rachel Dowle
Type: Coeducational Day
Age range: 11–16
Special needs catered for: EBD

LEICESTER

Gryphon School
Slater Street Lodge, Abbey Park,
Leicester LE1 3EJ
Tel: 07833 623420
Headteacher: Miss Christina Church
Type: Coeducational Day
Age range: 11–17
Special needs catered for: EBD

Oakwood School
20 Main Street, Glenfield,
Leicester LE3 8DG
Tel: 0116 2876218
Headteacher: Mr Peter Kilty
Type: Coeducational Day
Age range: 8–16
No. of pupils: 13
Special needs catered for: EBD

LEICESTERSHIRE

Claybrook Cottage School
Frolesworth Lane, Claybrook Magna,
Lutterworth, Leicestershire LE17 5DA
Tel: 01455 202049
Headteacher: Mrs Jennifer Collighan
Type: Coeducational Day
Age range: 8–16
Special needs catered for: BESD

Lewis Charlton School
North Street, Ashby-De-La-Zouch,
Leicestershire LE65 1HU
Tel: 01530 560775
Head: Ms Georgina Pearson
Type: Coeducational Boarding
Age range: 11–16
No. of pupils: 20
Special needs catered for: EBD

Meadow View Farm School
Cossington Road, Sileby, Leicester,
Leicestershire LE12 7RT
Tel: 07789537329
Headteacher: Mr J Read
Type: Coeducational Day
Age range: 6–11
Special needs catered for: ASD BESD
SCD

The Cedars
33 Ashby Road, Stapleton, Hinckley,
Leicestershire LE9 8JF
Tel: 01455 844205
Principal Teacher: Mr Troy Scrimshaw
Type: Boys' Boarding
Age range: B11–16
No. of pupils: 5
Special needs catered for: SEBD

Trinity College
Moor Lane, Loughborough,
Leicestershire LE11 1BA
Tel: 01509 218906
Headteacher: Mr Adam Brewster
Type: Coeducational Day
Age range: 9–16
No. of pupils: 36
Special needs catered for: EBD MLD

LINCOLNSHIRE

Broughton House
Brant Broughton, Lincolnshire LN5 0SL
Tel: 0800 288 9779
Head of Service: Mr Michael Semilore
Type: Coeducational Boarding
Age range: 16–25
Special needs catered for: AUT BESD LD
SCD SCLD SEBD SLD

NORTHAMPTONSHIRE

**Advanced Education - Northampton
School**
67 Queens Park Parade, Kingsthorpe,
Northampton,
Northamptonshire NN2 6LR
Tel: 01604 719711
Headteacher: Rob Bilbe
Type: Coeducational Day
Age range: 11–16
Special needs catered for: EBD MLD

Ashmead School
Buccleuch Farm, Haigham Hill, Burton
Latimer, Kettering,
Northamptonshire NN15 5PH
Tel: 01536 725998
Headteacher: Joyce Kuwazo
Type: Coeducational Day
Age range: 11–16
No. of pupils: 12
Special needs catered for: EBD

Belview School
124b Midland Road, Wellingborough,
Northamptonshire NN8 1NF
Tel: 01933 441877
Headteacher: Ms Candy Shaw
Type: Coeducational Day
Age range: 11–17
No. of pupils: 4
Special needs catered for: BESD

Thornby Hall School
Thornby Hall, Thornby, Northampton,
Northamptonshire NN6 8SW
Tel: 01604 740001
Director: Ms Rene Kennedy CertEd,
DipArt Therapy
Type: Coeducational Boarding
Age range: 12–18
No. of pupils: 20
Special needs catered for: EBD

NOTTINGHAM

Beech Trees School
Beech Trees House, Old Melton Road,
Widmerpoole, Nottingham NG12 5QH
Tel: 01949 81937
Headteacher: Ms Jennifer Collighan
Type: Coeducational Day
Age range: 8–16
No. of pupils: 3
Special needs catered for: BESD

NOTTINGHAMSHIRE

Freyburg School
The Poppies, Greenmile Lane, Babworth,
Nottinghamshire DN22 8JW
Tel: 01777 709061
Headteacher: Mr David Carr
Type: Boys' Day
Age range: B11–16
Special needs catered for: BESD

Hope House School
Barnby Road, Newark,
Nottinghamshire NG24 3NE
Tel: 01636 700 380
Headteacher: Mrs Teri Westmoreland
Type: Coeducational Day
Age range: 4–19
No. of pupils: 3
Special needs catered for: ADD ADHD
ASD ASP AUT BESD DEL EBD SCD SEBD

**NoRSACA Whitegates Further Education
Unit**
The Dukeries Centre, Park Street,
Worksop, Nottinghamshire S80 1HH
Tel: 01909 509400
Principal: Ms Karen Bulmer
Type: Coeducational Day
Special needs catered for: AUT LD

WINGS SCHOOL, NOTTINGHAMSHIRE
For further details see p.121
Kirklington Hall, Kirklington, Newark,
Nottinghamshire NG22 8NB
Tel: 01636 817430
Email: info@wingsnottsschool.co.uk
Website: www.wingsschool.co.uk
Director of Education & Care: Mrs Pam
Redican
Type: Coeducational Independent
Residential Special School
Age range: 9–17
No. of pupils: 45 B25 G20
Special needs catered for: ADD ADHD
ASP BESD EBD

RUTLAND

The Grange Therapuetic School
Knossington, Oakham, Rutland LE15 8LY
Tel: 01664 454264
Director: Dr A J Smith MA, MEd, PhD,
CPsychol, AFBPs
Type: Boys' Boarding
Age range: B8–16
No. of pupils: 75
Special needs catered for: EBD

GREATER LONDON

ESSEX

Barnardos
Tanners Lane, Barkingside, Ilford,
Essex IG6 1QG
Tel: 020 8550 8822
Type: Coeducational Day & Boarding
Special needs catered for: AUT EBD MLD
PH PMLD SLD SPLD SP&LD

MIDDLESEX

Unity School
62 The Ride, Hounslow,
Middlesex TW8 9LA
Type: Coeducational Boarding
Age range: 11–16
No. of pupils: 4
Special needs catered for: EBD

West Middlesex College
Colne Lodge, Longbridge Way, Uxbridge,
Middlesex UB8 2YG
Tel: 01895 619700
Principal: Ms Alison White
Type: Coeducational Day
Special needs catered for: ASP AUT

SURREY

Cressey College
Croydon, Surrey CR0 6XJ
Tel: 020 86545373
Headteacher: Ms Adrienne Barnes
Type: Coeducational Day
Age range: 11–17
Special needs catered for: BESD EBD
SCD

Kingsdown Secondary School
112 Orchard Road, Sanderstead,
Croydon, Surrey CR2 9LQ
Tel: 020 8657 1200
Headteacher: Ms Carole Nicholson
Type: Coeducational Boarding
Age range: 11–16
No. of pupils: 12
Special needs catered for: ASD ASP EBD
SPLD

LONDON

LONDON

Cavendish School
58 Hawkstone Road, Southwark Park,
London SE16 2PA
Tel: 020 73940088
Headteacher: Mrs Sara Craggs
Type: Coeducational Day
Age range: 11–16
No. of pupils: 42
Special needs catered for: EBD

**East London Independent Special
School**
Unit 7, Ibex House, 1c Maryland Park,
Stratford, London E15 1HB
Tel: 020 82211247
Headteacher: Mr David O'connor
Type: Coeducational Day
Age range: 7–16
No. of pupils: 40
Special needs catered for: ASD BESD

**Gloucester House the Tavistock
Children's Day Unit**
33 Daleham Gardens, London NW3 5BU
Tel: 020 77943353
Headteacher: Ms Ellenore Nicholson
Type: Boys' Day
Age range: B5–12
Special needs catered for: BESD

Insights Independent School
3-5 Alexandria Road, Ealing,
London W13 0NP
Tel: 020 8840 9099
Headteacher: Ms Barbara Quartey
Type: Coeducational Day
Age range: 7–18
No. of pupils: 24
Special needs catered for: BESD MLD

Leaways School London
Theydon Road, Clapton, London E5 9NZ
Tel: 020 8815 4030
Headmaster: Richard Gadd
Type: Coeducational Day
Age range: 10–17
Special needs catered for: SEBD

**North West London Independent Special
School**
85 Old Oak Road, Ealing, London W3 7DD
Tel: 020 87495403
CEO: Thomas Keaney
Type: Coeducational Day
Age range: 7–17
No. of pupils: 40
Special needs catered for: ASD BESD

Trinity School
4 Recreation Road, Sydenham,
London SE26 4ST
Headteacher: Mr Philip Lee
Type: Coeducational Day
Age range: 11–16
Special needs catered for: BESD

NORTH-EAST

DARLINGTON

Priory Pines House
Middleton St George, Darlington DL2 1TS
Tel: 01325 331177
Principal: Mr John Anderson
Type: Coeducational Day & Residential
Age range: 7–16
No. of pupils: 16
Special needs catered for: EBD

DURHAM

Highcroft School
The Green, Cockfield, Bishop Auckland,
Durham DL13 5AG
Tel: 077 02916189
Headteacher: Mr David Laheney
Type: Coeducational Day
Age range: 11–16
No. of pupils: 3
Special needs catered for: BESD

EAST RIDING OF YORKSHIRE

Advanced Education - Beverley School
Units 19-20 Priory Road Industrial Estate,
Beverley,
East Riding of Yorkshire HU17 0EW
Tel: 01482 307830
School Manager: Melanie Jackson
Type: Coeducational Day
Age range: 10–18
Special needs catered for: EBD LD

HARTLEPOOL

**Advanced Education - Hartlepool School
& Vocational Centre**
Sovereign Park, Brenda Road,
Hartlepool TS25 1NN
Tel: 01429 224965
Headteacher: Mr Paul Barnfather
Type: Coeducational Day
Age range: 11–16
No. of pupils: 10
Special needs catered for: EBD

NORTHUMBERLAND

Cambois School
Cambois, Blyth,
Northumberland NE24 1SF
Tel: 01670 857689
Headteacher: Mr David Smith
Type: Coeducational Day
Age range: 11–16
No. of pupils: 8
Special needs catered for: BESD EBD

TYNE & WEAR

Talbot House School
Hexham Road, Walbottle, Newcastle
upon Tyne, Tyne & Wear NE15 8HW
Tel: 0191 229 0111
Director of Services: A P James DAES,
BPhil, CRCCYP
Type: Coeducational Day
Age range: 7–18
No. of pupils: 40
Special needs catered for: ADD ADHD
ASD BESD EBD MLD

Thornbeck College
14 Thornhill Park, Sunderland,
Tyne & Wear SR2 7LA
Tel: 0191 5102038
Principal: Ms Christine Dempster
Type: Coeducational Day
Special needs catered for: ASP AUT

WEST YORKSHIRE

Broadwood School
252 Moor End Road, Halifax,
West Yorkshire HX2 0RU
Tel: 01422 355925
Headteacher: Mrs Deborah Nash
Type: Coeducational Day
Age range: 11–16
No. of pupils: 38
Special needs catered for: EBD

Meadowcroft School
145 Bolton Lane, Bradford,
West Yorkshire BD2 4AT
Tel: 01274 634666
Headteacher: Mrs Susan Smith
Type: Coeducational Day
Age range: 10–19
Special needs catered for: EBD

NORTH-WEST

BLACKPOOL

Pennsylvania House
1 Barclay Avenue, Blackpool FY4 4HH
Tel: 01253 313101
Head Teacher: Mr Bill Baker
Type: Boys' Boarding
Age range: B11–17
No. of pupils: 6
Special needs catered for: EBD

Piers House
334 St Anne's Road, Blackpool FY4 2QN
Tel: 01253 319651
Headteacher: Mr Keith Parker
Type: Boys' Boarding
Age range: B11–16
No. of pupils: 5
Special needs catered for: EBD

Primrose Cottage
c/o Northern Care, 214 Whitegate Drive,
Blackpool FY3 9JL
Tel: 01253 316160
Head of Education: Valerie Gardener
Type: Girls' Boarding
Age range: G11–16
No. of pupils: 6
Special needs catered for: EBD MLD

CHESHIRE

**Advanced Education - Warrington
School**
2 Forrest Way, Gatewarth Industrial
Estate, Warrington, Cheshire WA5 1DF
Tel: 01925 237580
Headteacher: Olufemi Onasanya
Type: Coeducational Day
Age range: 11–18
No. of pupils: 10
Special needs catered for: BESD EBD
SEBD

Halton School
33 Main Street, Halton Village, Runcorn,
Cheshire WA7 2AN
Tel: 01928 589810
Headteacher: Emma McAllester
Type: Coeducational Day
Age range: 7–14
No. of pupils: 14
Special needs catered for: EBD

CUMBRIA

Appletree School
Natland, Kendal, Cumbria LA9 7QS
Tel: 015395 60253
Head of Education: Mr R Davies BEd, MSpEd
Type: Independent Coeducational School
Age range: 6–12
No. of pupils: 20 B12 G6
Special needs catered for: ADD ADHD BESD DEL DYS DYSP EBD GLD HA LD MLD SCD SEBD

Eden Grove School
Bolton, Appleby, Cumbria CA16 6AJ
Tel: 01768 361346
Principal: Mr John McCaffrey
Type: Coeducational Day & Residential
Age range: 8–19
No. of pupils: 65
Special needs catered for: ADHD ASP AUT BESD CP DYS EBD EPI MLD PH SP&LD

Fell House School
Grange Fell Road, Grange-Over-Sands, Cumbria LA11 6AS
Tel: 01539 535926
Headteacher: Mr Rob Davies
Type: Coeducational Boarding
Age range: 7–12
No. of pupils: 8
Special needs catered for: EBD

Kirby Moor School
Longtown Road, Brampton, Cumbria CA8 2AB
Tel: 016977 42598
Headteacher: Mrs Catherine Garton
Type: Boys' Boarding
Age range: B10–18
Special needs catered for: BESD CLD EBD

Radical Education
119 Warwick Road, Carlisle, Cumbria CA1 1JZ
Tel: 01228 631770
Headteacher: Mr Jim Danson
Type: Coeducational Day
Age range: 14–16
No. of pupils: 6
Special needs catered for: EBD

Underley Garden School
Kirkby Lonsdale, Carnforth, Cumbria LA6 2DZ
Tel: 01524 271569
Headteacher: Ellie Forrest
Type: Coeducational Boarding
Age range: 9–19
No. of pupils: 43
Special needs catered for: ADD ADHD ASP SLD SP&LD

Whinfell School
110 Windermere Road, Kendal, Cumbria LA9 5EZ
Tel: 01539 723322
Headteacher: Mr R D Tyson
Type: Boys' Boarding
Age range: B11–19
No. of pupils: 5
Special needs catered for: AUT EBD

WINGS SCHOOL, CUMBRIA
For further details see p.122
Whassett, Milnthorpe, Cumbria LA7 7DN
Tel: 01539 562006
Email: info@wingsschool.co.uk
Website: www.wingsschool.co.uk
Director of Education & Care: Mrs Pam Redican
Type: Coeducational Independent Residential Special School
Age range: 11–17
No. of pupils: 56 B28 G28
Special needs catered for: ADD ADHD ASP BESD EBD

Witherslack Hall School
Witherslack, Grange-Over-Sands, Cumbria LA11 6SD
Tel: 01539 552397
Head Teacher: Ms Tina McIntosh MBA
Type: Boys' Boarding, Flexible Boarding & Day
Age range: B10–19
No. of pupils: 55
Special needs catered for: ADHD ASP BESD EBD MLD SPLD

GREATER MANCHESTER

Acorns School
19b Hilbert Lane, Marple, Stockport, Greater Manchester SK6 7NN
Tel: 0161 449 5820
Headteacher: Naseem Akhtar
Type: Coeducational Day
Age range: 5–17
No. of pupils: 40
Special needs catered for: EBD

Ashcroft School (CYCES)
Schools Hill, Cheadle, Greater Manchester SK8 1JE
Tel: 0161 283 4832
Principal: Stephen Grimley MA, CertEd
Type: Coeducational Day
Age range: 8–16
No. of pupils: 40
Special needs catered for: BESD

Birch House School
98-100 Birch Lane, Longsight, Manchester, Greater Manchester M13 0WN
Tel: 0161 2247500
Headteacher: Mr Bilal Mahmud
Type: Coeducational Day
Age range: 11–16
No. of pupils: 22
Special needs catered for: BESD EBD SEBD

Lime Meadows
73 Taunton Road, Ashton-Under-Lyne, Greater Manchester OL7 9DU
Tel: 0161 3399412
Type: Boys' Boarding
Age range: B14–19
No. of pupils: 5
Special needs catered for: EBD

Nugent House School
Carr Mill Road, Billinge, Wigan, Greater Manchester WN5 7TT
Tel: 01744 892551
Principal: Miss W Sparling BA(Hons), QTS, MA(SEN), PG Dip (Autism), NPQH
Type: Boys' Boarding & Day
Age range: B7–19
No. of pupils: 65
Special needs catered for: EBD

St John Vianney School
Rye Bank Road, Firswood, Stretford, Greater Manchester M16 0EX
Tel: 0161 8817843
Type: Coeducational Day
Age range: 4–19
No. of pupils: 80
Special needs catered for: MLD

LANCASHIRE

Belmont School
Haslingden Road, Rawtenstall,
Rossendale, Lancashire BB4 6RX
Tel: 01706 221043
Headteacher: Mr M J Stobart
Type: Boys' Day
Age range: B10–16
No. of pupils: 70
Special needs catered for: ADD ADHD
ASD ASP AUT BESD DEL EBD SCD SEBD

Cedar House School
Bentham, Lancaster, Lancashire LA2 7DB
Tel: 01524 261149
Headteacher: Mrs G Ridgway BEd, ALCM
Type: Coeducational Day & Boarding
Age range: 7–16
No. of pupils: 46
Special needs catered for: ADD ADHD
ASD ASP BESD DYS DYSP EPI HI MLD
SP&LD

Crookhey Hall School
Crookhey Hall, Garstang Road,
Cockerham, Lancaster,
Lancashire LA2 0HA
Tel: 01524 792618
Headteacher: Mr D P Martin
Type: Boys' Day
Age range: B11–16
No. of pupils: 64
Special needs catered for: ADD ADHD
BESD DEL EBD SCD SEBD

Cumberland School
Church Road, Bamber Bridge, Preston,
Lancashire PR5 6EP
Tel: 01772 284435
Head Teacher: Nigel Hunt
Type: Coeducational Day
Age range: 11–16
No. of pupils: 49
Special needs catered for: ADHD ASD
BESD MLD

Darwen School
3 Sudell Road, Darwen,
Lancashire BB3 3HW
Tel: 01254 777154
Headteacher: Mr Sean Naylor
Type: Coeducational Day
Age range: 7–16
No. of pupils: 10
Special needs catered for: EBD

Egerton Street Independent School
48/50 Egerton Street, Heywood,
Rochdale, Lancashire OL10 3BG
Tel: 01706 625982
Manager: Dave Edwards
Type: Coeducational Day
Age range: 11–16
Special needs catered for: EBD

Elland House School
Unit 7, Roman Road, Royton,
Lancashire OL2 5PJ
Tel: 0161 6283600
Headteacher: Mrs Jan Murray
Type: Coeducational Day
Age range: 11–16
Special needs catered for: BESD

Keyes Barn
Station Road, Salwick, Preston,
Lancashire PR4 0YH
Tel: 01772 673672
Headteacher: Mr Gary Holliday
Type: Coeducational Day
Age range: 5–12
Special needs catered for: EBD

Learn 4 Life
Quarry Bank Community Centre, 364
Ormskirk Road, Tanhouse, Skelmersdale,
Lancashire WN8 9AL
Tel: 01695 558698
Headteacher: Ms Elaine Booth
Type: Coeducational Day
Age range: 11–16
No. of pupils: 4
Special needs catered for: BESD EBD

Moorland View
Manchester Road, Dunnockshaw,
Burnley, Lancashire BB11 5PQ
Tel: 01282 431144
Head Teacher: Wayne Carradice
Type: Coeducational Day
Age range: 11–16
No. of pupils: 12
Special needs catered for: EBD

Roselyn House School
Moss Lane, Off Wigan Road, Leyland,
Lancashire PR25 4SE
Tel: 01772 435948
Headteacher: Miss S Damerall
Type: Coeducational Day
Age range: 11–16
No. of pupils: 21
Special needs catered for: AUT EBD

The Birches
106 Breck Road, Poulton-le-Fylde,
Lancashire FY6 7HT
Tel: 01253 899102
Head Teacher: Mr Mike Simpkins
Type: Boys' Boarding
Age range: B11–17
No. of pupils: 6
Special needs catered for: EBD

The Brambles
159 Longmeanygate, Midge Hill, Leyland,
Lancashire PR26 7BT
Tel: 01772 454826
Headteacher: Mr G Holiday
Type: Boys' Day
Age range: B11–16
Special needs catered for: EBD

The Nook School
The Nook, Knotts Lane, Colne,
Lancashire BB8 8HH
Tel: 01282 868840
Headteacher: Mr Paul Heaven
Type: Boys' Boarding
Age range: B8–16
Special needs catered for: EBD

The Willows at Oakfield House School
Station Road, Salwick, Preston,
Lancashire PR4 0YH
Tel: 01772 672630
Headteacher: June Redhead
Type: Coeducational Day
Age range: 5–11
No. of pupils: 23
Special needs catered for: EBD SLD

Waterloo Lodge School
Preston Road, Chorley,
Lancashire PR6 7AX
Tel: 01257 230894
Headteacher: Mrs J Taylor
Type: Coeducational Day
Age range: 11–16
No. of pupils: 45
Special needs catered for: ADD ADHD
BESD DEL EBD SCD SEBD

MERSEYSIDE

Balmoral Independent School
41 Balmoral Road, Newsham Park,
Liverpool, Merseyside L6 8ND
Tel: 0151 2910787
Manager: Alison Morris
Type: Coeducational Day
Age range: 10–16
Special needs catered for: EBD

Clarence High School
West Lane, Freshfield,
Merseyside L37 7AS
Tel: 01704 872151
Head: Ms Carol Parkinson
Type: Coeducational Day & Boarding
Age range: 7–17
Special needs catered for: EBD

West Kirby Residential School
Meols Drive, West Kirby, Wirral,
Merseyside CH48 5DH
Tel: 0151 632 3201
Principal: Mr G W Williams MEd,
AdDipSpecEd
Type: Coeducational Day & Weekly
Boarding
Age range: 5–19
No. of pupils: 90
Special needs catered for: ADD ADHD
ASD ASP BESD CLD DYSP SCD SP&LD

WARRINGTON

Chaigeley
Thelwall, Warrington WA4 2TE
Tel: 01925 752357
Principal: Mr Drew Crawshaw
Type: Boys' Boarding & Day
Age range: B8–16
No. of pupils: 75
Special needs catered for: ADD ADHD
ASD ASP AUT BESD DYS EBD GLD HA LD
MLD SCD SEBD SLD

Cornerstones
2 Victoria Road, Grappenhall,
Warrington WA4 2EN
Tel: 01925 211056
Head: Ms Caron Bethell
Type: Boys' Boarding
Age range: B7–18
No. of pupils: 11
Special needs catered for: AUT EBD

SOUTH-EAST

BRACKNELL FOREST

Cressex Lodge (SWAAY)
Terrace Road South, Binfield, Bracknell,
Bracknell Forest RG42 4DE
Tel: 01344 862221
Headteacher: Ms Sarah Snape
Type: Boys' Day
Age range: B11–16
No. of pupils: 9
Special needs catered for: BESD

BRIGHTON & HOVE

Springboard Education Junior
39 Whippingham Road, St Wilfred's
Upper Hall, Brighton,
Brighton & Hove BN2 3PS
Tel: 01273 885109
Headteacher: Elizabeth Freeman
Type: Coeducational Day
Age range: 7–13
Special needs catered for: ADHD BESD

The Lioncare School
87 Payne Avenue, Hove,
Brighton & Hove BN3 5HD
Tel: 01273 734164
Headteacher: Mrs J Dance
Type: Coeducational Day
Age range: 7–16
No. of pupils: 9
Special needs catered for: EBD

BUCKINGHAMSHIRE

Unity College
150 West Wycombe Road, High
Wycombe, Buckinghamshire HP12 3AE
Tel: 077 02916189
Headteacher: Mrs Lois Hubbard
Type: Coeducational Day
Age range: 11–16
No. of pupils: 12
Special needs catered for: BESD MLD
SEBD

EAST SUSSEX

Headstart School
Crouch Lane, Ninfield, Battle,
East Sussex TN33 9EG
Tel: 01424 893803
Headteacher: Ms Nicola Dann
Type: Coeducational Day
Age range: 7–18
Special needs catered for: BESD

The Mount Camphill Community
Faircrouch Lane, Wadhurst,
East Sussex TN5 6PT
Tel: 01892 782025
Type: Coeducational Day & Boarding
Age range: 16–22
No. of pupils: 33
Special needs catered for: ADD ADHD
ASD ASP AUT BESD CLD CP DEL DYS
DYSP EBD EPI GLD HI LD MLD MSI PD PH
Phe PNI SCD SLD SLI SPLD SP&LD

HAMPSHIRE

Coxlease Abbeymead
Palace Lane, Beaulieu,
Hampshire SO42 7YG
Tel: 02380 283 633
Principal: Mr Rick Tracey
Type: Coeducational Day & Residential
Age range: 9–16
No. of pupils: 5
Special needs catered for: EBD

Coxlease School
Clay Hill, Lyndhurst,
Hampshire SO43 7DE
Tel: 023 8028 3633
Principal: Mr Rick Tracey
Type: Coeducational Day & Residential
Age range: 9–18
No. of pupils: 55
Special needs catered for: BESD MLD

Hillcrest Hayling Island
24 Alexandra Avenue, Hayling Island,
Hampshire PO11 9AL
Tel: 02392 469691
Headteacher: Mr David Macaskill
Type: Boys' Boarding
Age range: B8–14
Special needs catered for: EBD

St Edward's School
Melchet Court, Sherfield English,
Romsey, Hampshire SO51 6ZR
Tel: 01794 885252
Head: L Bartel BEd(Hons)
Type: Boys' Weekly Boarding & Day
Age range: B10–17
No. of pupils: 44
Special needs catered for: BESD DYS
EBD MLD SPLD

KENT

Brewood Middle School
146 Newington Road, Ramsgate,
Kent CT12 6PT
Tel: 01843 597088
Head of School: Mr Daniel Radlett
Type: Coeducational Day
Age range: 5–13
No. of pupils: 8 B5 G3
Special needs catered for: ADD ADHD
ASD ASP AUT BESD CLD DEL EBD EPI
GLD HA HI LD MLD PH SCD SLD SLI
SP&LD

Brewood Secondary School
86 London Road, Deal, Kent CT14 9TR
Tel: 01304 363000
Head of School: Mr Daniel Radlett
Type: Coeducational Day
Age range: 11–18
No. of pupils: 12 B7 G5
Special needs catered for: ADD ADHD
ASD ASP AUT BESD CLD DEL EBD EPI
GLD HA HI LD MLD PH SCD SLD SLI
SP&LD

Browns School
Cannock House, Hawstead Lane,
Chelsfield, Orpington, Kent BR6 7PH
Tel: 01689 876816
Headteacher: Mr M F Brown
Type: Coeducational Day
Age range: 7–12
No. of pupils: 32
Special needs catered for: EBD SPLD

Caldecott Foundation School
Hythe Road, Smeeth, Ashford,
Kent TN25 6PW
Tel: 01303 815678
Acting Head: Mrs Valerie Miller
Type: Coeducational Boarding
Age range: 5–18
No. of pupils: 56 B42 G14
Special needs catered for: EBD

Greenfields School
Tenterden Road, Biddenden,
Kent TN27 8BS
Tel: 01580 292523
Director: Gary Yexley
Type: Coeducational Day
Age range: 5–11
No. of pupils: 13 B7 G6
Special needs catered for: EBD

Heath Farm School
Egerton Road, Charing Heath, Ashford,
Kent TN27 0AX
Tel: 01233 712030
Head: Liz Cornish
Type: Coeducational Day
Age range: 5–16
No. of pupils: 70 B50 G20
Special needs catered for: EBD

Hope View School
Station Approach, Chilham, Canterbury,
Kent CT4 8EG
Tel: 01227 738000
Type: Coeducational Day
Age range: 11–17
No. of pupils: 16 B16
Special needs catered for: ADD ADHD
ASD ASP BESD

Hythe House Education
Power Station Road, Sheerness,
Kent ME12 3AB
Tel: 01795 581006
Headteacher: Mr Robert Duffy
Type: Coeducational Day
Age range: 11–16
No. of pupils: 20
Special needs catered for: EBD

ISP Sittingbourne School
Church Street, Sittingbourne,
Kent ME10 3EG
Tel: 01795 422 044
Headteacher: Craig Walter
Type: Coeducational Day
Age range: 11–16
Special needs catered for: BESD SCD
SEBD

Learning Opportunities Centre
Ringwould Road, Ringwould, Deal,
Kent CT14 8DN
Tel: 01304 381906
Headteacher: Mrs Diana Ward
Type: Coeducational Day & Boarding
Age range: 11–16
No. of pupils: 40
Special needs catered for: EBD

Little Acorns School
London Beach Farm, Ashford Road, St
Michael's, Tenterden, Kent TN30 6SR
Tel: 01233 850422
Headteacher: Miss Angela Flynn
Type: Coeducational Boarding
Age range: 4–14
No. of pupils: 7 B5 G2
Special needs catered for: EBD

Meadows School and Meadows 16+
London Road, Southborough,
Kent TN4 0RJ
Tel: 01892 529144
Principal: Mike Price BEd(Hons), DipSEN,
MA
Type: Coeducational Day & Boarding
Age range: 11–19
No. of pupils: 45 B32 G13
Special needs catered for: ADHD ASP
AUT DYS DYSP EBD MLD SEBD

Ripplevale School
Chapel Lane, Ripple, Deal, Kent CT14 8JG
Tel: 01304 373866
Principal: Mr Ted Schofield CRSW
Type: Boys' Boarding & Day
Age range: B9–16
No. of pupils: 30
Special needs catered for: ADD ADHD
ASD ASP AUT BESD CLD DYS DYSP EBD
GLD HA LD MLD PMLD SCD SCLD SPLD
SP&LD

The Ashbrook Centre
8 Almond Close, Broadstairs,
Kent CT10 2NQ
Tel: 01843 869240
Principal: Mr Nigel Troop
Type: Coeducational Day
Age range: 5–18
No. of pupils: 5
Special needs catered for: BESD SEBD

The Boulters Learning and Skills Centre
Units 12-13, Oare Gunpowder Works, Off
Bysingwood Road, Faversham,
Kent ME13 7UD
Tel: 01795 529184
Headteacher: Ms L Scott
Type: Coeducational Day
Age range: 12–17
No. of pupils: 9
Special needs catered for: BESD

The Davenport School
Princess Margaret Avenue, Ramsgate,
Kent CT12 6HX
Tel: 01843 589018
Headteacher: Mr Franklyn Brown
Type: Boys' Day
Age range: B7–12
Special needs catered for: EBD

THE NEW SCHOOL AT WEST HEATH
For further details see p.124
Ashgrove Road, Sevenoaks,
Kent TN13 1SR
Tel: 01732 460553
Email: principal@westheathschool.com
Website: www.westheathschool.com
Principal: Mrs Christina Wells
Type: Coeducational Day & Boarding
Age range: 10–19
No. of pupils: B80 G31 VIth40
Special needs catered for: ADD ADHD
ASD ASP BESD DEL EBD SCD SPLD
SP&LD

The Old Priory School
Priory Road, Ramsgate, Kent CT11 9PG
Tel: 01843 599322
Head: Jack Banner
Type: Boys' Day
Age range: B10–15
Special needs catered for: EBD

The Old School
Capel Street, Capel-le-Ferne, Folkestone,
Kent CT18 7EY
Tel: 01303 251116
Headteacher: Martyn Jordan
Type: Boys' Day
Age range: B9–17
No. of pupils: 24
Special needs catered for: EBD

SOUTHAMPTON

The Serendipity Centre
399 Hinkler Road,
Southampton SO19 6DS
Tel: 023 8042 2255
Head Teacher: Mrs Linda Atkinson
Type: Girls' Day
Age range: G11–16
No. of pupils: 9
Special needs catered for: BESD

SURREY

Cornfield School
53 Hanworth Road, Redhill,
Surrey RH1 5HS
Tel: 01737 779578
Headteacher: Mrs Jayne Telfer
Type: Girls' Day
Age range: G11–18
No. of pupils: 25
Special needs catered for: EBD

Grafham Grange School
Nr Bramley, Guildford, Surrey GU5 0LH
Tel: 01483 892214
Acting Headteacher: Mr Phil Thompson
Type: Boys' Boarding
Age range: B10–16
No. of pupils: 44
Special needs catered for: EBD

Tudor Lodge School
92 Foxley Lane, Woodcote, Purley,
Surrey CR8 3NA
Tel: 020 8763 8785
Headteacher: Ms Patricia Lines
Type: Coeducational Day & Boarding
Age range: 12–16
No. of pupils: 7
Special needs catered for: SEBD

WEST SUSSEX

Brantridge School
Staplefield Place, Staplefield, Haywards
Heath, West Sussex RH17 6EQ
Tel: 01444 400228
Headteacher: Tamsin Blythe
Type: Boys' Boarding
Age range: B6–13
No. of pupils: 27
Special needs catered for: EBD

Farney Close School
Bolney Court, Bolney,
West Sussex RH17 5RD
Tel: 01444 881811
Head: Mr B Robinson MA, BEd(Hons)
Type: Coeducational Boarding & Day
Age range: 11–16
No. of pupils: 78
Special needs catered for: ADHD ASP
DYS EBD MLD SP&LD

Hillcrest Slinfold School
Stane Street, Slinfold, Horsham,
West Sussex RH13 0QX
Tel: 01403 790939
Principal: Mark Birkbeck BEd(Hons)
Type: Boys' Boarding
Age range: B11–16
Special needs catered for: ADD ADHD
ASD ASP BESD DYS DYSP EBD GLD MLD
SCD SEBD

Muntham House School Ltd
Barns Green, Muntham Drive, Horsham,
West Sussex RH13 0NJ
Tel: 01403 730302
Principal: Mr R Boyle MEd, BEd,
AdvDipSE
Type: Boys' Boarding
Age range: B8–18
No. of pupils: 51 VIth12
Special needs catered for: ADD ADHD
ASD BESD DYS EBD MLD SPLD SP&LD

PHILPOTS MANOR SCHOOL
For further details see p.123
West Hoathly, East Grinstead,
West Sussex RH19 4PR
Tel: 01342 810268
Email:
jill.roberts@philpotsmanorschool.co.uk
Website:
www.philpotsmanorschool.co.uk
Education Co-ordinator: Ms Linda
Churnside BEd
Type: Coeducational Boarding
Age range: 7–19
No. of pupils: 34 B22 G12
Special needs catered for: ADD ADHD
ASD ASP AUT BESD DEL DYS EBD EPI
GLD LD MLD SCD SP&LD

Southways School
The Vale House, Findon Road, Worthing,
West Sussex BN14 0RA
Tel: 01903 877448
Headteacher: Gail Jay
Type: Coeducational Day
Age range: 6–11
Special needs catered for: EBD

Springboard Education Senior
55 South Street, Lancing,
West Sussex BN15 8HA
Tel: 01903 605980
Head Teacher: Mr Simon Yorke-Johnson
Type: Independent Special School (Day)
Age range: 11–18
No. of pupils: 10
Special needs catered for: ADD ADHD
ASD ASP AUT BESD EBD

WOKINGHAM

High Close School
Wiltshire Road, Wokingham RG40 1TT
Tel: 0118 9785767
Head: Mrs Zoe Lattimer BSc(Hons), PGCE
Type: Coeducational Residential & Day
Age range: 7–18
Special needs catered for: ADHD ASD
ASP BESD EBD MLD

SOUTH-WEST

DEVON

Advanced Education - Devon School
Oaklands Park, Oaklands Road,
Buckfastleigh, Devon TQ11 0BW
Tel: 01364 644 823
Headteacher: Swavek Nowakiewicz
Type: Coeducational Day
Age range: 10–16
Special needs catered for: ASP AUT EBD
SEBD

Chelfham Mill School
Chelfham, Barnstaple, Devon EX32 7LA
Tel: 01271 850448
Principal: Mrs K T Roberts BEd,
BPhil(EBD)
Type: Boys' Boarding & Day
Age range: B9–16
No. of pupils: 40
Special needs catered for: ADD ADHD
ASP DYS DYSP EBD GLD LD MLD

Oakwood Court
7/9 Oak Park Villas, Dawlish,
Devon EX7 0DE
Tel: 01626 864066
Principal: J F Loft BEd, BPhil(SEN),
HNDHIM
Type: Coeducational Boarding
Age range: 16–25
No. of pupils: B13 G14
Special needs catered for: ADHD ASP
DYS DYSP EBD EPI MLD SLD

The Libra School
Edgemoor Court, South Radworthy,
South Molton, Devon EX36 3LN
Tel: 01598 740044
Headteacher: Ms J E Wilkes
Type: Coeducational Day
Age range: 8–18
Special needs catered for: EBD

Whitstone Head School
Whitstone, Holsworthy, Devon EX22 6TJ
Tel: 01288 341251
Principal: Mr D R McLean-Thorne
Type: Coeducational Day & Boarding
Age range: 10–16
No. of pupils: 37
Special needs catered for: ADD ADHD
ASD ASP AUT BESD CLD DEL DYS DYSP
EBD GLD MLD SCD SPLD

DORSET

Ivers College
Ivers, Hains Lane, Marnhull, Sturminster
Newton, Dorset DT10 1JU
Tel: 01258 820164
Principal: Linda Matthews
Type: Coeducational Residential Special
Age range: 18
No. of pupils: 23
Special needs catered for: EBD LD MLD
SCD

GLOUCESTERSHIRE

Marlowe Education Unit
Hartpury Old School, Gloucester Road,
Hartpury, Gloucestershire GL19 3BG
Tel: 01452 700855
Head Teacher: Diane McQueen
Type: Coeducational Day
Age range: 8–16
No. of pupils: 8
Special needs catered for: EBD MLD

SOMERSET

Advanced Education - Somerset School
Westport House, Langport Road,
Hambridge, Somerset TA10 0BH
Tel: 01460 281216
Headteacher: Mr Will Houghton
Type: Coeducational Day
Age range: 10–16
Special needs catered for: AUT EBD HI
SEBD

Aethelstan College
Newton Road, North Petherton,
Somerset TA6 6NA
Tel: 01626 8663233
Headteacher: Mrs Ros Hagley
Type: Coeducational Day
Age range: 11–16
Special needs catered for: EBD

Lillesdon School
Sedgemoor House, Lillesdon, Taunton,
Somerset TA3 6BY
Tel: 01823 492021
Headteacher: Mrs Alison Dobbie
Type: Coeducational Day
Age range: 7–17
No. of pupils: 16
Special needs catered for: BESD HI

Merryhay School
Merryhay House, Ilton Business Park,
Ilminster, Somerset TA19 9DU
Tel: 01460 55524
Head of School: Mr Edward Underwood
Type: Coeducational Day
Age range: 11–16
No. of pupils: 8
Special needs catered for: EBD MLD

New Horizon Centre School
Bath House Farm, West Hatch, Taunton,
Somerset TA3 5RH
Tel: 01823 481902
Headteacher: Jennie Meadows
Type: Coeducational Day
Age range: 11–16
No. of pupils: 20
Special needs catered for: EBD

THE MARCHANT-HOLLIDAY SCHOOL
For further details see p. 126
North Cheriton, Templecombe,
Somerset BA8 0AH
Tel: 01963 33234
Email: office@marchant-holliday.co.uk
Website: www.marchantholliday.co.uk
Head Teacher: Mr T J Kitts MEd,
BEd(Hons), DPSE(SEN)
Type: Boys' Boarding, Flexible Boarding
& Day
Age range: B5–13
Special needs catered for: ADD ADHD
ASD ASP BESD DYS DYSP

WILTSHIRE

Wessex College
Wessex Lodge, Nunney Road, Frome,
Wiltshire BA11 4LA
Tel: 01373 453414
Headteacher: Ms C Smith
Type: Coeducational Day
Age range: 11–16
No. of pupils: 6
Special needs catered for: EBD

WEST MIDLANDS

HEREFORDSHIRE

Queenswood School
Callows Hills Farm, Hereford Road,
Ledbury, Herefordshire HR8 2PZ
Tel: 01531 670632
Principal: Mr James Imber
Type: Coeducational Day & Residential
Age range: 11–19
No. of pupils: 15
Special needs catered for: BESD SEBD

The Larches School
Coningsby Road, Leominster,
Herefordshire HR6 8LL
Tel: 01568 780094
Head: Nigel Kedword
Type: Coeducational Day
Age range: 11–16
Special needs catered for: EBD

SHROPSHIRE

Acorn School
Dale Acre Way, Hollinswood, Telford,
Shropshire TF3 2EN
Tel: 01952 200410
Head: Ms Sarah Morgan
Type: Coeducational Day
Age range: 11–16
No. of pupils: 16
Special needs catered for: EBD

Care UK Children's Services
46 High Street, Church Stretton,
Shropshire SY6 6BX
Tel: 01694 724488
Director: Simon W Rouse BA(Hons), CSS,
DipPTh
Type: Coeducational Day
Age range: 10–18
No. of pupils: 24
Special needs catered for: EBD

Ditton Priors School
Station Road, Ditton Priors, Bridgnorth,
Shropshire WV16 6SS
Tel: 01746 712985
Headteacher: Mr Stephen Piper
Type: Coeducational Day
Age range: 11–16
No. of pupils: 10
Special needs catered for: BESD EBD

Smallbrook School
Smallbrook Lodge, Smallbrook Road,
Whitchurch, Shropshire SY13 1BX
Tel: 01948 661110
Headteacher: Ms Sarah Morgan
Type: Coeducational Day
Age range: 11–19
No. of pupils: 15
Special needs catered for: EBD

YOUNG OPTIONS COLLEGE
For further details see p. 127
Lamledge Lane, Shifnal,
Shropshire TF11 8SD
Tel: 01952 468220
Email: info@youngoptions.co.uk
Website: www.optionsgroup.co.uk
Headteacher: Louise De-Hayes
Type: Coeducational Residential & Day
Age range: 7–19
Special needs catered for: SEBD

STAFFORDSHIRE

Bloomfield College
Bloomfield Road, Tipton,
Staffordshire DY4 9AH
Tel: 0121 5209408
Headteacher: Mr Andrew Harding
Type: Coeducational Day
Age range: 11–16
Special needs catered for: EBD

Hillcrest Oaklands College
Alrewas Road, Kings Bromley,
Staffordshire DE13 7HR
Tel: 01543 473772
Principal: Jo Morris MEd, NPQH
Type: Girls' Boarding
Age range: G14–18
Special needs catered for: ADD ADHD
ASD ASP BESD DYS DYSP EBD GLD MLD
SCD SEBD

Horizon School Staffordshire
Venture House, 12 Prospect Park,
Longford Road, Cannock,
Staffordshire WS11 0LG
Tel: 01543 572 143
Consultant Head Teacher: Mr Stephen
Ellis
Type: Coeducational Day
Age range: 11–16
Special needs catered for: EBD

Longdon Hall School
Longdon Hall, Rugeley,
Staffordshire WS15 4PT
Tel: 01543 491051
Headteacher: Mr Matt Storey
Type: Coeducational Day
Age range: 7–18
Special needs catered for: BESD EBD

The Croft Independent School
4 Horsecroft Terrace, Leek,
Staffordshire ST13 6QL
Tel: 01538 386106
Manager: Beverley Salt
Type: Coeducational Day
Age range: 10–16
Special needs catered for: EBD

STOKE-ON-TRENT

Aidenswood
47 Liverpool Road East, Kidsgrove,
Stoke-on-Trent ST7 3AD
Tel: 01253 316160
Headteacher: Mr Paul Heaven
Type: Boys' Boarding
Age range: B13–17
No. of pupils: 6
Special needs catered for: EBD MLD

Draycott Moor College
Draycott Old Road, Draycott-in-the-
Moors, Stoke-on-Trent ST11 9AH
Tel: 01782 399849
Headteacher: Mr David Rutter
Type: Coeducational Day
Age range: 11–16
Special needs catered for: EBD

The Roaches Independent School
Tunstall Road, Knypersley, Stoke-on-
Trent ST8 7AB
Tel: 01782 523479
Head of Education: The Principal
Type: Coeducational Boarding & Day
Age range: 7–16
No. of pupils: 16
Special needs catered for: EBD

YOUNG OPTIONS PATHWAY COLLEGE STOKE
For further details see p. 128
Phoenix House, Marlborough Road,
Longton, Stoke-on-Trent ST3 1EJ
Tel: 01782 377270
Email: info@pathwaystoke.co.uk
Website: www.optionsgroup.co.uk
Headteacher: Mel Callaghan
Type: Coeducational Day & Boarding
Age range: 11–19
Special needs catered for: BESD

WARWICKSHIRE

Arc School
Church End, Ansley, Nuneaton,
Warwickshire CV10 0QR
Tel: 024 7639 4801
Headmistress: Pauline Garret
Type: Coeducational Day & Boarding
No. of pupils: 30
Special needs catered for: BESD

Wathen Grange School
Church Walk, Mancetter, Atherstone,
Warwickshire CV9 1PZ
Tel: 01827 714454
Head of Education Service: Mr Chris
Nock
Type: Coeducational Day
Age range: 11–16
No. of pupils: 15
Special needs catered for: EBD

WEST MIDLANDS

Blue River Academy
36 Medley Road, Greet, Birmingham,
West Midlands B11 2NE
Tel: 0121 7667981
Type: Boys' Day
Age range: B14–16
Special needs catered for: BESD

Oaklands School
215 Barrows Lane, Yardley, Birmingham,
West Midlands B26 1QS
Headteacher: Ms Rebecca Hill
Type: Coeducational Day
Age range: 11–16
No. of pupils: 4
Special needs catered for: BESD

The Collegiate Centre for Values Education for Life
51-54 Hockley Hill, Hockley, Birmingham,
West Midlands B18 5AQ
Tel: 0121 5230222
Headteacher: Mrs Val Russell
Type: Coeducational Day
Age range: 11–17
No. of pupils: 25
Special needs catered for: BESD

YORKSHIRE & HUMBERSIDE

KINGSTON UPON HULL

Horton House School
Hilltop Farm, Sutton Road, Wawne, Hull,
Kingston upon Hull HU7 5YY
Tel: 01482 875191
Head: Mr Matthew Stubbins
Type: Coeducational Residential & Day
Age range: 8–23
No. of pupils: B18 G5
Special needs catered for: ADD ADHD
ASD ASP AUT BESD CLD DYS DYSP EBD
EPI GLD LD MLD SCD SCLD SEBD SLD
SPLD

NORTH YORKSHIRE

Advanced Education - Scarborough School
Unit 11, Plaxton Park, Cayton Low Road,
Eastfield, Scarborough,
North Yorkshire YO11 1JR
Tel: 01723 581 475
Headteacher: Ms Anne Wood
Type: Coeducational Day
Age range: 8–16
Special needs catered for: SEBD

BRECKENBROUGH SCHOOL
For further details see p. 130
Sandhutton, Thirsk,
North Yorkshire YO7 4EN
Tel: 01845 587238
Email: office@breckenbrough.org.uk
Website: www.breckenbrough.org.uk
Headmaster: Geoffrey Brookes BEd
Type: Boys' Boarding & Day
Age range: B9–19
No. of pupils: 49
Special needs catered for: ADD ADHD
ASP BESD DEL DYS EBD HA

Clervaux Trust
Clow Beck Eco Centre, Jolby Lane, Croft
on Tees, North Yorkshire DL2 2TF
Tel: 01325 729860
Executive Director: Cate McQueen
Type: Coeducational Day & Residential
Age range: 14–25+

SPRING HILL SCHOOL

For further details see p.131

Palace Road, Ripon,
North Yorkshire HG4 3HN
Tel: 01765 603320
Email:
springhill.school@barnardos.org.uk
Website:
www.barnardos.org.uk/springhillschool
Principal: Linda Nelson
Type: Coeducational Day & Boarding
Age range: 9–19
No. of pupils: 31
Special needs catered for: ADHD ASP
AUT CP DEL DYS DYSP EBD EPI MLD SLD
SP&LD

SOUTH YORKSHIRE

BRANTWOOD SPECIALIST SCHOOL

For further details see p.129

1 Kenwood Bank, Nether Edge, Sheffield,
South Yorkshire S7 1NU
Tel: 0114 258 9062
Email: admin@brantwood.rmt.org
Website: www.rmt.org
Headteacher: Constantin Court
Type: Coeducational Day & Residential
Age range: 7–19
Special needs catered for: ADD ADHD
ASD ASP BESD CLD EBD GLD LD MLD
PMLD SCD SCLD SEBD SPLD

Chrysalis Therapeutic Educational Centre

48 Wostenholm Road, Nether Edge,
South Yorkshire S7 1LL
Tel: 0114 2509455
Headteacher: Mrs Sarah Allkins
Type: Coeducational Day
Age range: 8–14
No. of pupils: 4
Special needs catered for: BESD

Dove School

194 New Road, Staincross, Barnsley,
South Yorkshire S75 6PP
Tel: 01226 381380
Headteacher: Mrs Helen Mangham
Type: Coeducational Day
Age range: 9–16
Special needs catered for: BESD

WEST YORKSHIRE

Denby Grange School

Stocksmoor Road, Midgley, Wakefield,
West Yorkshire WF4 4JQ
Tel: 01924 830096
Head: Miss Jennie Littleboy
Type: Coeducational Day
Age range: 11–17
No. of pupils: 36
Special needs catered for: EBD SCD

New Gables School

2 New Close Road, Shipley,
West Yorkshire BD18 4AB
Tel: 01274 584705
Teacher-in-charge: Caroline Matson
Type: Coeducational Day
Age range: 11–16
Special needs catered for: SEBD

The Grange School

2 Milner Way, Ossett, Wakefield,
West Yorkshire WF5 9JE
Tel: 01924 378957
Headteacher: Phil Bennett
Type: Coeducational Day
Age range: 7–14
No. of pupils: 12
Special needs catered for: BESD

William Henry Smith School

Boothroyd, Brighouse,
West Yorkshire HD6 3JW
Tel: 01484 710123
Principal: B J Heneghan BA, PGCE,
DipSpEd
Type: Boys' Boarding
Age range: B8–16
Special needs catered for: ADD ADHD
BESD SCD SEBD

NORTHERN IRELAND

COUNTY DOWN

Camphill Community Glencraig

Craigavad, Holywood,
County Down BT18 0DB
Tel: 028 9042 3396
School Co-ordinator: Vincent Reynolds
Type: Learning Disabilities,
Coeducational
Age range: 7–19
No. of pupils: 32
Special needs catered for: ADHD ASP
AUT CP DYSP EBD EPI HI MLD PH PMLD
SLD SPLD SP&LD VIS

COUNTY TYRONE

Parkanaur College

57 Parkanaur Road, Dungannon,
County Tyrone BT70 3AA
Tel: 028 87761272
Principal: Mr Wilfred Mitchell
Type: Coeducational Day
Age range: 18–65
Special needs catered for: ADD ADHD
ASP AUT BESD CLD CP DYS DYSP EBD EPI
GLD HA HI LD MLD PD PH Phe PMLD PNI
SCD SCLD SLD SPLD VIS

SCOTLAND

EDINBURGH

Harmeny Education Trust Ltd

Harmeny School, Balerno,
Edinburgh EH14 7JY
Tel: 0131 449 3938
Chief Executive: Peter Doran
BA(Hons)Econ, CQSW, MA Social Work,
AdvCert SW
Type: Coeducational Boarding
Age range: 6–13
No. of pupils: 36
Special needs catered for: ADD ADHD
ASP DYS EBD SPLD

FIFE

Falkland House School
Falkland Estate, Cupar, Fife KY15 7AE
Tel: 01337 857268
Head: Mr Stuart Jacob
Type: Boys' Boarding
Age range: B5–18
No. of pupils: 30
Special needs catered for: ADD ADHD ASP BESD DYS EBD EPI SCD SPLD

Hillside School
Hillside, Aberdour, Fife KY3 0RH
Tel: 01383 860731
Principal: Mrs Anne Smith
Type: Boys' Boarding
Age range: B10–16
No. of pupils: 39
Special needs catered for: DYS EBD SPLD

Starley Hall School
Aberdour Road, Burntisland,
Fife KY3 OAG
Tel: 01383 860314
Head: Philip Barton BA
Type: Coeducational Boarding & Day
Age range: 10–16
No. of pupils: 48 B40 G8
Special needs catered for: EBD MLD

NORTH AYRSHIRE

Geilsland School
Beith, North Ayrshire KA15 1HD
Tel: 01505 504044
Type: Boys' Day & Boarding
Age range: B14–18
No. of pupils: 26
Special needs catered for: EBD MLD SEBD

Seafield School
86 Eglington Road, Ardrossan,
North Ayrshire KA22 8NL
Tel: 01294 470355
Head: Ian MacReady
Type: Boys' Day & Boarding
Age range: B5–16
Special needs catered for: EBD

NORTH LANARKSHIRE

St Philip's School
10 Main Street, Plains, Airdrie,
North Lanarkshire ML6 7SF
Tel: 01236 765407
Head: Mr P Hanrahan
Type: Boys' Day & Boarding
Age range: B12–16
No. of pupils: 61
Special needs catered for: EBD

PERTH & KINROSS

Balnacraig School
Fairmount Terrace, Perth,
Perth & Kinross PH2 7AR
Tel: 01738 636456
Head: Charles Kiddie
Type: Coeducational Day
Age range: 12–16
No. of pupils: 24 B12 G12
Special needs catered for: BESD EBD

Seamab House School
Rumbling Bridge, Kinross,
Perth & Kinross KY13 0PT
Tel: 01577 840307
Head: Mrs A W Anderson
Type: Coeducational Day & Boarding
Age range: 5–12
No. of pupils: 15
Special needs catered for: EBD

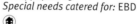

RENFREWSHIRE

Kibble Education and Care Centre
Goudie Street, Paisley,
Renfrewshire PA3 2LG
Tel: 0141 889 0044
Head: Graham Bell
Type: Co-educational Boarding & Day
Age range: 12–16
No. of pupils: 93
Special needs catered for: EBD MLD SCD SLD SPLD

Spark of Genius
Trojan House, Phoenix Business Park,
Paisley, Renfrewshire PA1 2BH
Tel: 0141 587 2710
Director: Mr Tom McGhee
Type: Coeducational Day & Boarding
Age range: 5–18
No. of pupils: 106
Special needs catered for: ASD EBD

The Good Shepherd Secure/Close Support Unit
Greenock Road, Bishopton,
Renfrewshire PA7 5PW
Tel: 01505 864500
Head: Mr Sand Cunningham
Type: Girls' Boarding & Day
Age range: G12–17
Special needs catered for: EBD MLD

STIRLING

Ballikinrain Residential School
Fintry Road, Balfron, Stirling G63 0LL
Tel: 01360 440244
Manager: Mr Paul Gilroy
Type: Boys' Boarding & Day
Age range: B8–14
No. of pupils: 40
Special needs catered for: BESD

Snowdon School
31 Spittal Street, Stirling FK8 1DU
Tel: 01786 464746
Headteacher: Annette P Davison
Type: Girls' Boarding
Age range: G13–17
Special needs catered for: BESD

WEST LOTHIAN

Moore House School
21 Edinburgh Road, Bathgate,
West Lothian EH48 1EX
Tel: 01506 652312
Type: Coeducational Day & Boarding
Age range: 8–16
No. of pupils: 37
Special needs catered for: ADHD EBD

WALES

DENBIGHSHIRE

The Branas School
Branas Isaf, Llandrillo, Corwen,
Denbighshire LL21 0TA
Tel: 01490 440545
Type: Boys' Day
Age range: B12–17
No. of pupils: 12
Special needs catered for: EBD

MONMOUTHSHIRE

Talocher School
Talocher Farm, Wonastow Road,
Monmouth, Monmouthshire NP25 4DN
Tel: 01600 740777
Principal: Mr Mike Borland
Type: Coeducational Day & Residential
Age range: 11–18
No. of pupils: 25
Special needs catered for: BESD SEBD

PEMBROKESHIRE

St David's Education Unit
Pembroke House, Brawdy Business Park,
Haverfordwest, Pembrokeshire SA62 6NP
Tel: 01437 721234
Head: Mrs Alison Wilkinson
Type: Coeducational Day
Age range: 8–17
No. of pupils: 7
Special needs catered for: EBD

POWYS

Hillcrest Pentwyn
Clyro, Powys HR3 5SE
Tel: 01497 821420
Principal: Linda Hagland
Type: Boys' Boarding
Age range: B11–17
Special needs catered for: ADD ADHD
ASD ASP BESD DYS DYSP EBD GLD MLD
SCD SEBD

SWANSEA

Blackwood School
Ferryboat House, Ellwood Jersey Marine,
Neath, Swansea SA10 6NG
Headteacher: Nicky Jones
Type: Boys' Boarding
Age range: B11–18
No. of pupils: 4
Special needs catered for: EBD SPLD

WREXHAM

Woodlands Children's Development Centre
27 Pentrefelyn Road, Wrexham LL13 7NB
Tel: 01978 262777
Head: Ms Vivien Devereaux
Type: Boys' Day
Age range: B11–18
No. of pupils: 8
Special needs catered for: BESD EBD

Special Educational Needs and the independent and non-maintained schools that cater for them

Attention Deficit Disorder (ADD)

Abingdon House School, London	D158
Action for Children Headlands School, Vale of Glamorgan	110, D164
Appleford School, Wiltshire	D156
Appletree School, Cumbria	D172
Belgrave School, Bristol	D155
Belmont School, Lancashire	D173
Birtenshaw Hall School, Greater Manchester	D159
Bladon House School, Staffordshire	D162
Blossom House School, London	D158
Bramfield House, Suffolk	D168
Brantwood Specialist School, South Yorkshire	129, D180
Breckenbrough School, North Yorkshire	130, D179
Brewood Middle School, Kent	D175
Brewood Secondary School, Kent	D175
Camphill School Aberdeen, Aberdeen	D142
Cedar House School, Lancashire	D173
Centre Academy London	100, D158
Chaigeley, Warrington	D174
Chelfham Mill School, Devon	D177
Coleg Elidyr, Carmarthenshire	D151
Cotswold Chine School, Gloucestershire	D167
Crookhey Hall School, Lancashire	D173
Cruckton Hall, Shropshire	84, D150
Demeter House, North Lincolnshire	D150
Eastwood Grange School, Derbyshire	D168
Falkland House School, Fife	D181
Farleigh College Mells, Somerset	D149
Harmeny Education Trust Ltd, Edinburgh	D180
Hillcrest Oaklands College, Staffordshire	D178
Hillcrest Park School, Oxfordshire	D167
Hillcrest Pentwyn, Powys	D182
Hillcrest Slinfold School, West Sussex	D176
Holme Court School, Bedfordshire	D156
Hope House School, Nottinghamshire	D169
Hope View School, Kent	D175
Horton House School, Kingston upon Hull	D179
Kisharon School, London	D158
Lakeside School, Merseyside	D159
Linkage College - Toynton Campus, Lincolnshire	D157
Linkage College - Weelsby Campus, North-East Lincolnshire	D163
MacIntyre Womaston School, Powys	D164
Mencap Pengwern College, Denbighshire	D164
Moor House School, Surrey	D139
Muntham House School Ltd, West Sussex	D176
North Hill House, Somerset	D149
Northease Manor School, East Sussex	D160
Ochil Tower, Perth & Kinross	D164
Orchard Hill College of Further Education, Surrey	D161
Owlswick School, East Sussex	D160
Parkanaur College, County Tyrone	D180
Philpots Manor School, West Sussex	123, D176
Potterspury Lodge School, Northamptonshire	77, D146
Queen Elizabeth's Training College, Surrey	D139
Ripplevale School, Kent	D175
Rossendale School, Lancashire	D147

Sheiling School, Thornbury, Bristol	D155
Sheridan School, Norfolk	D168
Springboard Education Senior, West Sussex	D177
St Andrews School, Norfolk	D156
St Dominic's School, Surrey	D161
St John's School & College, Brighton & Hove	D160
St Piers School and College, Surrey	D139
Talbot House School, Tyne & Wear	D171
The Linnet Independent Learning Centre, Derbyshire	D168
The Loddon School, Hampshire	D160
The Marchant-Holliday School, Somerset	126, D178
The Mount Camphill Community, East Sussex	D174
The New School at West Heath, Kent	124, D176
The Royal School for Deaf Children Margate and Westgate College, Kent	D139
The Ryes College & Community, Suffolk	D168
Underley Garden School, Cumbria	D172
Waterloo Lodge School, Lancashire	D173
West Kirby Residential School, Merseyside	D174
Whitstone Head School, Devon	D177
William Henry Smith School, West Yorkshire	D180
Wings School, Cumbria	122, D172
Wings School, Nottinghamshire	121, D170
Woodcroft School, Essex	D156

Attention Deficit and Hyperactive Disorder (ADHD) (Hyperkinetic Disorder)

3 Dimensions, Somerset	D149
Abingdon House School, London	D158
Action for Children Headlands School, Vale of Glamorgan	110, D164
Appleford School, Wiltshire	D156
Appletree School, Cumbria	D172
Aran Hall School, Gwynedd	D164
Belmont School, Lancashire	D173
Birtenshaw Hall School, Greater Manchester	D159
Bladon House School, Staffordshire	D162
Blossom House School, London	D158
Bracken School, Lancashire	D147
Bramfield House, Suffolk	D168
Brantwood Specialist School, South Yorkshire	129, D180
Breckenbrough School, North Yorkshire	130, D179
Brewood Middle School, Kent	D175
Brewood Secondary School, Kent	D175
Camphill Community Glencraig, County Down	D180
Camphill School Aberdeen, Aberdeen	D142
Cedar House School, Lancashire	D173
Centre Academy East Anglia, Suffolk	100, D156
Centre Academy London	100, D158
Chaigeley, Warrington	D174
Chelfham Mill School, Devon	D177
Chelfham Senior School, Devon	D149
Coleg Elidyr, Carmarthenshire	D151
Cotswold Chine School, Gloucestershire	D167
Crookhey Hall School, Lancashire	D173
Cruckton Hall, Shropshire	84, D150
Cumberland School, Lancashire	D173
Eastwood Grange School, Derbyshire	D168

Autistic Spectrum Disorder(s) (ASD)

Asperger Syndrome (ASP)

Hinwick Hall College of Further Education, Northamptonshire — D137
Holly Bank School, West Yorkshire — D141
Ingfield Manor School, West Sussex — D140
Kisharon School, London — D158
Langside School, Poole — D140
Linkage College - Toynton Campus, Lincolnshire — D157
Linkage College - Weelsby Campus, North-East Lincolnshire — D163
Meldreth Manor School, Hertfordshire — D137
Mencap Dilston College, Northumberland — D159
Mencap Pengwern College, Denbighshire — D164
Nash College, Kent — D138
National Institute for Conductive Education, West Midlands — D141
National Star College, Gloucestershire — D137
Orchard Hill College of Further Education, Surrey — D161
Paces High Green School for Conductive Education, South Yorkshire — D141
Parayhouse School, London — 101, D158
Parkanaur College, County Tyrone — D180
Portland College, Nottingham — D138
Queen Elizabeth's Training College, Surrey — D139
RNIB Pears Centre for Specialist Learning, West Midlands — 62, D141
Royal Blind School, Edinburgh — D142
Royal London Society for the Blind, Dorton House School, Kent — D139
Royal School for the Blind, Merseyside — D138
Rutherford School, Surrey — D158
Seashell Trust, Greater Manchester — D138
Sheiling School, Thornbury, Bristol — D155
Spring Hill School, North Yorkshire — 131, D180
St Christopher's School, Bristol — D155
St Elizabeth's School, Hertfordshire — D137
St John's Catholic School for the Deaf, West Yorkshire — 64, D141
St John's School & College, Brighton & Hove — D160
St Mary's School & College, East Sussex — D139
St Piers School and College, Surrey — D139
St Rose's School, Gloucestershire — D137
Stanmore House School, South Lanarkshire — D142
The David Lewis School, Cheshire — D159
The Fortune Centre of Riding Therapy, Dorset — D140
The Mount Camphill Community, East Sussex — D174
The PACE Centre, Buckinghamshire — D137
The Royal School for Deaf Children Margate and Westgate College, Kent — D139
The School for Profound Education (formerly St Margaret's School), Surrey — 60, D140
Treloar School, Hampshire — D139
Vranch House, Devon — D140
Woodcroft School, Essex — D156

Deaf (D) *see also Hearing Impairment (HI)*
Camphill School Aberdeen, Aberdeen — D142
Chailey Heritage School, East Sussex — 59, D139
Donaldson's School, West Lothian — D142

Exeter Royal Academy for Deaf Education, Devon — D140
Henshaws College, North Yorkshire — 70, D141
Jordanstown Schools, County Antrim — D142
Kisharon School, London — D158
Linkage College - Toynton Campus, Lincolnshire — D157
Linkage College - Weelsby Campus, North-East Lincolnshire — D163
Mary Hare School, West Berkshire — D137
Meldreth Manor School, Hertfordshire — D137
RNIB Pears Centre for Specialist Learning, West Midlands — 62, D141
Royal School for the Deaf Derby — 57, D137
Rutherford School, Surrey — D158
Seashell Trust, Greater Manchester — D138
St John's Catholic School for the Deaf, West Yorkshire — 64, D141
St John's School & College, Brighton & Hove — D160
St Mary's School & College, East Sussex — D139
St Rose's School, Gloucestershire — D137
The Royal School for Deaf Children Margate and Westgate College, Kent — D139

Delicate (DEL)
Appletree School, Cumbria — D172
Belgrave School, Bristol — D155
Belmont School, Lancashire — D173
Birtenshaw Hall School, Greater Manchester — D159
Bramfield House, Suffolk — D168
Breckenbrough School, North Yorkshire — 130, D179
Brewood Middle School, Kent — D175
Brewood Secondary School, Kent — D175
Calder House School, Wiltshire — D156
Camphill School Aberdeen, Aberdeen — D142
Coleg Elidyr, Carmarthenshire — D151
Corseford School, Renfrewshire — D142
Crookhey Hall School, Lancashire — D173
Derwen College, Shropshire — D141
East Park, Glasgow — D163
Hereward College of Further Education, West Midlands — D141
Hope House School, Nottinghamshire — D169
Kisharon School, London — D158
Lakeside School, Merseyside — D159
Linkage College - Toynton Campus, Lincolnshire — D157
Linkage College - Weelsby Campus, North-East Lincolnshire — D163
National Star College, Gloucestershire — D137
Orchard Hill College of Further Education, Surrey — D161
Parayhouse School, London — 101, D158
Philpots Manor School, West Sussex — 123, D176
Royal Blind School, Edinburgh — D142
Sheiling School, Thornbury, Bristol — D155
Spring Hill School, North Yorkshire — 131, D180
St Dominic's School, Surrey — D161
St John's School & College, Brighton & Hove — D160
St Mary's School & College, East Sussex — D139
St Rose's School, Gloucestershire — D137
The Fortune Centre of Riding Therapy, Dorset — D140

Dyslexia (DYS); see also SPLD below

Epilepsy (EPI)

General Learning Difficulties (GLD)

High Ability (HA)

Alderwasley Hall School & Callow Park College, Derbyshire	D156
Appleford School, Wiltshire	D156
Appletree School, Cumbria	D172
Belgrave School, Bristol	D155
Breckenbrough School, North Yorkshire	130, D179
Brewood Middle School, Kent	D175
Brewood Secondary School, Kent	D175
Camphill School Aberdeen, Aberdeen	D142
Centre Academy East Anglia, Suffolk	100, D156
Centre Academy London	100, D158
Chaigeley, Warrington	D174
Eastwood Grange School, Derbyshire	D168
Fairley House School, London	D158
Hereward College of Further Education, West Midlands	D141
Holme Court School, Bedfordshire	D156
Kisharon School, London	D158
Lakeside School, Merseyside	D159
Orchard Hill College of Further Education, Surrey	D161
Parkanaur College, County Tyrone	D180
Ripplevale School, Kent	D175
Rossendale School, Lancashire	D147
Sheiling School, Thornbury, Bristol	D155
St Dominic's School, Surrey	D161
St John's School & College, Brighton & Hove	D160
The Royal National College for the Blind (RNC), Herefordshire	D140

Hearing Impairment (HI)

Action for Children Penhurst School, Oxfordshire	D155
Advanced Education - Somerset School, Somerset	D177
Beaumont College, Lancashire	D138
Birtenshaw Hall School, Greater Manchester	D159
Brewood Middle School, Kent	D175
Brewood Secondary School, Kent	D175
Camphill Community Glencraig, County Down	D180
Camphill School Aberdeen, Aberdeen	D142
Cedar House School, Lancashire	D173
Chailey Heritage School, East Sussex	59, D139
Corseford School, Renfrewshire	D142
Craig-y-Parc School, Cardiff	D142
Derwen College, Shropshire	D141
Donaldson's School, West Lothian	D142
Doncaster College for the Deaf, South Yorkshire	D141
Doncaster School for the Deaf, South Yorkshire	63, D141
East Park, Glasgow	D163
Exeter Royal Academy for Deaf Education, Devon	D140
Hamilton Lodge School, Brighton & Hove	D139
Henshaws College, North Yorkshire	70, D141
Hereward College of Further Education, West Midlands	D141
Jordanstown Schools, County Antrim	D142
Kisharon School, London	D158
Lakeside School, Merseyside	D159
Langdon College, Greater Manchester	D159
Lillesdon School, Somerset	D177

Linkage College - Toynton Campus, Lincolnshire	D157
Linkage College - Weelsby Campus, North-East Lincolnshire	D163
Mary Hare Primary School for the Deaf, West Berkshire	D137
Mary Hare School, West Berkshire	D137
Meldreth Manor School, Hertfordshire	D137
Mencap Dilston College, Northumberland	D159
Mencap Lufton College, Somerset	D162
Mencap Pengwern College, Denbighshire	D164
Northern Counties School, Tyne & Wear	D138
Orchard Hill College of Further Education, Surrey	D161
Overley Hall School, Telford & Wrekin	107, D162
Parkanaur College, County Tyrone	D180
Penn School, Buckinghamshire	D137
Percy Hedley School, Tyne & Wear	D138
Portland College, Nottingham	D138
RNIB Pears Centre for Specialist Learning, West Midlands	62, D141
Royal London Society for the Blind, Dorton House School, Kent	D139
Royal School for the Blind, Merseyside	D138
Rutherford School, Surrey	D158
Seashell Trust, Greater Manchester	D138
Sheiling School, Thornbury, Bristol	D155
St Dominic's School, Surrey	D161
St John's Catholic School for the Deaf, West Yorkshire	64, D141
St John's School & College, Brighton & Hove	D160
St Mary's School & College, East Sussex	D139
St Rose's School, Gloucestershire	D137
The David Lewis School, Cheshire	D159
The Fortune Centre of Riding Therapy, Dorset	D140
The Mount Camphill Community, East Sussex	D174
The PACE Centre, Buckinghamshire	D137
The Royal School for Deaf Children Margate and Westgate College, Kent	D139
The School for Profound Education (formerly St Margaret's School), Surrey	60, D140
Treloar School, Hampshire	D139

Learning Difficulties (LD)

Acorn Park School, Norfolk	D145
Advanced Education - Beverley School, East Riding of Yorkshire	D171
Appletree School, Cumbria	D172
Arden College, Merseyside	D147
Birtenshaw Hall School, Greater Manchester	D159
Brantwood Specialist School, South Yorkshire	129, D180
Brewood Middle School, Kent	D175
Brewood Secondary School, Kent	D175
Broughton House, Lincolnshire	D169
Cambian Southwick Park School, Gloucestershire	D155
Camphill School Aberdeen, Aberdeen	D142
Centre Academy East Anglia, Suffolk	100, D156
Chaigeley, Warrington	D174
Chelfham Mill School, Devon	D177
Coleg Elidyr, Carmarthenshire	D151

Moderate Learning Difficulties (MLD)

Multi-sensory Impairment (MSI)

Partially Hearing (Phe)

Profound and Multiple Learning Difficulties (PMLD)

Physical Neurological Impairment (PNI)

Social and Communication Difficulties (SCD)

Acorn Park School, Norfolk	D145
Appletree School, Cumbria	D172
Beaumont College, Lancashire	D138
Belmont School, Lancashire	D173
Birtenshaw Hall School, Greater Manchester	D159
Blossom House School, London	D158
Boveridge House School (formerly Philip Green Memorial School), Dorset	D161
Brantwood Specialist School, South Yorkshire	129, D180
Brewood Middle School, Kent	D175
Brewood Secondary School, Kent	D175
Broughton House, Lincolnshire	D169
Cambian Southwick Park School, Gloucestershire	D155
Camphill School Aberdeen, Aberdeen	D142
Chaigeley, Warrington	D174
Chelfham Senior School, Devon	D149
Coleg Elidyr, Carmarthenshire	D151
Cressey College, Surrey	D170
Crookhey Hall School, Lancashire	D173
Denby Grange School, West Yorkshire	D180
Donaldson's School, West Lothian	D142
Eagle House School (Mitcham), Surrey	D148
Eastwood Grange School, Derbyshire	D168
Falkland House School, Fife	D181
Foxes Academy, Somerset	D162
Freeman College, South Yorkshire	117, D163
Glasshouse College, West Midlands	116, D163
Henshaws College, North Yorkshire	70, D141
Hill House School, Hampshire	D148
Hillcrest Oaklands College, Staffordshire	D178
Hillcrest Park School, Oxfordshire	D167
Hillcrest Pentwyn, Powys	D182
Hillcrest Slinfold School, West Sussex	D176
Hinwick Hall College of Further Education, Northamptonshire	D137
Holme Court School, Bedfordshire	D156
Homefield College, Leicestershire	D137
Hope House School, Nottinghamshire	D169
Horton House School, Kingston upon Hull	D179
I CAN'S Dawn House School, Nottinghamshire	96, D157
ISP Sittingbourne School, Kent	D175
Ivers College, Dorset	D177
Kibble Education and Care Centre, Renfrewshire	D181
Kisharon School, London	D158
Lakeside School, Merseyside	D159
Langdon College, Greater Manchester	D159
Langside School, Poole	D140
Link Primary Day School, Surrey	D157
Link Secondary Day School, Surrey	D158
Linkage College - Toynton Campus, Lincolnshire	D157
Linkage College - Weelsby Campus, North-East Lincolnshire	D163
Linn Moor Residential School, Aberdeen	D163
MacIntyre Wingrave School, Buckinghamshire	D155
Meadow View Farm School, Leicestershire	D169
Mencap Dilston College, Northumberland	D159
Mencap Pengwern College, Denbighshire	D164
Nash College, Kent	D138
National Star College, Gloucestershire	D137
Northease Manor School, East Sussex	D160
Ochil Tower, Perth & Kinross	D164
Orchard Hill College of Further Education, Surrey	D161
Owlswick School, East Sussex	D160
Parayhouse School, London	101, D158
Parkanaur College, County Tyrone	D180
Philpots Manor School, West Sussex	123, D176
Pontville, Lancashire	D159
Potterspury Lodge School, Northamptonshire	77, D146
Rainbow School for Children and Young People with Autism, London	D146
Ripplevale School, Kent	D175
Ruskin Mill College, Gloucestershire	115, D155
Seashell Trust, Greater Manchester	D138
Sheiling School, Ringwood, Hampshire	D160
Sheiling School, Thornbury, Bristol	D155
St Andrews School, Norfolk	D156
St Catherine's School, Isle of Wight	D139
St Dominic's School, Surrey	D161
St John's School & College, Brighton & Hove	D160
St Mary's School & College, East Sussex	D139
St Piers School and College, Surrey	D139
St Rose's School, Gloucestershire	D137
The David Lewis School, Cheshire	D159
The Linnet Independent Learning Centre, Derbyshire	D168
The Mount Camphill Community, East Sussex	D174
The New School at West Heath, Kent	124, D176
The Royal School for Deaf Children Margate and Westgate College, Kent	D139
The Ryes College & Community, Suffolk	D168
Waterloo Lodge School, Lancashire	D173
West Kirby Residential School, Merseyside	D174
Whitstone Head School, Devon	D177
William Henry Smith School, West Yorkshire	D180

Severe and Complex Learning Difficulties (SCLD)

Acorn Park School, Norfolk	D145
Beaumont College, Lancashire	D138
Birtenshaw Hall School, Greater Manchester	D159
Brantwood Specialist School, South Yorkshire	129, D180
Broughton House, Lincolnshire	D169
Cambian Southwick Park School, Gloucestershire	D155
Camphill School Aberdeen, Aberdeen	D142
Chailey Heritage School, East Sussex	59, D139
Chelfham Senior School, Devon	D149
Craig-y-Parc School, Cardiff	D142
Freeman College, South Yorkshire	117, D163
Glasshouse College, West Midlands	116, D163
Hill House School, Hampshire	D148
Holly Bank School, West Yorkshire	D141
Horton House School, Kingston upon Hull	D179
Kisharon School, London	D158
Kisimul School, Lincolnshire	98, D157
Kisimul School - Woodstock House, Surrey	104, D161
Langside School, Poole	D140
Linkage College - Toynton Campus, Lincolnshire	D157

Linkage College - Weelsby Campus, North-East Lincolnshire	D163
Linn Moor Residential School, Aberdeen	D163
MacIntyre Womaston School, Powys	D164
Mencap Pengwern College, Denbighshire	D164
Nash College, Kent	D138
National Star College, Gloucestershire	D137
Ochil Tower, Perth & Kinross	D164
Orchard Hill College of Further Education, Surrey	D161
Parkanaur College, County Tyrone	D180
Prior's Court School, West Berkshire	74, D145
Progress School, Lancashire	D159
Ripplevale School, Kent	D175
RNIB Pears Centre for Specialist Learning, West Midlands	62, D141
Rowden House School, Herefordshire	D162
Royal School for the Blind, Merseyside	D138
Ruskin Mill College, Gloucestershire	115, D155
Seashell Trust, Greater Manchester	D138
Sheiling School, Ringwood, Hampshire	D160
Sheiling School, Thornbury, Bristol	D155
St Christopher's School, Bristol	D155
St John's School & College, Brighton & Hove	D160
St Joseph's School, Surrey	D161
St Piers School and College, Surrey	D139
St Rose's School, Gloucestershire	D137
Stanmore House School, South Lanarkshire	D142
The Loddon School, Hampshire	D160
The PACE Centre, Buckinghamshire	D137
The Royal School for Deaf Children Margate and Westgate College, Kent	D139
Woodcroft School, Essex	D156

Severe Emotional and Behavioural Difficulties (SEBD); see also BESD and EBD above

Advanced Education - Devon School, Devon	D177
Advanced Education - Scarborough School, North Yorkshire	D179
Advanced Education - Somerset School, Somerset	D177
Advanced Education - Warrington School, Cheshire	D171
Advanced Education - Wisbech School & Vocational Centre, Cambridgeshire	D167
Appletree School, Cumbria	D172
Avocet House, Norfolk	D168
Beaumont College, Lancashire	D138
Belmont School, Lancashire	D173
Birch House School, Greater Manchester	D172
Brantwood Specialist School, South Yorkshire	129, D180
Broughton House, Lincolnshire	D169
Cambian Southwick Park School, Gloucestershire	D155
Camphill School Aberdeen, Aberdeen	D142
Chaigeley, Warrington	D174
Crookhey Hall School, Lancashire	D173
Freeman College, South Yorkshire	117, D163
Geilsland School, North Ayrshire	D181
Glasshouse College, West Midlands	116, D163
Hillcrest Oaklands College, Staffordshire	D178
Hillcrest Park School, Oxfordshire	D167

Hillcrest Pentwyn, Powys	D182
Hillcrest Slinfold School, West Sussex	D176
Hope House School, Nottinghamshire	D169
Hopewell School, Essex	D167
Horton House School, Kingston upon Hull	D179
ISP Sittingbourne School, Kent	D175
Jacques Hall, Essex	D168
Kisharon School, London	D158
Leaways School London, London	D170
Linn Moor Residential School, Aberdeen	D163
MacIntyre Womaston School, Powys	D164
Meadows School and Meadows 16+, Kent	D175
Mencap Pengwern College, Denbighshire	D164
New Gables School, West Yorkshire	D180
Orchard Hill College of Further Education, Surrey	D161
Queenswood School, Herefordshire	D178
Ravenswood School, Derbyshire	D168
Rossendale School, Lancashire	D147
Ruskin Mill College, Gloucestershire	115, D155
Sheiling School, Thornbury, Bristol	D155
Sheridan School, Norfolk	D168
St John's School & College, Brighton & Hove	D160
Talocher School, Monmouthshire	D182
The Ashbrook Centre, Kent	D175
The Cedars, Leicestershire	D169
The Linnet Independent Learning Centre, Derbyshire	D168
The Ryes College & Community, Suffolk	D168
Tudor Lodge School, Surrey	D176
Unity College, Buckinghamshire	D174
Waterloo Lodge School, Lancashire	D173
William Henry Smith School, West Yorkshire	D180
Young Options College, Shropshire	127, D178

Severe Learning Difficulties (SLD)

49 King Street, South Yorkshire	D163
Acorn Park School, Norfolk	D145
Action for Children Penhurst School, Oxfordshire	D155
Aran Hall School, Gwynedd	D164
Barnardos, Essex	D170
Beaumont College, Lancashire	D138
Beechwood College, Vale of Glamorgan	D151
Birtenshaw Hall School, Greater Manchester	D159
Bladon House School, Staffordshire	D162
Boveridge House School (formerly Philip Green Memorial School), Dorset	D161
Brewood Middle School, Kent	D175
Brewood Secondary School, Kent	D175
Bristol Dyslexia Centre, Bristol	D155
Broughton House, Lincolnshire	D169
Cambian Southwick Park School, Gloucestershire	D155
Camphill Community Glencraig, County Down	D180
Camphill School Aberdeen, Aberdeen	D142
Chaigeley, Warrington	D174
Chailey Heritage School, East Sussex	59, D139
Chilworth House School, Oxfordshire	D167
Coleg Elidyr, Carmarthenshire	D151
Craig-y-Parc School, Cardiff	D142
Derwen College, Shropshire	D141

Specific Language Impairment (SLI)

Specific Learning Difficulties (SPLD);
see also Dyslexia above

Speech and Language Difficulties (SP&LD)

Visually Impaired (VIS)

Useful associations and websites

Action for Blind People

14-16 Verney Road
London SE16 3DZ

Tel: 020 7635 4800
Helpline: 0303 123 9999

Email: helpline@rnib.org.uk
Website: www.actionforblindpeople.org.uk

A UK based charity (nos. 205913, SCO40050) that works to inspire change and create opportunities to enable blind and partially sighted people to have an equal voice and equal choice. They enable visually impaired people to transform their lives through work, housing, leisure and support. Part of the RNIB.

Action for Sick Children

32b Buxton Road
High Lane
Stockport SK6 8BH

Tel: 01663 763 004 Helpline: 0800 0744 519
Website: www.actionforsickchildren.org

Healthcare charity (no. 296295) formed in the 1960s to help parents whose children have to spend extended stays in hospital.

Action on Hearing Loss

19-23 Featherstone Street
London EC1Y 8SL

Tel: 020 7296 8000 Textphone: 020 7296 8001   Fax: 020 7296 8199
Email: informationline@hearingloss.org.uk   Website: www.actiononhearingloss.org.uk

Action on Hearing Loss, formerly the Royal National Institute for Deaf People, is the largest national charity (nos. 207720, SCO38926) representing the nine million deaf and hard of hearing people in the UK. As a membership charity we aim to achieve a radically better quality of life for deaf and hard of hearing people. We do this by campaigning and lobbying vigorously, by raising awareness of deafness and hearing loss, by providing services and through social medical and technical research.

Follow us on Twitter.

Action on Hearing Loss Cymru

16 Cathedral Road
Cardiff CF11 9LJ

Tel: 02920 333 034 Text: 02920 333 036   Fax: 02920 333 035
Email: informationline@hearingloss.org.uk

See main entry above.

Action on Hearing Loss Northern Ireland

4-8 Adelaide Street
Belfast
BT2 8GA

Tel: 028 9023 9619
Textphone: 028 9024 9462
Email: information.nireland@hearingloss.org.uk

Fax: 028 9031 2032

See main entry above.

Action on Hearing Loss Scotland

Empire House
131 West Nile Street
Glasgow
G1 2RXJ

Tel: 0141 341 5330 Text: 0141 341 5347
Email: scotland@hearingloss.org.uk

Fax: 0161 354 0176

See main entry above.

ADDISS – National Attention Deficit Disorder Information & Support Service

Premier House
112 Station Road
Edgware, Middlesex HA8 7BJ

Tel: 020 8952 2800
Email: info@addiss.co.uk

Fax: 020 8952 2909
Website: www.addiss.co.uk

ADDISS provides information and assistance for those affected by ADHD. Registered charity no. 1070827.

Advisory Centre for Education – (ACE)

36 Nicholay Road
London N19 3EZ

Tel: 020 8407

Email: enquiries@ace-ed.org.uk

Website: www.ace-ed.org.uk

ACE is an independent national advice centre for parents/carers of children aged 5 to 16. Advice booklets can be downloaded or ordered from the website. Training courses and seminars for LA officers, schools and governors are available. As well as a training package for community groups advising parents on education matters. Has Facebook page and you can follow them on Twitter.

AFASIC – Unlocking Speech and Language

20 Bowling Green Lane
London EC1R 0BD

Tel: 020 7490 9410
Fax: 020 7251 2834   Helpline: 0845 3 55 55 77
Website: www.afasicengland.org.uk

Helps children and young people with speech and language impairments. Provides: training/conferences for parents and professionals; a range of publications; support through local groups; and expertise in developing good practice. Registered charity nos. 1045617, SCO39170. Has a Facebook page.

AFASIC – Cymru

Titan House
Cardiff Bay Business Centre
Lewis Road
Ocean Park
Cardiff CF24 5BS

Tel: 029 2046 5854
Website: www.afasiccymru.org.uk   Fax: 029 2046 5854

See main entry above.

AFASIC – Northern Ireland

Cranogue House
19 Derry Courtney Road
Caledon
County Tyrone BT68 4UF

Tel: 028 3756 9611 (M-F 10.30am-2.30pm)
Email: mary@afasicnorthernireland.org.uk   Website: www.afasicnorthernireland.org.uk

See main entry above.

AFASIC – Scotland

The Vine
43 Magdalen Yard Road
Dundee DD1 4NE

Tel: 01382 250060   Fax: 01382 568391
Email: info@afasicscotland.org.uk

Registered charity no. SCO39170. See main entry above.

Association of Blind and Partially-Sighted Teachers and Students (ABAPTAS)

BM Box 6727
London
WC1N 3XX

Tel: 0117 966 4839
Website: www.abapstas.org.uk

National organisation of visually impaired people that focuses on education and employment issues. Registered charity no. 266056.

Association of Sign Language Interpreters (ASLI)
Suite 165
Milton Keynes Business Centre
Foxhunter Drive
Linford Wood
Milton Keynes
MK14 6GD

Tel: 0871 474 0522 Textphone: 18001 0871 474 0522 Fax: 01908 325259
Email: office@asli.org.uk   Website: www.asli.org.uk

Has a useful online directory of sign language interpreters.

Asthma UK
Summit House
70 Wilson Street
London
EC2A 2DB

Tel: 0800 121 6255   UK Advice Line: 0800 121 6244 (Mon-Fri 9am-5pm)
Fax: 020 7256 6075
Email: info@asthma.org.uk   Website: www.asthma.org.uk

Charity dedicated to helping the 5.2 million people in the UK who are affected by asthma. Registered charity nos. 802364, SCO39322. Has a Facebook page and you can follow them on Twitter.

Ataxia (UK)
Lincoln House, Kennington Park
1-3 Brixton Road
London SW9 6DE

Tel: 020 7582 1444
Helpline: 0845 644 0606
Email: office@ataxia.org.uk   Website: www.ataxia.org.uk

Aims to support all people affected by ataxia. Registered charity nos. 1102391 and SCO406047. Has a Facebook page and you can follow them on Twitter.

AVM Support UK
Suite G03, Blyth CEC
Ridley Street
Blyth
Northumberland
NE24 3AG

Email: info@avmsupport.org.uk
Website: www.avmsupport.org.uk

Offers support and information for those affected by Arteriovenous Malformation (AVM).

BCS – IT Can Help
c/o Information Technologists
39a Bartholomew Close
London
EC1A 7JN

Freephone & text phone helpline: 0800 269 545

Email: enquiries@abilitynet.org.uk
Website: www.itcanhelp.org.uk

Provides onsite volunteers to help individuals with disabilities who have computer problems Registered charity no. 292786.

BIBIC (British Institute for Brain Injured Children)
Knowle Hall
Bridgwater
Somerset
TA7 8PJ

Tel: 01278 684060   Fax: 01278 685573
Email: info@bibic.org.uk
Website: www.bibic.org.uk

As a registered charity (no. 1057635) BIBIC helps children with a disability or learning difficulty caused by conditions such as cerebral palsy, Down's syndrome and other genetic disorders; acquired brain injury caused by trauma or illness; and developmental disorders such as autism, ADHD, Asperger syndrome and dyspraxia.

All children are assessed by a multi-professional team who put together a report and a therapy plan that is taught to the family by the child's key worker. This provides support for the family to learn about their child and how they can make a positive difference to their development. Sections of the plan are designed to be shared with the child's school and social groups to ensure a consistent approach in areas such as communication, behaviour and learning. Families return on a regular basis for reassessments and updated therapy programmes.

Has a Facebook page and you can follow them on Twitter.

Brain and Spine Foundation
3.36 Canterbury Court
Kennington Park
1-3 Brixton Road
London SW9 6DE

Tel: 020 7793 5900 Helpline: 0808 808 1000
Fax: 020 7793 5939 Fax helpline: 020 7793 5939
Email: info@brainandspine.org.uk
Website: www.brainandspine.org.uk

Registered charity (no. 1098528), which was founded in 1992 to help those people affected by brain and spine conditions.

British Blind Sport (BBS)

Pure Offices
Plato Close
Tachbrook Park
Leamington Spa
Warwickshire CV34 6WE

Tel: 01926 424247   Fax: 01926 427775
Email: info@britishblindsport.org.uk
Website: www.britishblindsport.org.uk

A registered charity (no. 271500) providing sport and recreation for blind and partially sighted people.

British Deaf Association England

Head Office
18 Leather Lane
London
EC1N 7SU

Tel: 020 7405 0090 Textphone: 05603 115295   Fax: 01772 561610
Email: bda@bda.org.uk   Website: www.bda.org.uk

The BDA is a democratic, membership-led national charity (no. 1031687) campaigning on behalf of deaf sign language users in the UK. It exists to advance and protect the interests of the deaf community, to increase deaf people's access to facilities and lifestyles that most hearing people take for granted and to ensure greater awareness of their rights and responsibilities as members of society. The association has several main service areas, with teams covering education and youth, information, health promotions, video production and community services, offering advice and help. There is a national helpline that provides information and advice on a range of subjects such as welfare rights, the Disability Discrimination Act (DDA) and education.

British Deaf Association of Northern Ireland

Unit 5c, Weavers Court
Linfield Road
Belfast
BT12 5GH

Tel: 02890 437486 Textphone: 02890 437480   Fax: 02890 437487
Email: northernireland@bda.org   Website: www.bda.org.uk

See main entry under British Deaf Association England.

British Deaf Association Scotland

1st Floor Central Chambers, Suite 58
93 Hope Street
Glasgow G2 6LD

Tel: 0141 248 5554   Fax: 0141 248 5565
Email: scotland@bda.org.uk   Website: www.bda.org.uk

See main entry under British Deaf Association England.

British Deaf Association Wales

British Sign Language Cultural Centre
47 Newport Road
Cardiff
CF24 0AD

Tel: 0845 130 2851 Textphone: 0845 1302 853   Fax: 0845 130 2852
Email: wales@bda.org.uk   Website: www.bda.org.uk

See main entry under British Deaf Association England.

British Dyslexia Association

Unit 8, Bracknell Beeches
Old Bracknell Lane
Bracknell RG12 7BW

Tel: 0845 251 9002 (Helpline) or 0845 251 9003 (Admin)
Fax: 0845 251 9005
Email: helpline@bdadyslexia.org.uk   Website: www.bdadyslexia.org.uk

Helpline/information service open between 10am and 4.00pm (M-F) also open late on Wednesdays 5-7pm. Has a Facebook page. Registered charity no. 289243.

British Institute of Learning Disabilities (BILD)

Campion House
Green Street
Kidderminster,
Worcestershire DY10 1JL

Tel: 01562 723010   Fax: 01562 723029
Email: enquiries@bild.org.uk   Website: www.bild.org.uk

Registered charity (no. 1019663) committed to improving the quality of life of people with learning disabilities. They do this by advancing education, research and practice and by promoting better ways of working with children and adults with learning disabilities. BILD provides education, training, information, publications, journals, membership services, research and consultancy. Has a Facebook page and you can follow them on Twitter.

British Psychological Society

St Andrews House
48 Princess Road East
Leicester LE1 7DR

Tel: 0116 254 9568   Fax: 0116 227 1314
Email: enquiries@bps.org.uk   Website: www.bps.org.uk

The representative body for psychology and psychologists in the UK. Has search facility for details on psychologists. Registered charity nos. 229642 & SCO39452.

Brunel Able Children's Education (BACE) Centre

Brunel University
School of Sport & Education,
Kingston Lane
Uxbridge, Middlesex UB8 3PH

Tel: 01895 267152   Fax: 01895 269806
Email: catherina.emery@brunel.ac.uk
Website: www.brunel.ac.uk/sse/education/research/bace

Conducts research into all aspects of identification and provision for able and exceptionally able children. The centre has been involved in supporting the education of able children in inner city schools for a number of years. A number of courses are run for teachers to train them to make effective provision for able pupils.

Capability Scotland (ASCS)

Head Office, Westerlea
11 Ellersly Road
Edinburgh
Midlothian EH12 6HY

Tel: 0131 337 9876 Textphone: 0131 346 2529
Fax: 0131 346 7864   Website: www.capability-scotland.org.uk

ASCS is a national disability advice and information service, which provides free confidential advice and information on a range of disability issues including advice on cerebral palsy. Registered charity no. SCO11330.

Carers UK

20 Great Dover Street
London SE1 4LX

Tel: 020 7378 4999   Fax: 020 7378 9781
Adviceline: 0808 808 7777 (W & Th 10-12 and 2-4pm) or Email: adviceline@carersuk.org
Email: info@carersuk.org   Website: www.carersuk.org

For carers run by carers. Registered charity nos. 246329 & SCO39307. Has a Facebook page and you can follow them on Twitter.

Carers Northern Ireland

58 Howard Street
Belfast BT1 6PJ

Tel: 028 9043 9843
Email: info@carersni.org   Website: www.carersuk.org/northern-ireland

See main entry under Carers UK.

Carers Scotland

The Cottage
21 Pearce Street
Glasgow G51 3UT

Tel: 0141 445 3070
Email: info@carersscotland.org   Website: www.carersuk.org/scotland

See main entry under Carers UK.

Carers Wales

River House
Gwaelod-y-Garth
Cardiff CF15 9SS

Tel: 029 2081 1370
Email: info@carerswales.org

Website: www.carersuk.org/wales

See main entry under Carers UK.

Centre for Studies on Inclusive Education (CSIE)

The Park
Daventry Road
Knowle
Bristol BS4 1DQ

Tel: 0117 353 3150
Email: admin@csie.org.uk

Fax: 0117 353 3151
Website: www.csie.org.uk

Promoting inclusion for all children in restructured mainstream schools. Registered charity no. 327805.

Challenging Behaviour Foundation

c/o The Old Courthouse
New Road Avenue
Chatham, Kent
ME4 6BE

Tel: 01634 838739 Family support line: 0845 602 7885
Email: info@thecbf.org.uk

Website: www.challengingbehaviour.org.uk

Supports families, professionals and stakeholders who live/work with people with severe learning disabilities who have challenging behaviour. Registered charity no. 1060714.

Child Brain Injury Trust (CBIT)

Unit 1, The Great Barn
Baynards Green Farm
Bicester, Oxfordshire
OX27 7SG

Tel: 01869 341075
Email: info@cbituk.org

Website: www.childbraininjurytrust.org.uk

Formerly known as the Children's Head Injury Trust (CHIT) this organisation was originally set up in 1991. It offers support to children and families affected by brain injuries that happen after birth. Registered charity nos. 1113326 & SCO39703. Has Facebook page and you can follow them on Twitter.

Children's Legal Centre
Head Office
University of Essex, Wivenhoe Park
Colchester, Essex CO4 3SQ

Tel: 01206 877 910
Email: clc@essex.ac.uk

Fax: 01206 877 963
Website: www.childrenslegalcentre.com

The Children's Legal Centre is an independent national charity (no. 281222) concerned with law and policy affecting children and young people. The centre runs a free and confidential legal advice and information service covering all aspects of law and the service is open to children, young people and anyone with concerns about them. The Education Legal Advocacy unit provides advice and representation to children and/or parents involved in education disputes with a school or a local education authority. Has a Facebook page and you can follow them on Twitter.

Communication Matters
Catchpell House
Carpet Lane
Edinburgh
EH6 6SP

Tel/Fax: 0845 456 8211
Email: admin@communications.org.uk

Website: www.communicationmatters.org.uk

Support for people who find communication difficult.

Contact a Family
209-211 City Road
London
EC1V 1JN

Tel: 020 7608 8700 Helpline: 0808 808 3555 Textphone: 0808 808 3556   Fax: 020 7608 8701
Email: helpline@cafamily.org.uk

Website: www.cafamily.org.uk

Registered charity (nos. 284912, SCO39169) that provides support, advice and information to families with disabled children. Has a Facebook page and you can follow them on Twitter.

Council for Disabled Children
National Children's Bureau
8 Wakley Street
London EC1V 7QE

Tel: 020 7843 1900
Email: cdc@ncb.org.uk

Fax: 020 7843 6313
Website: www.councilfordisabledchildren.org.uk

The council promotes collaborative work and partnership between voluntary and non-voluntary agencies, parents and children and provides a national forum for the discussion, development and dissemination of a wide range of policy and practice issues relating to service provision and support for children and young people with disabilities and special educational needs. Has a particular interest in inclusive education, special education needs, parent partnership services, play and leisure and transition. Registered charity no. 258825. Has a Facebook page and you can follow them on Twitter.

Cystic Fibrosis Trust

11 London Road
Bromley
Kent BR1 1BY

Tel: 020 8464 7211 Helpline: 0300 373 1000
Email: enquiries@cftrust.org.uk

Fax: 020 8313 0472
Website: www.cftrust.org.uk

The Cystic Fibrosis Trust is a national registered charity (nos. 1079049, SCO40196) established in 1964. It offers information and support to people with cystic fibrosis, their families, their carers and anyone affected by cystic fibrosis. It funds research, offers some financial support to people with cystic fibrosis and campaigns for improved services. It provides a wide range of information including fact sheets, publications and expert concensus documents on treatment and care for people with cystic fibrosis. Has a Facebook page.

Department for Education (DfE) – formerly the DCSF

Castle View House
East Lane
Runcorn
Cheshire WA7 2GJ

Website: www.education.gov.uk/schools/pupilsupport/sen

Disabled Living Foundation

380-384 Harrow Road
London W9 2HU

Tel: 020 7289 6111 Helpline: 0845 130 9177
Email: info@dlf.org.uk

Website: www.dlf.org.uk

This foundation provides free, impartial advice about products for disabled people. Registered charity no. 290069. Has a Facebook page and you can follow them on Twitter.

Down's Syndrome Education International

The Sarah Duffen Centre
Belmont Street, Southsea
Portsmouth, Hampshire
PO5 1NA

Tel: 023 9285 5330
Email: enquiries@downsed.org

Fax: 023 9285 5320
Website: www.downsed.org

Down's Syndrome Education International works around the world to improve the development, education and social achievements of many thousands of people living with Down's syndrome. We undertake and support scientific research and disseminate quality information and advice widely through our websites, books, films and training courses.

Our education services support families and professionals to help people with Down's syndrome achieve sustained gains in all areas of their development.

For 30 years, we have disseminated the latest research findings in practical and accessible formats to the widest audiences, from birth to adulthood. Please visit our website for more information. Registered charity no. 1062823. We have a Facebook page and you can follow us on Twitter.

Down's Syndrome Association

Langdon Down Centre
2a Langdon Park
Teddington TW11 9PS

Tel: 020 8614 5100   Fax: 0845 230 0373
Email: info@downs-syndrome.org.uk   Website: www.downs-syndrome.org.uk

We provide information and support for people with Down's syndrome, their families and carers, and the professionals who work with them. We strive to improve knowledge of the condition. We champion the rights of people with Down's syndrome. Registered charity no. 1061474.

Down's Syndrome Association Northern Ireland

Unit 2, Marlborough House
348 Lisburn Road
Belfast BT9 6GH

Tel: 028 90666 5260   Fax: 028 9066 7674
Email: enquiriesni@downs-syndrome.org.uk

See main entry above.

Down's Syndrome Association Wales

Suite 1, 206 Whitchurch Road
Heath, Cardiff CF14 3NB

Tel: 029 2052 2511
Email: wales@downs-syndrome.org.uk

See main entry above.

Dyslexia Action

Park House
Wick Road
Egham
Surrey TW20 0HH

Tel: 01784 222300   Fax: 01784 222333
Email: info@dyslexiaaction.org.uk   Website: www.dyslexiaaction.org.uk

Registered charity (nos. 268502, SCO39177) and the UK's leading provider of services and support for people with dyslexia and literacy difficulties. We specialise in assessment, teaching and training. We also develop and distribute teaching materials and undertake research.

Dyslexia Action is the largest supplier of specialist training in this field and is committed to improving public policy and practice. We partner with schools, LAs, colleges, universities, employers, voluntary sector organisations and government to improve the quality and quantity of help for people with dyslexia and specific learning difficulties.

Our services are available through our 26 centres around the UK. We have a Facebook page and you can follow us on Twitter.

Dyslexia Scotland

2nd floor – East Suite
Wallace House
17-21 Maxwell Place
Stirling FK8 1JU

Tel: 01786 446 650
Email: info@dyslexiascotland.org.uk

Fax: 01786 471235
Website: www.dyslexiascotland.org.uk

Scottish association set up to support and campaign on behalf of people affected by dyslexia. They have a useful and easy to use website. Registered charity no. SCO00951.

Dyspraxia Foundation

8 West Alley
Hitchin
Hertfordshire SG5 1EG

Tel: 01462 455016 Helpline: 01462 454 986 (M-F 10am-1pm)   Fax: 01462 455052
Email: dyspraxia@dyspraxiafoundation.org.uk   Website: www.dyspraxiafoundation.org.uk

The foundation exists to support individuals and families affected by dyspraxia; to promote better diagnostic and treatment facilities for those who have dyspraxia; to help professionals in health and education to assist those with dyspraxia; and to promote awareness and understanding of dyspraxia. As well as various publications, the Dyspraxia Foundation organises conferences and talks and supports a network of local groups across the United Kingdom.

Registered charity no. 1058352. Has a Facebook page and you can follow them on Twitter.

Education Scotland

Denholm House
Almondvale Business Park
Almondvale Way
Livingston
EH54 6GA

Tel: 0141 282 5000
Email: enquiries@educationscotland.org.uk

Textphone: 01506 600236
Website: www.educationscotland.gov.uk

Education Scotland is an executive non-departmental public body sponsored by the Scottish government. It is the main organisation for the development and support of the Scottish curriculum and is at the heart of all major developments in Scottish education, moving education forward with its partners.

Has a Facebook page and you can follow them on Twitter.

ENABLE Scotland

2nd Floor
146 Argyle Street
Glasgow
G2 8BL

Tel: 0141 226 4541   Fax: 0141 204 4398
Email: enabledirect@enable.org.uk   Website: www.enable.org.uk

Contact the ENABLE Scotland Information Service about any aspect of learning disability. They offer jobs, training, respite breaks, day services, supported living, housing and support for people with learning disabilities in different parts of Scotland. Its legal service can assist families with wills and trusts. Registered charity no. SC009024. Has a Facebook page and you can follow them on Twitter.

English Federation of Disability Sport

Sport Park, Loughborough University
3 Oakwood Drive
Loughborough
Leicestershire LE11 3QF

Tel: 01509 227750   Fax: 0509 227777
Email: info@efds.org.uk   Website: www.efds.co.uk

Charity (no. 1075180) that creates opportunities for disabled people to participate in sporting activities.

Epilepsy Action

New Anstey House
Gate Way Drive,
Yeadon
Leeds LS19 7XY

Tel: 0113 210 880   Fax: 0113 391 0300
Email: helpline@epilepsy.org.uk   Website: www.epilepsy.org.uk

Epilepsy Action is the largest member-led epilepsy organisation in the UK. We are committed to supporting the needs of people with epilepsy, by working with individuals, families, carers and professionals to increase awareness and understanding of the condition. Our services to support people with epilepsy in education include a free telephone and email helpline, and a network of local branches. Epilepsy Action produces online resources for professionals and families, and information packs for schools and settings. Registered charity no. 234343. See our Facebook page and follow us on Twitter.

European Council for High Ability (ECHA)

Secretariat
NACE National Office,
PO Box 242,
Arnolds Way
Oxford OX2 9FR

Tel: 01865 861 879   Fax: 01865 861 880
Website: www.echa.info

ECHA is an international organisation of researchers, teachers, school administrators, and parents who are concerned with giftedness, talent, and high ability. Its goal is to promote awareness of gifted children and to provide information to the public on the best development of gifted young people. ECHA is a private non-profit organisation. Registered charity no. 40146782.

Foundation for Conductive Education
The National Institute of Conductive Education
Cannon Hill House
Russell Road
Moseley
Birmingham B13 8RD

Tel: 0121 449 1569
Email: info@conductive-education.org.uk   Website: www.conductive-education.org.uk

The National Institute of Conductive Education provides a range of direct services to physically disabled children including a Parent & Child Programme for up to three-years-old; an Ofsted (ref 103588) inspected nursery and primary school; sessional and outreach services. Conductive Education teaches children and adults with motor disorders (eg cerebral palsy and dyspraxia in children as well as Parkinson's, multiple sclerosis, stroke and head injury) how to overcome their movement problems to lead more independent, fulfilled and dignified lives.

The foundation undertakes research and consultancy and offers a comprehensive range of professionally oriented, skills-based training courses at all levels including the BA(Hons)(CE) with the University of Wolverhampton. Covers UK and overseas. Registered charity no. 295873.

GIFT
24 Martingale Road
Billericay
Essex
CM11 1SG

Tel: 01277 654228
Email: enquiries@giftltd.co.uk   Website: www.giftltd.co.uk

GIFT aims to offer a value-for-money education consultancy of quality, which meets the needs of gifted and talented children and those working to support them in the excitement and challenge of achieving their full potential as human beings. Residential and non-residential courses are organised for exceptionally able children aged five to 18 throughout the year (see our website). INSET courses for schools on provision, identification and school policy are provided with a special emphasis on workshops for practical activities.

Haringey Association for Independent Living (HAIL)
Tottenham Town Hall
Town Hall Approach Road
Tottenham
London N15 4RY

Tel: 020 8275 6550   Fax: 020 8275 6559
Email: admin@hailltd.org   Website: www.hailltd.org

Haringey Association for Independent Living is a support service for adults with learning difficulties moving towards independent living. You can follow them on Twitter.

Headway

Bradbury House
190 Bagnall Road
Old Basford
Nottingham NG6 8SF

Tel: 0115 924 0800 Helpline: 0808 800 2244   Fax: 0115 958 4446
Email: enquiries@headway.org.uk   Website: www.headway.org.uk

Registered charity no.1025852 supporting people with brain injuries and their carers. Has a Facebook page and you can follow them on Twitter.

Helen Arkell Dyslexia Centre

Arkell Lane
Frensham
Farnham, Surrey GU10 3BL

Tel: 01252 792400
Email: enquiries@arkellcentre.org.uk   Website: www.arkellcentre.org.uk

A registered charity (no. 1064646) providing comprehensive help and care for children with specific learning difficulties, including assessment, specialist tuition, speech and language therapy, summer schools and short courses. Initial consultations can be arranged in order to give advice on options for support. Professional teacher-training programmes and schools' support. Financial help available in cases of need. Has a Facebook page.

Huntington's Disease Association

Head Office
Suite 24
Liverpool Science Park
Innovation Centre 1
131 Mount Pleasant
Liverpool L3 5TF

Tel: 0151 331 5444   Fax: 0151 331 5441
Email: info@hda.org.uk   Website: www.hda.org.uk

Registered charity (no. 296453) offering support to people affected by Huntington's Disease (HD); which is sometimes referred to as Huntington's Chorea. Has a Facebook page.

Independent Panel for Special Education Advice (IPSEA)

Hunters Court
Debden Road
Saffron Walden CB11 4AA

Tel: 01799 582030 Adviceline: 0800 018 4016
Email: info@ipsea.org.uk   Website: www.ipsea.org.uk

IPSEA offers free and independent advice and support to parents of children with special educational needs including: free advice on LAs' legal duties towards children with free accompanied visits where necessary, free support and possible representation for those parents appealing to the Special Educational Needs Tribunal, free second opinions on a child's needs and the provision required to meet those needs. Registered charity no. 327691. Has a Facebook page and you can follow them on Twitter.

Institute for Neuro-Physiological Psychology (INPP)
1 Stanley Street
Chester
Cheshire
CH1 2LR

Tel: 01244 311414   Fax: 01244 311414
Website: www.inpp.org.uk

Established in 1975 to research into the effect central nervous system (CNS) dysfunctions have on children with learning difficulties, to develop appropriate CNS remedial and rehabilitation programmes, and to correct underlying physical dysfunctions in dyslexia, dyspraxia and attention deficit disorder (ADD).

Ivemark Syndrome Association
18 French Road
Poole
Dorset
BH17 7HB

Tel: 01202 699824

Support group for families with children affected by Ivemark Syndrome (also know as right atrial isomerism).

Jeans for Genes
1st Floor
Macmillan House
Paddington Station
London
W2 1FT

Tel: 0800 980 4800
Email: hello@jeanforgenes.com   Website: www.jeansforgenes.com

The first Friday of every October is Jeans for Genes Day. Their aim is to raise money to fund research into genetic disorders and their target figure is £3million each year. Has a Facebook page and you can follow them on Twitter. Registered charity no.1062206.

KIDS
49 Mecklenburgh Square
London
WC1N 2NY

Tel: 020 7520 0405
Website: www.kids.org.uk

KIDS was established in 1970 to help disabled children in their development and communication skills. Registered charity no. 275936. Has a Facebook page and you can follow them on Twitter.

Leonard Cheshire Disability England

66 South Lambeth Road
London SW8 1RL

Tel: 020 3242 0200
Email: info@lcdisability.org

Fax: 020 3242 0250
Website: www.lcdisability.org

Leonard Cheshire – the UK's largest voluntary-sector provider of support services for disabled people. They also support disabled people in 52 countries around the world. Registered charity nos. 218186 and SCO05117.

Leonard Cheshire Disability Northern Ireland

Unit 5, Boucher Plaza
Boucher Road
Belfast BT12 6HR

Tel: 028 9024 6247
Email: northernirelandoffice@lcdisability.org

Fax: 028 9024 6395

See main entry – Leonard Cheshire Disability England.

Leonard Cheshire Disability Scotland

Murrayburgh House
17 Corstorphine Road
Edinburgh EH12 6DD

Tel: 0131 346 9040
Email: scotlandoffice@lcdisability.org

Fax: 0131 346 9050

See main entry – Leonard Cheshire Disability England.

Leonard Cheshire Disability Wales

Centre for Business
Office 3
12 Devon Place
Newport
Gwent NP20 4NN

Tel: 01633 263807

See main entry – Leonard Cheshire Disability England.

Leukaemia Care Society

1 Birch Court
Blackpole East
Worcester WR3 8SG

Tel: 01905 755977 Careline: 08088 010 444   Fax: 01905 755 166
Email: care@leukaemiacare.org.uk   Website: www.leukaemiacare.org.uk

Registered charity (nos. 259483, SCO39207) that exists to provide care and support to anyone affected by leukaemia. Has a Facebook page and you can follow them on Twitter.

Leukaemia Care Scotland

Regus Management
Maxim 1, Maxim Office Park
2 Parklands Way, Eurocentral
Motherwell ML1 4WR

Tel: 01698 209073
Email: scotland@leukaemiacare.org.uk

See main entry above.

Listening Books

12 Lant Street
London SE1 1QH

Tel: 020 7407 9417   Fax: 020 7403 1377
Email: info@listening-books.org.uk   Website: www.listening-books.org.uk

Registered charity (no. 264221) that provides a postal and internet based audio library service to anyone who is unable to read in the usual way due to an illness, disability or learning difficulty such as dyslexia.

Has a range of educational audio material to support all aspects of the National Curriculum, as well as thousands of general fiction and non-fiction titles for all ages. There is no limit to the number of titles you may borrow during the year.

Manx Dyslexia Asociation

Coan Aalin
Greeba Bridge
Greba
Isle of Man IM4 3LD

Tel: 07624 315724
Email: manxdyslexia@gmail.com
Website: www.manxdyslexia.org

Charity (no. IM706) founded in 1993 to help raise the awareness of dyslexia on the Isle of Man.

MENCAP England

123 Golden Lane
London EC1Y 0RT

Tel: 020 7454 0454 Helpline: 0808 808 1111   Fax: 020 7608 3254
Email: information@mencap.org.uk   Website: www.mencap.org.uk

The Royal MENCAP Society is a registered charity (nos. 222377, SCO41079) that offers services to adults and children with learning disabilities. We offer help and advice in benefits, housing and employment via our helpline.

Helplines are open from Monday to Friday 9.30am-4.30pm; Wednesday – subject to change: (open am-closed pm). Language line is also used. Our office is open Monday-Friday 9-5pm.

We also offer help and advice to anyone who has any other issues or we can signpost them in the right direction. We can also provide information and support for leisure, recreational services (Gateway Clubs) residential services and holidays.

MENCAP Northern Ireland

Segal House
4 Annandale Avenue
Belfast BT7 3JH

Tel: 028 9069 1351
Email: helpline.ni@mencap.org.uk

See main entry – MENCAP England.

MENCAP Cymru

31 Lambourne Crescent
Cardiff Business Park
Llanishen, Cardiff CF14 5GF

Helpline: 02920 747588
Email: helpline.wales@mencap.org.uk

See main entry – MENCAP England.

MENSA

British Mensa Ltd
St John's House
St John's Square
Wolverhampton WV2 4AH

Tel: 01902 772771   Fax: 01902 392500
Email: enquiries@mensa.org.uk   Website: www.mensa.org.uk

MENSA aims to bring about awareness that giftedness in a child is frequently a specific learning difficulty and should be recognised and treated as such, train teachers to recognise giftedness in a child, train teachers to teach gifted children, establish mutually beneficial relationships with other organisations having similar aims to our own and to devise and implement strategies aimed, at ministerial and senior civil servant levels, at bringing about recognition of the importance of catering for the needs of gifted children.

Mind, the National Association for Mental Health

15-19 Broadway
Stratford
London E15 4BQ

Tel: 020 8519 2122   Fax: 020 8522 1725
Email: contact@mind.org.uk   Website: www.mind.org.uk

Mind (the National Association for Mental Health) is the leading mental health charity (no. 219830) in England and Wales. Mind works for a better life for everyone with experience of mental or emotional stress. It does this by: advancing the views, needs and ambitions of people experiencing mental distress; promoting inclusion and challenging discrimination; influencing policy through effective campaigning and education; providing quality services that meet the expressed needs of people experiencing mental distress and which reflect the requirements of a diverse community; achieving equal legal and civil rights through campaigning and education.

With over 60 years of experience, Mind is a major national network consisting of over 200 local Mind associations, which cover most major towns and rural areas in England and Wales. These are separately registered charities operating under the Mind brand. The Mind network is the largest charitable provider of mental health services in the community. The work of the local associations is strengthened and supported by staff and activities through its many offices in England and Wales. This ensures that, as a national charity, Mind keeps a distinct local perspective to their work.

Mind believes in the individual and equipping them to make informed choices about options open to them. Mind's mental health telephone information service (Mindinfoline) deals with thousands of calls each year. We offer a vital lifeline to people in distress, their relatives and carers, as well as providing mental health information to members of the public, professionals and students.

Visit our Facebook page and you can follow us on Twitter.

Mind Cymru

3rd Floor, Quebec House
Castlebridge, 5-19 Cowbridge Road East
Cardiff CF11 9AB

Tel: 029 2039 5123   Fax: 029 2034 6585
Email: contactwales@mind.org.uk

See main entry above.

Motability

Warwick House
Roydon Road
Harlow
Essex CM19 5PX

Tel: 01279 635999 Minicom/textphone: 01279 632213 Fax: 01279 632000
Website: www.motability.co.uk

Registered charity no. 299745. Motability helps disabled people to use their mobility allowance to obtain new transport.

MS Society
MS National Centre
372 Edgware Road
London NW2 6ND

Tel: 020 8438 0700   Fax: 020 8438 0701
Website: www.mssociety.org.uk

Multiple Sclerosis Society. Registered charity nos. 207495 and SCO16433. Has a Facebook page and you can follow them on Twitter.

MS Society Cymru
Temple Court
Cathedral Road
Cardiff CF11 9HA

Tel: 029 2078 6676   Fax: 029 2078 6677

See main entry above.

MS Society Northern Ireland
The Resource Centre
34 Annadale Avenue
Belfast BT7 3JJ

Tel: 02890 802 802

See main entry above.

MS Society Scotland
National Office, Ratho Park
88 Glasgow Road, Ratho Station
Newbridge EH28 8PP

Tel: 0131 335 4050   Fax: 0131 335 4051

See main entry above.

Muscular Dystrophy Campaign
61 Southwark Street
London SE1 0HL

Tel: 020 7803 4800
Email: info@muscular-dystrophy.org
Website: www.muscular-dystrophy.org

Registered charity (nos. 205395, SCO39445). Provides information and advice for families affected by muscular dystrophy and other neuromuscular conditions.

Has a Facebook page and you can follow them on Twitter.

NAS – The National Autistic Society – England

393 City Road
London EC1V 1NG

Tel: 020 7833 2299 Autism Helpline: 0800 800 4104 (M-F 10-4) Fax: 020 7833 9666
Email: nas@nas.org.uk   Website: www.autism.org.uk

The National Autistic Society is the UK's leading charity (nos. 269425, SCO39427) for people affected by autism. For more than 50 years we have worked to support children and young people with autism (including Asperger syndrome) to reach their goals. A well-rounded education, tailored to the needs of the individual, can help people to reach their full potential.

NAS Cymru

6/7 Village Way,
Greenmeadow Springs Business Park
Tongwynlais, Cardiff CF15 7NE

Tel: 02920 629 312 Fax: 02920 629 317   Email: wales@nas.org.uk

See main entry NAS – England.

NAS Northern Ireland

59 Malone Road
Belfast BT9 6SA

Tel: 02890 687 066   Fax: 02890 688 518
Email: northern.ireland@nas.org.uk

See main entry NAS – England.

NAS Scotland

Central Chambers
1st Floor, 109 Hope Street
Glasgow G2 6LL

Tel: 0141 221 8090   Fax: 0141 221 8118
Email: scotland@nas.org.uk

See main entry NAS – England.

nasen

4/5 Amber Business Village
Amber Close, Amington
Tamworth, Staffordshire B77 4RP

Tel: 01827 311500   Fax: 01827 313005
Email: welcome@nasen.org.uk   Website: www.nasen.org.uk

nasen promotes the interests of children and young people with exceptional learning needs and influences the quality of provision through strong and cohesive policies and strategies for parents and professionals.

Membership offers a number of journals, professional development and publications at a reduced cost, and provides a forum for members to share concerns and disseminate expertise and knowledge.

National Association for Able Children in Education (NAACE)

NACE National Office
The Core Business Centre
Milton Hill
Abingdon
Oxfordshire OX13 6AB

Tel: 01235 828280
Fax: 01235 828281
Email: info@nace.co.uk
Website: www.nace.co.uk

NAACE works with teachers to support able children in schools. The organisation also provides, publications, journals, booklets, courses and conferences. Registered charity no. 327230.

National Association for Gifted Children (NAGC)

Suite 1-2
Challenge House
Sherwood Drive
Bletchley,
Milton Keynes MK3 6DP

Tel: 01908 646433
Fax: 0870 770 3219
Email: amazingchildren@nagcbritain.org.uk
Website: www.potentialplusuk.org

Registered charity (no. 313182). It is a mutually supportive self-help organisation offering services both through local branches and nationally. Membership is open to individuals, families, education professionals and schools.

National Association of Independent Schools and Non-Maintained Special Schools (NASS)

PO Box 705
York
YO30 6WW

Tel: 01904 624446
Email: krippon@nasschools.org.uk
Website: www.nasschools.org.uk

NASS is a voluntary organisation that represents the interests of those special schools outside the maintained sector of the education system.

Our commitment is to achieve excellence and to attain the highest professional standards in working with unique children and young people who have physical, sensory and intellectual difficulties. We exist to promote, develop and maintain the highest professional standards for non-maintained and independent special schools. We offer free information and advice on our member schools to families and professionals. Registered charity no. 1083632.

National Blind Children's Society

Administration
Bradbury House
Market Street
Highbridge
Somerset TA9 3BW

Tel: 01278 764764
Fax: 0121 764790
Email: enquiries@nbcs.org.uk
Website: www.nbcs.org.uk

Founded in 1995 to offer advice and support for blind and partially sighted children and their families and carers. Registered charity no. 1051607. Has a Facebook page.

National Federation of the Blind of the UK

Sir John Wilson House
215 Kirkgate
Wakefield
Yorkshire WF1 1JG

Tel: 01924 291313
Email: nfbuk@nfbuk.org

Fax: 01924 200244
Website: www.nfbuk.org

Registered charity no. 236629 set up to better the understanding between blind and sighted people.

National Society for Epilepsy

Chesham Lane
Chalfont St Peter
Gerrards Cross,
Buckinghamshire SL9 0RJ

Tel: 01494 601300 Helpline 01494 601400 (Mon-Fri 10am-4pm)
Fax: 01494 871927

Website: www.epilepsysociety.org.uk

The NSE provides information and support to those affected by epilepsy. Registered charity no. 206186. Has a Facebook page and you can follow them on Twitter.

NDCS – The National Deaf Children's Society

Head Office
15 Dufferin Street
London EC1Y 8UR

Tel: 020 7490 8656 Minicom: 020 7490 8656
Email: ndcs@ndcs.org.uk

Fax: 020 7251 5020
Website: www.ndcs.org.uk

Leading provider of information, advice, advocacy and support for deaf children, their parents and professionals on all aspects of childhood deafness. This includes advice and information on education, including further and higher education, and support at Special Educational Needs Tribunals.

NDCS also provides advice on equipment and technology for deaf children at home and at school. Registered charity nos. 1016532 and SCO40779. You can follow them on Twitter.

NDCS Cmyru

4 Cathedral Road
Cardiff
CF11 9LJ

Tel: 029 2037 3474 Minicom: 029 2023 2739
Email: ndcswales@ndcs.org.uk

Fax: 029 2037 9800

See main entry above.

NDCS Northern Ireland

38-42 Hill Street
Belfast BT1 2LB

Tel: 028 9031 3170 Minicom: 028 9027 8177
Email: nioffice@ndcs.org.uk

Fax: 028 9027 8205

See main entry above.

NDCS Scotland

Second Floor, Empire House
131 West Nile Street
Glasgow G1 2RX

Tel: 0141 354 7850 Textphone: 0141 332 6133   Fax: 0141 331 2780
Email: ndcs.scotland@ndcs.org.uk

See main entry above.

Network 81

1-7 Woodfield Terrace
Stansted
Essex CM24 8AJ

Tel: 0845 077 4056 (Admin) Helpline: 0845 077 4055 Fax: 0845 077 4057
Email: info@network81.org   Website: www.network81.org

Network 81 offers practical help and support to parents throughout all stages of assessment and statementing as outlined in the Education Act 1996. Their national helpline offers an individual service to parents linked to a national network of local contacts.

NIACE

Chetwynd House
21 DeMontfort Street
Leicester LE1 7GE

Tel: 0116 204 4200 Minicom: 0116 255 6049   Fax: 0116 204 6988
Email: enquiries@niace.org.uk   Website: www.niace.org.uk

Works across sectors and age groups to raise national standards and encourage adults in achieving literacy, numeracy and language skills. Registered charity no. 1002775. You can follow them on Twitter.

NOFAS – UK

165 Beaufort Park
London
NW11 6DA

Tel: 0208 458 5951
Email: info@nofas-uk.org   Website: www.nofas-uk.org

Offers advice, support and information about Foetal Alcohol Spectrum Disorder. Registered charity no. 1101935.

OAASIS

The Croft, Vicars Hill
Boldre
Brockenhurst,
Hampshire SO41 5QB

Helpline: 0800 197 3907 (M-F 10-4.30)
Email: oaasis@cambiangroup.com   Website: www.oaasis.co.uk

OAASIS, a part of Cambian Education Services, is there to help anyone who has a question on SEN issues, be they parents, carers or any professional. Has a range of over 30 information sheets on a range of learning disabilities and other related SEN topics; publications for more in-depth knowledge on seven learning disabilities; advice on any aspect of SEN from a new diagnosis, local support groups, school issues including statementing and the tribunal system.

Paget Gorman Society
PGS Administrative Secretary
43 Westover Road
Fleet GU51 3DB

Tel: 01252 621 183
Website: www.pagetgorman.org

Advice and information for parents and professionals concerned with speech and language-impaired children.

Parents for Inclusion (PI)
336 Brixton Road
London
SW9 7AA

Tel: 020 7738 3888 Helpline: 0800 652 3145
Email: info@parentsforinclusion.org
Website: www.parentsforinclusion.org

A network of parents of disabled children and children with special needs. Registered charity no.1070675.

Physically Disabled and Able Bodied (PHAB Ltd)
Summit House
50 Wandle Road
Croydon
CR0 1DF

Tel: 020 8667 9443 Fax: 020 8681 1399
Email: info@phab.org.uk Website: www.phab.org.uk

Registered charity (no. 283931) that works to promote and encourage people with and without physical disabilities to work together to achieve inclusion for all in the wider community.

Qualifications and Curriculum Development Agency (QCDA)
53-55 Butts Road
Earlsdon Park
Coventry CV1 3BH

Tel: 0300 303 3010 Fax: 0300 303 3014
Email: info@qcda.gov.uk Website: www.qcda.gov.uk

QCDA's primary duty is to keep under review the school curriculum, pupil assessment and qualifications obtained in schools, colleges or in the workplace and to advise the Secretary of State for Education and Skills on any matters which affect them. QCDA's Equal Opportunities Team aims to ensure that arrangements for the curriculum, assessment and qualifications provide for the inclusion of all learners and take account of individual requirements arising from disability (including special educational needs), race, gender or high ability. Formerly known as QCA.

Royal National Institute for the Blind (RNIB)
105 Judd Street
London
WC1H 9NE

Tel: 020 7388 1266   Fax: 020 7388 2034
Helpline: 0303 123 9999
Email: helpline@rnib.org.uk   Website: www.rnib.org.uk

Every day another 100 people start to lose their sight – there are around two million people in the UK with sight problems, blindness being one of the major causes of disability in the UK. RNIB's pioneering work helps anyone with a sight problem – not just with Braille, Talking Books and computer training, but with imaginative and practical solutions to everyday challenges. They fight for equal rights for people with sight problems; fund pioneering research into preventing and treating eye disease; and campaign to change society's attitudes, actions and assumptions so that people with sight problems can enjoy the same rights, freedoms and responsibilties as fully-sighted people.

RNIB promotes eye health by running public health awareness campaigns and their schools and colleges help educate hundreds of children and students with sight problems. They run campaigns on a wide variety of issues, from community care to the design of banknotes and coins, from legislation about broadcasting to accessible information. They lobby national and local government, hold public meetings, organise letter-writing campaigns and work in coalitions to achieve their aims. Registered charity no. 226227.

Has a Facebook page and you can follow them on Twitter.

Scope
6 Market Road
London N7 9PW

Tel: 0808 800 3333 (Scope response)   Switchboard: 020 7619 7100
Text SCOPE plus message to 80039
Email: response@scope.org.uk   Website: www.scope.org.uk

Scope is a national disability organisation whose focus is people with cerebral palsy. We provide a range of support, information and campaigning services both locally and nationally in addition to providing opportunities in early years, education, employment and daily living. For more information about cerebral palsy and Scope services, contact Scope Response, which provides free information, advice and initial counselling. Open 9am-7pm weekdays and 10am-2pm Saturdays. Registered charity no. 208231.

Has a Facebook page and you can follow them on Twitter.

Scope Cymru
4 Ty Nant Court
Morganstown
Cardiff CF15 8LW

Tel: 029 20 815 450
Email: response@scope.org.uk

See main entry above.

Scottish Society for Autism

Hilton House,
Alloa Business Park
Whins Road
Alloa FK10 3SA

Tel: 01259 720044

Email: autism@scottishautism.org   Website: www.scottishautism.org

The Scottish Society for Autism is a registered charity (no. SC009068) established in 1968. They aim to work with individuals of all ages with autism spectrum disorder (ASD), their families and carers, to provide and promote exemplary services and training in education, care, support and life opportunities. Has a Facebook page and you can follow them on Twitter.

Sense – The National Deafblind Charity

101 Pentonville Road
London N1 9LG

Tel/Textphone: 0845 127 0066   Fax: 0845 127 0061
Email: info@sense.org.uk   Website: www.sense.org.uk

Sense is the leading national charity that supports and campaigns for children and adults who are deafblind. We provide expert advice and information as well as specialist services to deafblind people, their families, carers and the professionals who work with them. We also support people who have sensory impairments with additional disabilities.

Our services include on-going support for deafblind people and families. These range from day services where deafblind people have the opportunity to learn new skills and Sense-run houses in the community – where people are supported to live as independently as possible. We also provide leading specialist advice, for example on education options and assistive technology. Registered charity no. 289868. Has a Facebook page and you can follow them on Twitter.

Shine

42 Park Road
Peterborough
PE1 2UQ

Tel: 01733 421309   Fax: 01733 555985
Email: info@shinecharity.org.uk   Website: www.shinecharity.org.uk

The new name for the Association for Spina Bifida and Hydrocephalus (ASBAH). Europe's largest organisation dedicated to supporting individuals and families as they face the challenges arising from spina bifida and hydrocephalus.

Advisers are available to explain the problems associated with spina bifida and or hydrocephalus and may be able to arrange visits to schools and colleges to discuss difficulties. Registered charity no. 249338. Has a Facebook page and you can follow them on Twitter.

Signature

Mersey House
Mandale Business Park
Belmont
Country Durham DH1 1TH

Tel: 0191 383 1155 Text: 07974 121594
Email: enquiries@signature.org.uk

Fax: 0191 3837914
Website: www.signature.org.uk

Association promoting communication with deaf and deafblind people. NB: Signature Wales has a separate web page (www.signature.org.uk/wales) but as yet no specific contact details.

Signature Northern Ireland

Harvester House
4-8 Adelaide Street
Belfast BT2 8GA

Tel/text: 028 90 438161
Email: pam.tilson@signature.org.uk

Website: www.signature.org.uk/northernireland

See main entry above.

Signature Scotland

TouchBase Community Suite
43 Middlesex Street
Glasgow G41 1EE

Tel: 0141 418 719 Text: 0141 418 7193
Email: glasgow@signature.org.uk

Fax: 0141 418 7192
Website: www.signature.org.uk/scotland

See main entry above.

SNAP-CYMRU

Head Office
10 Coopers Yard
Curran Road, Cardiff CF10 5NB

Tel: 029 2038 4868 Helpline: 0845 120 3730
Email: headoffice@snapcymru.org

Fax: 029 2034 8998
Website: www.snapcymru.org

An all-Wales service for children and families, which provides: accurate information and impartial advice and support for parents, carers, and young people in relation to special educational needs and disability; disagreement resolution service; casework service; independent parental support service; advocacy for children and young people in receipt of services; training for parents, carers, young people; training for professionals in relation to SEN/disability. Has a Facebook page.

Spinal Injuries Association

SIA House
2 Trueman Place,
Oldbrook
Milton Keynes
MK6 2HH

Tel: 0845 678 6633 Adviceline: 0800 980 0501   Fax: 0845 070 6911
Email: sia@spinal.co.uk   Website: www.spinal.co.uk

Registered charity no.1054097 set up to provide services for people with spinal cord injuries. Has a Facebook page and you can follow them on Twitter.

The ACE Centre – North

Hollinwood Business Centre,
Albert Street
Hollinwood
Oldham OL8 3QL

Tel: 0161 358 0151   Fax: 0161 358 6152
Email: enquiries@ace-north.org.uk   Website: www.ace-north.org.uk

The centre offers independent advice and information, assessments and training in the use of assistive technology for individuals with physical and communication disabilities across the north of England. Registered charity no. 1089313.

The Alliance for Inclusive Education

336 Brixton Road
London SW9 7AA

Tel: 020 7737 6030
Email: info@allfie.org.uk   Website: www.allfie.org.uk

National network campaigning for the rights of disabled children in education.

The Association of National Specialist Colleges (NATSPEC)

c/o Derwen College
Oswestry
Shropshire SY11 3JA

Tel: 0117 923 2830
Email: chiefexecutive@natspec.org.uk   Website: www.natspec.org.uk

NATSPEC represents independent specialist colleges across England, Wales and Northern Ireland, providing for over 3000 learners with learning difficulties and/or disabilities, often with complex or additional needs. Most colleges offer residential provision. Member colleges support learners in their transition to adult life, participation in the community and where possible, employment. NATSPEC acts as a national voice for its member colleges and works in partnership with a range of other providers, agencies and organisations. You can contact colleges directly, via the website, or through your connexions/careers service.

The Brittle Bone Society

Grant-Paterson House
30 Guthrie Street
Dundee
DD1 5BS

Tel: 01382 204446   Fax: 01382 206771
Email: contact@brittlebone.org   Website: www.brittlebone.org

A UK registered charity (nos. 272100, SCO10951) providing support for people affected by Osteogenesis Imperfecta (OI). Has a Facebook page and you can follow them on Twitter.

The CALL Centre (Communications Aids for Language and Learning)

University of Edinburgh
Paterson's Land
Holyrood Road
Edinburgh
Midlothian
EH8 8AQ

Tel: 0131 651 6235   Fax: 0131 651 6234
Email: info@callcentrescotland.org.uk   Website: www.callcentrescotland.org.uk

The CALL Centre provides services and carries out research and development projects across Scotland for people, particularly children with severe communication disabilities, their families and people who work with them in augmentative communication techniques and technology, and specialised computer use.

The Disability Law Service

39-45 Cavell Street
London
E1 2BP

Tel: 020 7791 9800 Minicom: 020 7791 9801   Fax: 020 7791 9802
Email: advice@dls.org.uk   Website: www.dls.org.uk

The Disability Law Service (DLS) offers free, confidential legal advice to disabled people in the following areas: benefits; children; community care; consumer/contract; discrimination; further and higher education; and employment. In some cases they are able to offer legal representation. The Disability Law Service is made up of solicitors, advisers and trained volunteers who provide up-to-date, informed legal advice for disabled people, their families, enablers and carers. The advice they give is free, and the service offers complete confidentiality. They aim to offer a service that enables disabled people to access relevant information and clarify their rights. Registered charity no. 280805. Has a Facebook page and you can follow them on Twitter.

The Fragile X Society

Rood End House
6 Stortford Road
Great Dunmow,
Essex
CM6 1DA

Tel: 01371 875 100
Email: info@fragilex.org.uk

Fax: 01371 859 915
Website: www.fragilex.org.uk

The aims of The Fragile X Society are to provide support and comprehensive information to families whose children and adult relatives have fragile X syndrome, to raise awareness of fragile X and to encourage research. There is a link network of family contacts, national helplines for statementing, benefits and family support for epilepsy. They publish information booklets, leaflets, a publications list, video and three newsletters a year. There are also national conferences four times a year. Family membership (UK) is free. Welcomes associate membership from interested professionals. Registered charity no. 1127861. Has a Facebook page and you can follow them on Twitter.

The Guide Dogs for the Blind Association

Burghfield Common
Reading
Berkshire
RG7 3YG

Tel: 0118 983 5555
Email: guidedogs@guidedogs.org.uk

Fax: 0118 983 5433
Website: www.guidedogs.org.uk

The Guide Dogs for the Blind Association provides guide dogs, mobility and other rehabilitation services to blind and partially sighted people. Registered charity nos. 209617 and SCO38979. Has Facebook page and you can follow them on Twitter.

The Haemophilia Society

First Floor
Petersham House
57a Hatton Garden
London
EC1N 8JG

Tel: 020 7381 1020
Email: info@haemophilia.org.uk

Fax: 020 7405 4824 Helpline: 0800 018 6068
Website: www.haemophilia.org.uk

Founded in 1950, this registered charity (nos. 288260, SCO39732) has over 4000 members and a network throughout the UK providing information, advice and support services to sufferers of haemophilia, von Willebrand's and related bleeding disorders. You can follow them on Twitter.

The Hyperactive Children's Support Group (HACSG)

71 Whyke Lane
Chichester
Sussex
PO19 7PD

Tel: 01243 539966
Email: hacsg@hacsg.org.uk

Website: www.hacsg.org.uk

Support group. Will send information pack if you send a large SAE. Registered charity no. 277643.

The London Centre for Children with Cerebral Palsy

54 Muswell Hill
London
N10 3ST

Tel: 020 8444 7242
Email: info@cplondon.org.uk

Fax: 020 8444 7241
Website: www.cplondon.org.uk

Provides education for young children with cerebral palsy using the system of Conductive Education. Registered charity no. 1124524.

The Makaton Charity

Manor House
46 London Road
Blackwater
Camberley GU17 0AA

Tel: 01276 606760
Email: info@makaton.org

Fax: 01276 36725
Website: www.makaton.org

Makaton vocabulary is a language programme using speech, signs and symbols to provide basic means of communication and encourage language and literacy skills to develop in children and adults with communication and learning difficulties. Training workshops, courses and a variety of resource materials are available and there is a family support helpline too. Registered charity no. 1119819.

The Planned Environment Therapy Trust (PETT)

Archive and Study Centre
Church Lane
Toddington
Cheltenham
Gloucestershire GL54 5DQ

Tel: 01242 620125
Website: www.archive.pettrust.org.uk

Fax: 01242 620125

Founded to promote effective treatment for those with emotional and psychological disorders. Registered charity no. 248633.

The Social, Emotional and Behavioural Difficulties Association (SEBDA)

c/o Goldwyn School
Godinton Lane
Great Chart
Ashford
Kent
TN23 3BT

Tel: 01233 622958
Email: admin@sebda.org

Website: www.sebda.org

SEBDA exists to campaign on behalf of and to provide information, training and a support service to professionals who work with children and young people with social, emotional and behavioural difficulties. Registered charity no. 258730.

Please note: they do not provide any services to parents.

The Stroke Association

Stroke House
240 City Road
London EC1V 2PR

Tel: 020 7566 0300 Textphone: 020 7251 9096   Fax: 020 7490 2686
Email: info@stroke.org.uk   Website: www.stroke.org.uk

More than 250,000 people in the UK live with the disabilities caused by a stroke. The association's website provides information and advice for free. Registered charity nos. 211015, SCO37789, IOM945, NP0369 (Jersey). They have a Facebook page and you can follow them on Twitter.

The Thalidomide Society

Tel: 01462 438212
Email: info@thalsoc.demon.co.uk
Website: www.thalidomidesociety.co.uk

Registered charity no. 231708 created in 1962. Support group for impaired adults whose disabilities are a result of the drug Thalidomide.

Together for Short Lives

4th Floor
Bridge House
48-52 Baldwin Street
Bristol BS1 1QB

Tel: 0117 989 7820
Helpline: 0845 989 7820
Email: info@togetherforshortlives.org   Website: www.togetherforshortlives.org.uk

The new name for the Association for Children's Palliative Care (ACT). Helps families with children who have life-limiting or life threatening conditions. Has Facebook page.

Tourette's Action

Kings Court
91-93 High Street
Camberley
Surrey GU15 3RN

Tel: 01276 482903
Email: admin@tourettes-action.org.uk   Website: www.tourettes-action.org.uk

Registered charity no. 1003317 offering support and information about Tourette's. Has Facebook page and you can follow them on Twitter.

U Can Do IT

1 Taylors Yard
67 Alderbrook Road
London
SW12 8AD

Tel: 020 8673 3300   Fax: 020 8675 9571
Website: www.ucandoit.org.uk

U CAN DO IT is a London charity (no. 1070571) providing blind, deaf and physically disabled children and adults with the skills they need to utilise the internet. Tuition is one to one at home, by highly skilled police-vetted tutors (CRB level 2), with costs starting from £1 per lesson. You can follow them on Twitter.

WheelPower – British Wheelchair Sport

Stoke Mandeville Stadium
Guttman Road
Stoke Mandeville
Buckinghamshire HP21 9PP

Tel: 01296 395995   Fax: 01296 424171
Email: info@wheelpower.org.uk   Website: www.wheelpower.org.uk

The British Wheelchair Sports Foundation is the national organisation for wheelchair sport in the UK and exists to provide, promote and develop opportunities for men, women and children with disabilities to participate in recreational and competitive wheelchair sport. Registered charity no. 265498. Has a Facebook page and you can follow them on Twitter.

Young Minds

Suite 11
Baden Place
Crosby Row
London
SE1 1YW

Tel: 020 7089 5050   Fax: 020 7407 8887
Website: www.youngminds.org.uk   Email: ymenquiries@youngminds.org.uk

National charity (nos. 1016968, SCO39700) committed to improving the mental health of young people and children in the UK. Their website has advice, information and details of how you can help. They have a Facebook page and you can follow them on Twitter.

WEBSITES

UNITED KINGDOM

www.abilitynet.org.uk

Ability Net is a charity (no. 1067673) that provides impartial, expert advice about computer technology for disabled people. You can follow them on Twitter.

www.abilityonline.net

Disability information and news and views online. Registered charity no. 1089117.

www.apparelyzed.com

Spinal cord injury peer support – has a forum with useful links.

www.ukdpc.net

United Kingdom's Disabled People's Council – a national umbrella organisation set up by disabled people to represent their interests at a national level. Registered charity no. 1067873.

www.cae.org.uk

Centre for Accessible Environments – a registered charity (no. 1050820), which is the leading authority on providing a built enviroment that is accessible for everyone, including disabled people.

www.choicesandrights.org.uk

CRDC – Choices and Rights Disability Coalition. Run for and by disabled people in the Kingston upon Hull and East Riding of Yorkshire area. Registered charity no. 1106462.

www.amyandfriends.org

Website set up to support those families affected by Cockayne Syndrome in the UK. Registered charity no. 1119746.

www.deafcouncil.org.uk

UK Council on Deafness. Has interesting list of member websites.

www.disabilitynow.org.uk

Disability Now – award winning online newspaper for everyone with an interest in disability.

www.feapda.org

European Federation of Associations of teachers of the deaf.

www.focusondisability.org.uk

Focus on Disability – resource of general information regarding disability in the UK.

www.direct.gov.uk/disabledpeople

The UK government's web page for disabled people.

www.hafad.org.uk

HAFAD – Hammersmith and Fuham Action for Disability.

www.heartnsoul.co.uk

Heart 'n' Soul Music Theatre – a leading disability arts group. Has a Facebook page.

www.mugsy.org

National Autistic Society – Surrey branch. Website has pages dedicated to all areas of the UK as well as international pages.

Useful associations and websites

www.ncil.org.uk

National Centre for Independent Living. A resource on independent living and direct payments for disabled people and others working in the field. Registered charity no. 1113427.

www.qefd.org

Queen Elizabeth's Foundation – a national charity (no. 251051) supporting over 20,000 physically disabled people annually.

www.ssc.education.ed.ac.uk

Scottish Sensory Centre – for everyone who is involved in the education of children and young people with sensory impairment.

www.theark.org.uk

A registered charity (no. 1098204) set up to enhance the lives of people with multi-sensory impairment, learning difficulties and physical disabilities.

www.tuberous-sclerosis.org

Tuberous Sclerosis Association of Great Britain. Registered charity no. 1039549. Website provides information and support for people and families affected by TSC.

www.vitalise.org.uk

Vitalise (formerly The Winged Fellowship Trust) provides respite care for disabled children, adults and their carers. Registered charity no. 295072.

www.westminster.gov.uk/weldis

WELDIS – an online information resource of services in and around Westminster for older people, adults and children with disabilities and their carers.

www.youreable.com

Information, products and services for the disabled community including news, shopping, pen pals and discussion forums.

Maintained schools and colleges

BATH & NORTH EAST SOMERSET
CHILDREN'S SERVICES

Special Educational Needs, PO Box 25, Riverside, Temple Street, Keynsham, Bristol BS31 1DN
Tel: 01225 394306, *Fax:* 01225 394251

BATH

Fosse Way School
Longfellow Road, Midsomer Norton, BATH BA3 3AL
Tel: 01761 412198
Head: Mr David Gregory
Category: PH SLD SPLD ASD MLD MSI CLD (Coed 3-19)

The Link Centre
Frome Road, Odd Down, BATH BA2 5RF
Tel: 01225 832212
Head: Mr Colin Cattanach
Category: EBD (Coed 4-16)

Three Ways School
180 Frome Road, Odd Down, BATH BA2 5RF
Tel: 01225 838070
Head: Mrs Julie Dyer
Category: PH SLD SPLD ASD MLD MSI CLD (Coed 2-19)

BEDFORD BOROUGH COUNCIL
EDUCATION AUTHORITY

Borough Hall, Cauldwell Street, Bedford MK42 9AP
Tel: 01234 267422

BEDFORD

Grange School
Halsey Road, Kempston, BEDFORD, Bedfordshire MK42 8AU
Tel: 01234 407100
Head: Mr I Davidson
Category: ASD MLD (Coed 5-16)

Ridgeway Special School
Hill Rise, Kempston, BEDFORD MK42 7EB
Tel: 01234 402402
Head: Mr G Allard
Category: PD (Coed 2-19)

St Johns Special School & College
Austin Cannons, Kempston, BEDFORD MK42 8AA
Tel: 01234 345565
Head: Mr R Babbage
Category: SLD PMLD (Coed 2-19)

CENTRAL BEDFORDSHIRE COUNCIL

Priory House, Monks Walk, Chicksands, Shefford SG17 5TQ
Tel: 0300 300 8000

BIGGLESWADE

Ivel Valley Primary School
The Baulk, BIGGLESWADE, Bedfordshire SG18 0PT
Tel: 01767 601010
Head: Miss J Mudd
Category: SLD PMLD (Coed 3-19)

Ivel Valley Secondary School
Hitchmead Road, BIGGLESWADE, Bedfordshire SG18 0NL
Tel: 01767 601010
Head: Miss J Mudd
Category: SLD PMLD (Coed 3-19)

DUNSTABLE

The Chiltern Primary School
Beech Road, DUNSTABLE, Bedfordshire LU6 3LY
Tel: 01582 667106
Head: Mrs S Crosbie
Category: SLD PMLD

Weatherfield School
Brewers Hill Road, DUNSTABLE, Bedfordshire LU6 1AF
Tel: 01582 605632
Head: J Selmes
Category: MLD (7-16)

HOUGHTON REGIS

The Chiltern Secondary School
Parkside Drive, HOUGHTON REGIS, Bedfordshire LU5 5PX
Tel: 01582 866972
Head: Mrs S Crosbie
Category: SLD PMLD

LEIGHTON BUZZARD

Oak Bank Special School
Sandy Lane, LEIGHTON BUZZARD, Bedfordshire LU7 3BE
Tel: 01525 374559
Head: Mr P Cohen

WEST BERKSHIRE COUNCIL

SEN Team, West Street House, West Street, Newbury, Berkshire RG14 1BZ
Tel: 01635 519713

NEWBURY

The Castle School
Love Lane, Donnington, NEWBURY, Berkshire RG14 2JG
Tel: 01635 42976
Heads: Mr J Hewitt
Category: ASD SLD SPLD GLD PH (Coed 2-19)

READING

Brookfields Special School
Sage Road, Tilehurst, READING, Berkshire RG31 6SW
Tel: 0118 942 1382
Head: Mrs Jane Headland
Category: AUT MSI Complex Needs

BLACKBURN WITH DARWEN
BOROUGH COUNCIL, CHILDREN'S SERVICES DEPARTMENT

King William Street, Town Hall, Blackburn, Lancashire BB1 7DY
Tel: 01254 585585

BLACKBURN

Crosshill Special School
Shadsworth Road, BLACKBURN, Lancashire BB1 2HR
Tel: 01254 505700
Head: Mr Ian Maddison
Category: MLD

Newfield Special School
Old Bank Lane, Off Shadsworth Road,
BLACKBURN, Lancashire BB1 2PW
Tel: 01254 588600
Head: Mr Geoff Fitzpatrick
Category: Complex

BLACKPOOL
CHILDREN AND YOUNG PEOPLE'S DEPARTMENT

Children with Additional Needs Team,
Town Hall, Blackpool FY1 1AD
Tel: 01253 477477

BLACKPOOL

Highfurlong School
Blackpool Old Road, BLACKPOOL,
Lancashire FY3 7LR
Tel: 01253 392188
Head: Mr EV Jackson MA
Category: PH

Park School
158 Whitegate Drive, BLACKPOOL,
Lancashire FY3 9HF
Tel: 01253 764130
Head: Mr K Berry
Category: MLD CLD SEBD (Coed 4-16)

Woodlands Special School
Whitegate Drive, BLACKPOOL, Lancashire
FY3 9HF
Tel: 01253 316722
Head: Ms A Henderson
Category: SLD PMLD MSI (Coed 2-19)

BOURNEMOUTH
CHILDREN AND FAMILIES SERVICES

BOURNEMOUTH

Linwood School
Alma Road, BOURNEMOUTH, Dorset
BH9 1AJ
Tel: 01202 525107
Head: Mr S Brown
Category: ASD MLD SLD PMLD (Coed 3-18)

Tregonwell Academy
Petersfield Road, BOURNEMOUTH,
Dorset BH7 6QP
Tel: 01202 424361
Head: Mr Brian Hooper
Category: BESD (Coed 7-16)

BRACKNELL FOREST
CHILDREN, YOUNG PEOPLE AND LEARNING

Seymour House, 38 Broadway,
Bracknell, Berkshire RG12 1AU
Tel: 01344 354000, *Fax:* 01344 352000

BRACKNELL

Kennel Lane School
Kennel Lane, BRACKNELL, Berkshire
RG42 2EX
Tel: 01344 483872
Head: Miss A de Bunsen
Category: MLD SLD AUT PMLD

BRADFORD
DEPARTMENT OF CHILDREN'S SERVICES

Future House, Bolling Road, Bradford,
West Yorkshire BD4 7EB
Tel: 01274 385955

BRADFORD

Chellow Heights School
Thorn Lane, Bingley Road, BRADFORD,
West Yorkshire BD9 6AL
Tel: 01274 484242
Head: Ms S Haithwaite
Category: SLD PMLD ADS (Primary)

Delius School
Barkerend Road, BRADFORD, West
Yorkshire BD3 8QX
Tel: 01274 666472
Head: Ms S Joy
Category: SLD PMLD ASD (Primary)

Hazelbeck School
Wagon Lane, Bingley, BRADFORD, West
Yorkshire BD16 1EE
Tel: 01274 777107
Head: Ms S Pierce
Category: SLD PMLD ASD (Secondary)

High Park School
Netherlands Avenue, BRADFORD, West
Yorkshire BD6 1EA
Tel: 01274 696740
Head: Ms D Flavell
Category: ASD (Primary & Secondary)

Southfield School
Haycliffe Lane, BRADFORD, West
Yorkshire BD5 9ET
Tel: 01274 779662
Head: Mr D Wall
Category: SLD PMLD ASD (Secondary)

KEIGHLEY

Beechcliffe School
Green Head Road, KEIGHLEY, West
Yorkshire BD20 6ED
Tel: 01535 603041
Head: Mrs P Pearson
Category: SLD PMLD ASD (Secondary)

Phoenix School
Braithwaite Avenue, KEIGHLEY, West
Yorkshire BD22 6HZ
Tel: 01535 607038
Head: Mr M Harrison
Category: SLD PMLD ASD (Primary)

BRIGHTON & HOVE
CHILDREN'S SERVICES

SEN Team, PO Box 2503, King's House,
Grand Avenue, Hove, East Sussex
BN3 2SU
Tel: 01273 293552, *Fax:* 01273 293547

BRIGHTON

Alternative Centre for Education Queensdown Special School
Queensdown School Road, off Lewes
Road, BRIGHTON, East Sussex BN1 7LA
Tel: 01273 604472
Acting Head: Ms Lorraine Myles
Category: SEBD (Coed 5-16)

Cedar Centre
Lynchet Close, Hollingdean, BRIGHTON,
East Sussex BN1 7FP
Tel: 01273 558622
Head: Ms Chris Coleby
Category: MLD

Downs Park School
Foredown Road, Portslade, BRIGHTON,
East Sussex BN41 2FU
Tel: 01273 417448
Head: Ms Jackie Brooks
Category: ASD (Coed 5-16)

Downs View School
Warren Road, BRIGHTON, East Sussex
BN2 6BB
Tel: 01273 601680
Head: Mr Adrian Carver
Category: SLD ASD HI VIS (4-19)

Hillside Special School
Foredown Road, Portslade, BRIGHTON,
East Sussex BN41 2FU
Tel: 01273 416979
Head: Mr Bob Wall
Category: SLD

Patcham House School
Old London Road, Patcham, BRIGHTON,
East Sussex BN1 8XR
Tel: 01273 551028
Head: Mrs Kim Bolton
Category: PD Del ASP MLD SPLD (11-16)

BRISTOL
CHILDREN AND YOUNG PEOPLE'S SERVICES

City Hall, College Green, Bristol BS1 5TR
Tel: 0117 922 2000

BRISTOL

Briarwood Special School
Briar Way, Fishponds, BRISTOL BS16 4EA
Tel: 0117 353 2651
Head: Mr David Hussey
Category: SLD MLD AUT (Coed 3-19)

Bristol Gateway School
Long Cross, Lawrence Weston, BRISTOL
BS11 0QA
Tel: 0117 377 2275
Head: Ms Kaye Palmer-Green
Category: SEBD (Coed 10-16)

Claremont School
Henleaze Park, Henleaze, BRISTOL
BS9 4LR
Tel: 0117 353 3622
Head: Ms Alison Ewins
Category: PD SLD (Coed 3-19)

Elmfield School for Deaf Children
Greystoke Avenue, Westbury-on-Trym,
BRISTOL BS10 6AY
Tel: 0117 903 0366
Head: Mrs Kate Murray
Category: D (Coed 5-16)

Kingsweston Special School
Napier Miles Road, Kingsweston,
BRISTOL BS11 0UT
Tel: 0117 903 0400
Head: Mr Neil Galloway
Category: MLD SLD AUT (Coed 3-19)

Knowle DGE
Leinster Avenue, Knowle, BRISTOL
BS4 1NN
Tel: 0117 353 2011
Head: Mr Peter Evans
Category: BESD SEBD Complex Needs
(Coed 5-16)

New Fosseway Special School
Williams Jessop Way, Hartcliffe, BRISTOL
BS13 0RL
Tel: 0117 903 0220
Head: Mrs Shan Wynne-Jones
Category: SPLD (Coed 6-19)

Notton House Special School
28 Notton, Lacock, BRISTOL SN15 2NF
Tel: 01249 730407
Head: Mr Bobby Evans
Category: SEBD ASP (Boys 9-16)

Woodstock Special School
Rectory Gardens, Henbury, BRISTOL
BS10 7AH
Tel: 0117 377 2175
Head: Ms Hilary Harris
Category: SEBD (Primary)

BUCKINGHAMSHIRE
LOCAL AUTHORITY, ACHIEVEMENT & LEARNING

County Hall, Walton Street, Aylesbury,
Buckinghamshire HP20 1UA
Tel: 0845 3708090

AMERSHAM

Stony Dean School
Orchard End Avenue, Off Pineapple Road,
AMERSHAM, Buckinghamshire HP7 9JW
Tel: 01494 762538
Head: Mrs P Dichler
Category: Language & Communication
(Coed Secondary)

AYLESBURY

Booker Park School
Stoke Leys Close, AYLESBURY,
Buckinghamshire HP21 9ET
Tel: 01296 427221
Head: Ms A Parkin
Category: MLD SLD ASD (Coed Primary)

Pebble Brook School
Churchill Avenue, AYLESBURY,
Buckinghamshire HP21 8LZ
Tel: 01296 415761/2
Head: Mr David Miller
Category: MLD SLC (Coed Secondary
Day/boarding)

Stocklake Park Community School
Stocklake, AYLESBURY, Buckinghamshire
HP20 1DP
Tel: 01296 423507
Head: Ms A Parkin
Category: SLD (Coed Secondary)

BEACONSFIELD

Alfriston School
Penn Road, BEACONSFIELD,
Buckinghamshire HP9 2TS
Tel: 01494 673740
Head: Mrs Jinna Male
Category: MLD (Girls Secondary
Day/boarding)

CHESHAM

Heritage House School
Cameron Road, CHESHAM,
Buckinghamshire HP5 3BP
Tel: 01494 771445
Head: Mr J Boylan
Category: SLD (Coed Primary/Secondary)

GREAT MISSENDEN

Chiltern Way Federation - Prestwood Campus
Nairdwood Lane, Prestwood, GREAT MISSENDEN, Buckinghamshire HP16 0QQ
Tel: 01494 863514
Head: Mr I McCaul
Category: BESD (Boys Boarding)

HIGH WYCOMBE

Chiltern Gate School
Verney Avenue, HIGH WYCOMBE,
Buckinghamshire HP12 3NE
Tel: 01494 532621/2
Head: Mr John Headland
Category: MLD EBD ASD SLD
Communication difficulties (Coed Day/boarding 4-11)

Maplewood School
Faulkner Way, Downley, HIGH WYCOMBE,
Buckinghamshire HP13 5HB
Tel: 01494 525728
Head: Mr J Rumble
Category: SLD (Coed Primary/Secondary 5-18)

Westfield School
Highfield Road, Bourne End, HIGH
WYCOMBE, Buckinghamshire SL8 5BE
Tel: 01628 533125
Head: Mr G Allen
Category: BESD (Coed Primary)

WENDOVER

Chiltern Way Federation - Wendover Campus
Church Lane, WENDOVER,
Buckinghamshire HP22 6NL
Tel: 01296 622157
Head: Mr I McCaul
Category: BESD (Boys Secondary Boarding)

WINSLOW

Furze Down School
Verney Road, WINSLOW,
Buckinghamshire MK18 3BL
Tel: 01296 713385
Head: Mrs S Collins
Category: A Range Of Needs (Coed Primary/Secondary)

CAMBRIDGESHIRE
CHILDREN & YOUNG PEOPLE'S SERVICES

Shire Hall, Castle Hill, Cambridge
CB3 0AP
Tel: 0345 045 5200

CAMBRIDGE

Castle School
Courtney Way, CAMBRIDGE CB4 2EE
Tel: 01223 442400
Head: Ms Carol McCarthy
Category: PMLD SLD MLD (Coed 2-19)

Granta School
Cambridge Road, Linton, CAMBRIDGE
CB21 4JB
Tel: 01223 896890
Head: Mrs Lucie Calow
Category: ASD PMLD SLD MLD (Coed 2-19)

Trinity School
8 Station Road, Foxton, CAMBRIDGE,
Cambridgeshire CB22 6SA
Tel: 01223 712995
Head: Mr Jim Simon

COTTENHAM

The Centre School
High Street, COTTENHAM,
Cambridgeshire CB24 8UA
Tel: 01954 288789
Headteacher/Principal: Mr S Ellison & Mrs S Raven
Category: (Coed 11-16)

ELY

Highfield Special School
Downham Road, ELY, Cambridgeshire
CB6 1BD
Tel: 01353 662085
Head: Mr Simon Bainbridge
Category: PMLD SLD MLD ASD PD VIS (Coed 2-19)

The Harbour School
Station Road, Wilburton, ELY,
Cambridgeshire CB6 3RR
Tel: 01353 740229
Head: Mrs Mary Rayner
Category: ADD EBD MLD SEBN (Coed 5-17)

EYNESBURY

Samuel Pepys School
Cromwell Road, EYNESBURY,
Cambridgeshire PE19 2EZ
Tel: 01480 375012
Head: Ms Mandy Green
Category: ASD PMLD SLD Complex needs (Coed 2-19)

HUNTINGDON

Spring Common School
American Lane, HUNTINGDON,
Cambridgeshire PE29 1TQ
Tel: 01480 377403
Head: Ms Kim Taylor
Category: PMLD SLD MLD ASD EBD (Coed 2-19)

WISBECH

Meadowgate School
Meadowgate Lane, WISBECH,
Cambridgeshire PE13 2JH
Tel: 01945 461836
Head: Mrs Jackie McPherson
Category: SLD MLD (Coed 2-19)

CHESHIRE EAST
BOROUGH COUNCIL

Children, Families and Adults,
Westfields, Middlewich Road, Sandbach
CW11 1HZ
Tel: 0300 123 55 00

CREWE

Adelaide School
Adelaide Street, CREWE, Cheshire
CW1 3DT
Tel: 01270 685151
Head: Mr L Willday
Category: BESD (Coed 11-16)

Springfield School
Crewe Green Road, CREWE, Cheshire
CW1 5HS
Tel: 01270 685446
Head: Mr M Swaine
Category: SLD (Coed 2-19)

KNUTSFORD

St John's Wood Community School
Longridge, KNUTSFORD, Cheshire
WA16 8PA
Tel: 01625 383045
Head: Mrs S Clayton
Category: BESD (Coed Day 11-16)

MACCLESFIELD

Park Lane School
Park Lane, MACCLESFIELD, Cheshire
SK11 8JR
Tel: 01625 384040
Head: Mrs Lorraine Warmer
Category: SLD (Coed Day 2-19)

CHESHIRE WEST & CHESTER
COUNCIL

58 Nicholas Street, Chester CH1 2NP
Tel: 0300 123 8 123

CHESTER

Dee Banks School
Sandy Lane, Great Boughton, CHESTER,
Cheshire CH3 5UX
Tel: 01244 981031
Head: Rev R P Elliott
Category: ASD SLD PMLD (Coed Day 2-19)

Dorin Park School
Wealstone Lane, Upton, CHESTER,
Cheshire CH2 1HP
Tel: 01244 981193
Head: Miss Annie Hinchcliffe
Category: PD Complex needs (Coed Day 2-19)

ELLESMERE PORT

Capenhurst Grange School
Chester Road, Great Sutton, ELLESMERE
PORT, Cheshire CH66 2NA
Tel: 0151 338 2141
Head: Mrs S Myers-Whittaker
Category: BESD (Coed 11-16)

Hinderton School
Capenhurst Lane, Whitby, ELLESMERE
PORT, Cheshire CH65 7AQ
Tel: 0151 338 2200
Head: Mr L McCallion
Category: ASD with complex learning
needs (Coed Day 4-11)

NORTHWICH

Cloughwood School
Stones Manor Lane, Hartford,
NORTHWICH, Cheshire CW8 1NU
Tel: 01606 76671
Head: Mr Adrian Larkin
Category: BESD (Boys Day/Residential
11-16)

Greenbank Residential School
Greenbank Lane, Hartford, NORTHWICH,
Cheshire CW8 1LD
Tel: 01606 288028
Head: Mrs Chris Brennan
Category: ASD MLD (Coed
Day/Residential 11-19)

Rosebank School
Townfield Lane, Barnton, NORTHWICH,
Cheshire CW8 4PQ
Tel: 01606 74975
Head: Mrs Judith McGuiness
Category: ASD with complex learning
needs (Coed Day 2-11)

The Russett School
Middlehurst Avenue, Weaverham,
NORTHWICH, Cheshire CW8 3BW
Tel: 01606 853005
Head: Mrs Catherine Lewis
Category: SLD PMLD MSI (Coed Day 2-19)

WINSFORD

Hebden Green Community School
Woodford Lane West, WINSFORD,
Cheshire CW7 4EJ
Tel: 01606 594221
Head: Mr A W Farren
Category: PD Complex needs (Coed
Day/Residential 2-19)

Oaklands School
Montgomery Way, WINSFORD, Cheshire
CW7 1NU
Tel: 01606 551048
Head: Mr K D Boyle
Category: HI MLD SP&LD (Coed Day 11-16)

CORNWALL
CHILDREN, SCHOOLS AND FAMILIES

County Hall, Treyew Road, Truro,
Cornwall TR1 3AY
Tel: 0300 1234 101

PENZANCE

Nancealverne School
Madron Road, PENZANCE, Cornwall
TR20 8TP
Tel: 01736 365039
Head: Mrs Fiona Flindall
Category: SLD PMLD (Coed 2-19)

REDRUTH

Curnow School
Drump Road, REDRUTH, Cornwall
TR15 1LU
Tel: 01209 215432
Head: Dr R Coburn
Category: PMLD SLD (Coed 2-19)

ST AUSTELL

Doubletrees School
St Blazey Gate, St Blazey, Par, ST AUSTELL, Cornwall PL24 2DS
Tel: 01726 812757
Head: Ms Kim Robertson
Category: SLD PMLD (Coed 2-19)

TRURO

Pencalenick School
St Clement, TRURO, Cornwall TR1 1TE
Tel: 01872 520385
Head: Mr A Barnett
Category: SCLD (Coed 11-16)

CUMBRIA
CHILDREN'S SERVICES

Education Offices, 5 Portland Square, Carlisle, Cumbria CA1 1PU
Tel: 01228 226877

BARROW IN FURNESS

George Hastwell School
Moor Tarn Lane, Walney, BARROW IN FURNESS, Cumbria LA14 3LW
Tel: 01229 475253
Head: Mr B J Gummett
Category: SLD PMLD

CARLISLE

James Rennie School
California Road, Kingstown, CARLISLE, Cumbria CA3 0BX
Tel: 01228 554280
Head: Kris Williams
Category: SLD PMLD

KENDAL

Sandgate School
Sandylands Road, KENDAL, Cumbria LA9 6JG
Tel: 01539 792100
Head: Ms Joyce Fletcher
Category: SLD PMLD

ULVERSTON

Sandside Lodge School
Sandside Road, ULVERSTON, Cumbria LA12 9EF
Tel: 01229 588825
Head: Ms Susan Gill
Category: SLD PMLD

WHITEHAVEN

Mayfield School
Moresby Road, Hensingham, WHITEHAVEN, Cumbria CA28 8TU
Tel: 01946 691253
Head: Ms L Brownrigg
Category: SLD PMLD

DERBYSHIRE
CHILDREN & YOUNGER ADULTS

Special Needs Section, County Hall, Matlock, Derbyshire DE4 3AG
Tel: 01629 533190

ALFRETON

Alfreton Park Community Special School
Alfreton Park, ALFRETON, Derbyshire DE55 7AL
Tel: 01773 832019
Head: Mrs R MacKenzie
Category: SLD (2-19)

Swanwick School and Sports College
Hayes Lane, Swanwick, ALFRETON, Derbyshire DE55 1AR
Tel: 01773 602198
Head: Christopher Greenhough
Category: MLD (5-16)

BELPER

Holbrook Centre for Autism
Port Way, Holbrook, BELPER, Derbyshire DE56 0TE
Tel: 01332 880208
Head: Julian Scholefield
Category: AUT (5-19)

BUXTON

Peak School
Buxton Road, Chinley, High Peak, BUXTON, Derbyshire SK23 6ES
Tel: 01663 750324
Head: Mrs L Scowcroft
Category: SLD (2-19)

CHESTERFIELD

Ashgate Croft School
Ashgate Road, CHESTERFIELD, Derbyshire S40 4BN
Tel: 01246 275111
Head: Mr M Meaton
Category: MLD SLD (2-19)

Holly House School
Church Street North, Old Whittington, CHESTERFIELD, Derbyshire S41 9QR
Tel: 01246 450530
Head: Mr P Brandt
Category: EBD (7-14)

ILKESTON

Bennerley Fields Specialist Speech and Language College
Stratford Street, ILKESTON, Derbyshire DE7 8QZ
Tel: 0115 9326374
Head: Ms Debbie Gerring
Category: MLD (2-16)

LONG EATON

Brackenfield School and Specialist College of Cognition and Learning
Bracken Road, LONG EATON NG10 4DA
Tel: 0115 973 3710
Acting Head: Ms D Coombs
Category: MLD (5-16)

Stanton Vale School
Thoresby Road, LONG EATON NG10 3NP
Tel: 0115 972 9769
Head: Mr Chris White
Category: PMLD SLD (2-19)

SHIREBROOK

Stubbin Wood School
Burlington Avenue, Langwith Junction, SHIREBROOK, Derbyshire NG20 8QF
Tel: 01623 742795
Head: Lee Floyd
Category: MLD SLD (2-19)

DERBY CITY
EDUCATION & LEARNING

Children & Young People's Services, Middleton House, 27 St Mary's Gate, Derby, Derbyshire DE1 3NS
Tel: 01332 716924

DERBY

Ivy House School
Moorway Lane, Littleover, DERBY DE23 7FS
Tel: 01332 777920
Head: Mrs P Sillitoe
Category: SLD PMLD (Coed 2-19)

Kingsmead School
Bridge Street, DERBY DE1 3LB
Tel: 01332 715 970
Head: Ms Sue Bradley
Category: EBD (Coed 11-16)

St Andrew's School
St Andrew's View, Breadsall Hilltop, DERBY DE21 4EW
Tel: 01332 832746
Head: Mr P Harrison
Category: SLD (Coed 11-19)

St Clare's School
Rough Heanor Road, Mickleover, DERBY DE3 9AZ
Tel: 01332 511757
Head: Ms Carmel McKenna
Category: MLD SP&LD AUT PD SLD (Coed 11-16)

St Giles' School
Hampshire Road, Chaddesden, DERBY DE21 6BT
Tel: 01332 343039
Head: Ms Pamela Thomas
Category: SLD AUT (Coed 4-11)

St Martin's School
Wisgreaves Road, Alvaston, DERBY DE24 8RQ
Tel: 01332 571151
Head: Mr Gary Dodds
Category: MLD AUT EBD SLD (Coed 11-16)

DEVON
CHILDREN & YOUNG PEOPLE'S SERVICES

County Special Education Team, One Capital Court, Bittern Road, Sowton, Exeter, Devon EX2 7FW
Tel: 01392 383913, *Fax:* 01392 383972

BARNSTAPLE

Marland School (Day)
Springfield Court, Brannam Crescent, Roundswell Business Park, BARNSTAPLE, Devon EX31 3TD
Tel: 01271 384100
Head: Mr Keith Bennett
Category: SEBD (10-16)

Pathfield School
Abbey Road, Pilton, BARNSTAPLE, Devon EX31 1JU
Tel: 01271 342423
Head: Mrs Claire May
Category: SLD PMLD (3-19)

The Lampard Community School
St John's Lane, BARNSTAPLE, Devon EX32 9DD
Tel: 01271 345416
Head: Mrs Karen Rogers
Category: Complex and difficulties with communication and interaction (including SLCN and/or ASC) (7-16)

DAWLISH

Oaklands Park School
John Nash Drive, DAWLISH, Devon EX7 9SF
Tel: 01626 862363
Head: Mr Robert Pugh
Category: SLD ASC PMLD (Day/boarding 3-19)

Ratcliffe School
John Nash Drive, DAWLISH, Devon EX7 9RZ
Tel: 01626 862939
Head: Mrs Cherie White
Category: BESD (8-16)

EXETER

Barley Lane School
Barley Lane, St Thomas, EXETER, Devon EX4 1TA
Tel: 01392 430774
Head: Mr Michael MacCourt
Category: BESD (10-16)

Ellen Tinkham School
Hollow Lane, EXETER, Devon EX1 3RW
Tel: 01392 467168
Head: Mrs Jacqueline Warne
Category: SLD PMLD (3-19)

Southbrook School
Bishop Westall Road, EXETER, Devon EX2 6JB
Tel: 01392 258373
Head: Mrs Bronwen Caschere
Category: MLD ASC (11-16)

HONITON

Mill Water Community School
Honiton Bottom Road, HONITON, Devon EX14 2ER
Tel: 01404 43454
Head: Mr Alan Sheppard
Category: SLD PMLD (3-19)

TORRINGTON

Marland School (Residential)
Peters Marland, TORRINGTON, Devon EX38 8QQ
Tel: 01805 601324
Head: Mr Keith Bennett
Category: SEBD (10-16)

TOTNES

Bidwell Brook School
Shinner's Bridge, Dartington, TOTNES, Devon TQ9 6JU
Tel: 01803 864120
Acting Head: Mrs Jacqueline Warne
Category: SLD PMLD (3-19)

DORSET
COUNTY COUNCIL

Children's Services, County Hall,
Dorchester DT1 1XJ
Tel: 01305 224888, *Fax:* 01305 224547

BEAMINSTER

Mountjoy School
Tunnel Road, BEAMINSTER, Dorset
DT8 3HB
Tel: 01308 861155
Head: Mr J Franzen
Category: ASD SLD PMLD Complex (2-19)

STURMINSTER NEWTON

Yewstock School
Honeymead Lane, STURMINSTER
NEWTON, Dorset DT10 1EW
Tel: 01258 472796
Head: Mr S Kretz
Category: ASD MLD/Comlex PMLD SLD
(2-19)

WEYMOUTH

Westfield Arts College
Littlemoor Road, Preston, WEYMOUTH,
Dorset DT3 6AA
Tel: 01305 833518
Head: Mr A Penman
Category: MLD/Complex ASD (3-16)

Wyvern School
Dorchester Road, WEYMOUTH, Dorset
DT3 5AL
Tel: 01305 817917
Head: Mrs S Hoxey
Category: ASD PMLD SLD Complex (2-19)

WIMBORNE

Beaucroft Foundation School
Wimborne Road, Colehill, WIMBORNE,
Dorset BH21 2SS
Tel: 01202 886083
Head: Mr P McGill
Category: MLD/Complex ASD (4-16)

DURHAM
COUNTY COUNCIL

Children and Adult Services, County
Hall, Durham, County Durham DH1 5UJ
Tel: 0300 026 0000, *Fax:* 0191 386 0487

BISHOP AUCKLAND

Evergreen School
Warwick Road, BISHOP AUCKLAND,
Durham DL14 6LS
Tel: 01388 459721
Head: Mrs T A Hutchison
Category: MLD SLD PMLD AUT (2-11)

CONSETT

Villa Real School
Villa Real Road, CONSETT, Durham
DH8 6BH
Tel: 01207 503651
Head: Mrs G Stringer
Category: SLD PMLD AUT (2-19)

DURHAM

**Durham Trinity School and Sports
College**
Aykley Heads, DURHAM DH1 5TS
Tel: 0191 3864612
Head: Mrs J Connolly
Category: MLD SLD PMLD AUT (2-19)

FERRYHILL

Windlestone School
Chilton, FERRYHILL, Durham DL17 0HP
Tel: 01388 720337
Head: Mr T Bennett
Category: SEBD (11-16)

NEWTON AYCLIFFE

Walworth School
Bluebell Way, NEWTON AYCLIFFE,
Durham DL5 7LP
Tel: 01325 300194
Head: Mr P Wallbanks
Category: SEBD (4-11)

PETERLEE

Glendene Arts Academy
Crawlaw Road, Easington Colliery,
PETERLEE, Durham SR8 3LP
Tel: 0191 527 0304
Head: Mr E Baker
Category: MLD SLD PMLD AUT (2-19)

SHERBURN

Elemore Hall School
Littletown, SHERBURN, Durham
DH6 1QD
Tel: 0191 372 0275
Head: Mr R J Royle
Category: SEBD (11-16)

SPENNYMOOR

The Meadows
Whitworth Lane, SPENNYMOOR, Durham
DL16 7QW
Tel: 01388 811178
Head: Mrs S M Cook
Category: SEBD (11-16)

The Oaks Secondary School
Rock Road, SPENNYMOOR, Durham
DL16 7DB
Tel: 01388 827380
Head: Mrs A English
Category: MLD SLD PMLD AUT (11-19)

STANLEY

Hare Law School
Hare Law, STANLEY, Durham DH9 8DT
Tel: 01207 234547
Head: Mrs M Collins
Category: MLD SLD AUT (5-16)

ESSEX
ESSEX PARENT PARTNERSHIP SERVICE

County Hall, Chelmsford, Essex CM1 1QH
Tel: 01245 436036

BASILDON

Castledon School
Bromfords Drive, Wickford, BASILDON,
Essex SS12 0PW
Tel: 01268 761252
Head: Mrs C Clift
Category: ASD MLD (5-16)

BENFLEET

Cedar Hall School
Hart Road, Thundersley, BENFLEET, Essex
SS7 3UQ
Tel: 01268 774723
Head: Mr P Whelan
Category: MLD (4-16)

Glenwood School
Rushbottom Lane, New Thundersley,
BENFLEET, Essex SS7 4LW
Tel: 01268 792575
Head: Mrs J Salter
Category: SLD (3-19)

BRAINTREE

The Edith Borthwick School
Fennes Road, Church Street, BRAINTREE,
Essex CM7 5LA
Tel: 01376 529300
Head: Mr Ian Boatman
Category: ASD MLD SLD (3-19)

BRENTWOOD

The Endeavour School
Hogarth Avenue, BRENTWOOD, Essex
CM15 8BE
Tel: 01277 217330
Head: Mr M Southgate
Category: MLD (5-16)

CHIGWELL

Wells Park School
School Lane, Lambourne Road,
CHIGWELL, Essex IG7 6NN
Tel: 020 8502 6442
Head: Miss S Wraw
Category: BESD (5-12)

CLACTON ON SEA

Shorefields School
Ogilvie House, 114 Holland Road,
CLACTON ON SEA, Essex CO15 6HF
Tel: 01255 424412
Head: Mrs J Hodges
Category: ASD MLD SLD (3-19)

COLCHESTER

Kingswode Hoe School
Sussex Road, COLCHESTER, Essex
CO3 3QJ
Tel: 01206 576408
Head: Mrs E Drake
Category: MLD (5-16)

Lexden Springs School
Halstead Road, Lexden, COLCHESTER,
Essex CO3 9AB
Tel: 01206 563321
Head: Mrs J Wood
Category: SLD (3-19)

Market Field School
School Road, Elmstead Market,
COLCHESTER, Essex CO7 7ET
Tel: 01206 825195
Head: Mr G Smith
Category: ASD MLD SLD (4-16)

Ramsden Hall School
School Road, Langham, COLCHESTER,
Essex CO4 5PA
Tel: 01206 271571
Head: Mr S Grant
Category: BESD (Boys 11-16)

HARLOW

Harlow Fields School & College
Tendring Road, HARLOW, Essex
CM18 6RN
Tel: 01279 423670
Head: Ms Sue Davis
Category: ASD MLD SLD (3-19)

LOUGHTON

Oak View School
Whitehills Road, LOUGHTON, Essex
IG10 1TS
Tel: 020 8508 4293
Head: Mrs S Winter
Category: MLD SLD (3-19)

WITHAM

Southview School
Conrad Road, WITHAM, Essex CM8 2TA
Tel: 01376 503505
Head: Mr Paul Ellis
Category: PD (3-19)

GLOUCESTERSHIRE
CHILDREN & YOUNG PEOPLE'S SERVICES

Shire Hall, Westgate Street, Gloucester
GL1 2TG
Tel: 01452 425000

CHELTENHAM

Battledown Centre for Children and Families
Harp Hill, Battledown, CHELTENHAM,
Gloucestershire GL52 6PZ
Tel: 01242 525472
Head: Ms Jane Cummins
Category: All (0-7)

Belmont Special School
Warden Hill Road, CHELTENHAM,
Gloucestershire GL51 3AT
Tel: 01242 216180
Head: Dr Anne Maddison
Category: CLD MLD ASD (Coed 4-16)

Bettridge School
Warden Hill Road, CHELTENHAM,
Gloucestershire GL51 3AT
Tel: 01242 514934
Head: Ms Mandy Roberts
Category: SLD PMLD (2-19)

CIRENCESTER

Paternoster School
Watermoor Road, CIRENCESTER,
Gloucestershire GL7 1JR
Tel: 01285 652480
Head: Ms Julie Mantell
Category: SLD PMLD (2-17)

COLEFORD

Heart of the Forest Community School
Speech House Road, Coalway,
COLEFORD, Gloucestershire GL16 7EJ
Tel: 01594 822175
Head: Mrs Melissa Bradshaw
Category: SLD PMLD (Coed 3-19)

FAIRFORD

Coln House School
Horcott Road, FAIRFORD, Gloucestershire
GL7 4DB
Tel: 01285 712308
Deputy Head: Mr Lewis
Category: BESD (Coed Day/boarding 9-16)

GLOUCESTER

The Milestone School
Longford Lane, GLOUCESTER,
Gloucestershire GL2 9EU
Tel: 01452 874000
Head: Mrs Lyn Dance
Category: MLD SLD PMLD CLD (Coed 2-16)

STONEHOUSE

The Shrubberies School
Oldends Lane, STONEHOUSE,
Gloucestershire GL10 2DG
Tel: 01453 822155
Head: Ms Jane Jones
Category: SLD PMLD (Coed 2-19)

TEWKESBURY

Alderman Knight School
Ashchurch Road, TEWKESBURY,
Gloucestershire GL20 8JJ
Tel: 01684 295639
Head: Mrs Clare Steel
Category: CLD MLD ASD SLD PMLD (4-16)

SOUTH GLOUCESTERSHIRE COUNCIL

Special Educational Needs Section,
Department for Children, Adults and
Health, PO Box 2083, Council Offices,
Castle Street, Thornbury, South
Gloucestershire BS35 9BQ
Tel: 01454 863301 or 01454 863173

KINGSWOOD

New Horizons Learning Centre
Mulberry Drive, KINGSWOOD, South
Gloucestershire BS15 4ED
Tel: 01454 865340
Head: Mrs T Craig
Category: BESD

THORNBURY

New Siblands School
Easton Hill Road, THORNBURY, South
Gloucestershire BS35 2JU
Tel: 01454 866754
Head: Mr A Buckton
Category: SLD

WARMLEY

Warmley Park School
Tower Road North, WARMLEY, South
Gloucestershire BS30 8XL
Tel: 01454 867272
Head: Mr S Morris
Category: SLD (Day 3 -19)

YATE

Culverhill School
Kelston Close, YATE, South
Gloucestershire BS37 8SZ
Tel: 01454 866930
Head: Ms N Jones
Category: CLD (Day 7 - 16)

HALTON BOROUGH COUNCIL

Halton Parent Partnership, Rutland
House, Halton Lea, Runcorn, Cheshire
WA7 2GW
Tel: 0151 511 7733

RUNCORN

Cavendish School
Lincoln Close, RUNCORN, Cheshire
WA7 4YX
Tel: 01928 561706
Head: Mrs C Dickinson
Category: SLD (11-19)

WIDNES

Ashley School
Cawfield Avenue, WIDNES, Cheshire
WA8 7HG
Tel: 0151 424 4892
Head: Mrs Linda King
Category: MLD Complex emotional needs
(11-16)

Brookfields School
Moorfield Road, WIDNES, Cheshire
WA8 3JA
Tel: 0151 424 4329
Head: Mr Andreas Chryssafi
Category: SLD (2-11)

Chesnut Lodge School
Green Lane, WIDNES, Cheshire WA8 7HF
Tel: 0151 424 0679
Head: Mrs Heather Austin
Category: PH (2-16)

HAMPSHIRE COUNTY COUNCIL

Children's Services Department,
Elizabeth II Court, The Castle,
Winchester, Hampshire SO23 8UG
Tel: 0845 603 5620

ANDOVER

Icknield School
River Way, ANDOVER, Hampshire
SP11 6LT
Tel: 01264 365297
Head: Sharon Ghiacy
Category: SLD (Coed 2-19)

Norman Gate School
Vigo Road, ANDOVER, Hampshire
SP10 1JZ
Tel: 01264 323423
Head: Christine Gayler
Category: MLD ASD (Coed 2-11)

The Mark Way School
Batchelors Barn Road, ANDOVER,
Hampshire SP10 1HR
Tel: 01264 351835
Head: Sonia Longstaff
Category: MLD ASD (Coed 11-16)

Wolverdene Special School
22 Love Lane, ANDOVER, Hampshire
SP10 2AF
Tel: 01264 362350
Head: Paul Van Walwyk
Category: BESD (Coed 5-11)

BASINGSTOKE

Dove House School
Sutton Road, BASINGSTOKE, Hampshire
RG21 5SU
Tel: 01256 351555
Head: Colin House
Category: MLD ASD (Coed 11-16)

Limington House School
St Andrews Road, BASINGSTOKE,
Hampshire RG22 6PS
Tel: 01256 322148
Head: Petra Smillie
Category: SLD (Coed 2-19)

Maple Ridge School
Maple Crescent, BASINGSTOKE,
Hampshire RG21 5SX
Tel: 01256 323639
Head: Deborah Gooderham
Category: MLD ASD (Coed 4-11)

Saxon Wood School
Rooksdown, Barron Place,
BASINGSTOKE, Hampshire RG24 9NH
Tel: 01256 356635
Head: Richard Parratt
Category: PD (Coed 2-11)

BORDON

Hollywater School
Mill Chase Road, BORDON, Hampshire
GU35 0HA
Tel: 01420 474396
Head: Steph Clancy
Category: LD (Coed 2-19)

CHANDLERS FORD

Lakeside School
Winchester Road, CHANDLERS FORD,
Hampshire SO53 2DW
Tel: 023 8026 6633
Head: Gareth Evans
Category: BESD (Boys 11-16)

FAREHAM

Baycroft School
Gosport Road, Stubbington, FAREHAM,
Hampshire PO14 2AE
Tel: 01329 664151
Head: Chris Toner
Category: MLD ASD (Coed 11-16)

Heathfield School
Oldbury Way, FAREHAM, Hampshire
PO14 3BN
Tel: 01329 845150
Head: Nicky Cunningham
Category: MLD ASD PD (Coed 2-11)

St Francis Special School
Patchway Drive, Oldbury Way, FAREHAM,
Hampshire PO14 3BN
Tel: 01329 845730
Head: Steve Hollinghurst
Category: SLD (Coed 2-19)

FARNBOROUGH

Henry Tyndale School
Ship Lane, FARNBOROUGH, Hampshire
GU14 8BX
Tel: 01252 544577
Head: Rob Thompson
Category: LD ASD (Coed 2-19)

The Samuel Cody Specialist Sports College
Ballantyne Rode, Cove, FARNBOROUGH,
Hampshire GU14 6SS
Tel: 01252 514194
Head: Anna Dawson
Category: MLD ASD (Coed 11-16)

HAVANT

Prospect School
Freeley Road, HAVANT, Hampshire
PO9 4AQ
Tel: 023 9248 5150
Head: Marijke Miles
Category: BESD (Boys 11-16)

PORTSMOUTH

Glenwood School
Washington Road, Emsworth,
PORTSMOUTH, Hampshire PO10 7NN
Tel: 01243 373120
Head: Philip Johnson
Category: MLD ASD (Coed 11-16)

SOUTHAMPTON

Forest Park Primary School
Ringwood Road, Totton, SOUTHAMPTON,
Hampshire SO40 8EB
Tel: 023 8086 4949
Head: Nicola Dando
Category: LD (Coed 2-11)

Forest Park Secondary School
Commercial Road, Totton,
SOUTHAMPTON, Hampshire SO40 3AF
Tel: 023 8086 4211
Head: Nicola Dando
Category: LD (Coed 11-19)

Lord Wilson School
Montiefiore Drive, Sarisbury Green,
SOUTHAMPTON, Hampshire SO31 7NL
Tel: 01489 582684
Head: Stuart Parker-Tyreman
Category: BESD (Male 11-16)

Oak Lodge School
Roman Road, Dibden Purlieu,
SOUTHAMPTON, Hampshire SO45 4RQ
Tel: 023 8084 7213
Head: Beverley Hawker
Category: MLD ASD (Coed 11-16)

WATERLOOVILLE

Rachel Madocks School
Eagle Avenue, Cowplain,
WATERLOOVILLE, Hampshire PO8 9XP
Tel: 023 9224 1818
Head: Jacqueline Sumner
Category: SLD (Coed 2-19)

Riverside Community Special School
Scratchface Lane, Purbrook,
WATERLOOVILLE, Hampshire PO7 5QD
Tel: 023 9225 0138
Head: Catherine Marsh
Category: MLD ASD (Coed 3-11)

The Waterloo School
Warfield Avenue, WATERLOOVILLE,
Hampshire PO7 7JJ
Tel: 023 9225 5956
Head: Anna Brown
Category: BESD (Boys 4-11)

WINCHESTER

Osborne School
Athelstan Road, WINCHESTER,
Hampshire SO23 7GA
Tel: 01962 854537
Head: Sonia O'Donnell
Category: LD ASD (Coed 11-19)

Shepherds Down Special School
Shepherds Lane, Compton,
WINCHESTER, Hampshire SO21 2AJ
Tel: 01962 713445
Head: Jane Sansome
Category: LD ASD (Coed 4-11)

HARTLEPOOL
BOROUGH COUNCIL

Child and Adult Services Department,
Civic Centre, Victoria Road, Hartlepool
TS24 8AY
Tel: 01429 266522

HARTLEPOOL

Catcote School
Catcote Road, HARTLEPOOL TS25 4EZ
Tel: 01429 264036
Head: Mr A Chapman
Category: MLD SLD PMLD ASD BESD

Springwell School
Wiltshire Way, HARTLEPOOL TS26 0IB
Tel: 01429 280600
Head: Mr K Telfer
Category: MLD SLD PMLD ASD BESD

HEREFORDSHIRE
THE CHILDREN, YOUNG PEOPLE AND FAMILIES DIRECTORATE

Special Educational Needs Team, Blackfriars, Blackfriars Street, Hereford, Herefordshire HR4 9ZR
Tel: 01432 260871

HEREFORD

Barrs Court School
Barrs Court Road, HEREFORD HR1 1EQ
Tel: 01432 265035
Head: Mr R Aird
Category: CLD PMLD MSI PD ADHD ASD OCD SP&LD SLD (Coed 11-19)

Blackmarston School
Honddu Close, HEREFORD HR2 7NX
Tel: 01432 272376
Head: Mrs S Bailey
Category: SLD ASD PMLD(Coed 3-11)

The Brookfield School & Specialist College
Grandstand Road, HEREFORD HR4 9NG
Tel: 01432 265153
Head: Mrs O Evans
Category: ESBD (Coed 7-16)

LEOMINSTER

Westfield School
Westfield Walk, LEOMINSTER HR6 8HD
Tel: 01568 613147
Acting Head: Ms N Gilbert
Category: SLD ASD PMLD (Coed 2-19)

HERTFORDSHIRE
CHILDREN'S SERVICES

County Hall, Pegs Lane, Hertford SG13 8DQ
Tel: 0300 123 4043

BALDOCK

Brandles School
Weston Way, BALDOCK, Hertfordshire SG7 6EY
Tel: 01462 892189
Head: Mr David Vickery
Category: EBD (Boys 11-16)

BUSHEY

Meadow Wood School
Cold Harbour Lane, BUSHEY, Hertfordshire WD23 4NN
Tel: 020 8420 4720
Head: Ms Elizabeth Stratton
Category: PI (Coed Day 3-12)

HATFIELD

Southfield School
Travellers Lane, HATFIELD, Hertfordshire AL10 8TJ
Tel: 01707 258259
Head: Ms Libby Duggan
Category: MLD (Coed Day 4-11)

HEMEL HEMPSTEAD

Haywood Grove School
St Agnells Lane, HEMEL HEMPSTEAD, Hertfordshire HP2 7BG
Tel: 01442 250077
Head: Ms Jacqui Donley
Category: EBD (Coed Day 5-11)

The Collett School
Lockers Park Lane, HEMEL HEMPSTEAD, Hertfordshire HP1 1TQ
Tel: 01442 398988
Head: Mr Stephen Hoult-Allen
Category: MLD AUT (Coed 4-16)

Woodfield School
Malmes Croft, Leverstock Green, HEMEL HEMPSTEAD, Hertfordshire HP3 8RL
Tel: 01442 253476
Head: Mrs Gill Waceba
Category: SLD AUT (Coed Day 3-19)

HERTFORD

Hailey Hall School
Hailey Lane, HERTFORD, Hertfordshire SG13 7PB
Tel: 01992 465208
Head: Ms Heather Boardman
Category: EBD (Boys 11-16)

LETCHWORTH GARDEN CITY

Woolgrove School
Pryor Way, LETCHWORTH GARDEN CITY, Hertfordshire SG6 2PT
Tel: 01462 622422
Head: Mrs Susan Selley
Category: MLD AUT (Coed Day 5-11)

REDBOURN

St Luke's School
Crouch Hall Lane, REDBOURN, Hertfordshire AL3 7ET
Tel: 01582 626727
Head: Mr P Johnson
Category: MLD (Coed Day 9-16)

ST ALBANS

Batchwood School
Townsend Drive, ST ALBANS, Hertfordshire AL3 5RP
Tel: 01727 868021
Acting Head: Mrs Anne Spencer
Category: EBD (Coed 11-16)

Heathlands School
Heathlands Drive, ST ALBANS, Hertfordshire AL3 5AY
Tel: 01727 754060
Head: Ms Deborah Jones-Stevens
Category: HI (Coed Day & boarding 3-16)

Watling View School
Watling View, ST ALBANS, Hertfordshire AL1 2NU
Tel: 01727 850560
Head: Mr Tom Jackson-Owens
Category: SLD (Coed Day 2-19)

STEVENAGE

Greenside School
Shephall Green, STEVENAGE, Hertfordshire SG2 9XS
Tel: 01438 315356
Head: Mr David Victor
Category: SLD AUT (Coed Day 2-19)

Larwood School
Webb Rise, STEVENAGE, Hertfordshire
SG1 5QU
Tel: 01438 236333
Head: Mr Sean Trimble
Category: EBD (Coed Day & boarding 5-11)

Lonsdale School
Brittain Way, STEVENAGE, Hertfordshire
SG2 8BL
Tel: 01438 726999
Head: Mrs Maria White
Category: PH (Coed Day & boarding 5-11)

The Valley School
Valley Way, STEVENAGE, Hertfordshire
SG2 9AB
Tel: 01438 747274
Head: Mr David Harrison
Category: MLD (Coed Day 11-19)

WARE

Amwell View School & Specialist Sports College
Stanstead Abbotts, WARE, Hertfordshire
SG12 8EH
Tel: 01920 870027
Head: Mrs Janet Liversage
Category: SLD AUT (Coed Day 2-19)

Middleton School
Walnut Tree Walk, WARE, Hertfordshire
SG12 9PD
Tel: 01920 485152
Head: Ms Donna Jolly
Category: MLD AUT (Coed Day 5-11)

Pinewood School
Hoe Lane, WARE, Hertfordshire SG12 9PB
Tel: 01920 412211
Head: Mr Adrian Lloyd
Category: MLD (Coed Residential 11-16)

WATFORD

Breakspeare School
Gallows Hill Lane, Abbots Langley,
WATFORD, Hertfordshire WD5 0BU
Tel: 01923 263645
Head: Mrs Gill Williamson
Category: SLD (Coed Day 3-19)

Colnbrook School
Hayling Road, WATFORD, Hertfordshire
WD19 7UY
Tel: 020 8428 1281
Head: Mr Richard Hill
Category: MLD AUT (Coed Day 4-11)

Falconer School
Falconer Road, Bushey, WATFORD,
Hertfordshire WD23 3AT
Tel: 0208 950 2505
Head: Mr Mark Williamson
Category: EBD (Boys Day/boarding 11-16)

Garston Manor School
Horseshoe Lane, Garston, WATFORD,
Hertfordshire WD25 7HR
Tel: 01923 673757
Head: Ms Julie Lowman
Category: MLD (Coed Day 11-16)

WELWYN GARDEN CITY

Knightsfield School
Knightsfield, WELWYN GARDEN CITY,
Hertfordshire AL8 7LW
Tel: 01707 376874
Head: Mrs Lucy Leith
Category: HI (Coed Day & boarding 11-18)

Lakeside School
Stanfield, Lemsford Lane, WELWYN
GARDEN CITY, Hertfordshire AL8 6YN
Tel: 01707 327410
Head: Mrs Judith Chamberlain
Category: SLD PD (Coed Day 2-19)

ISLE OF WIGHT
CHILDREN'S SERVICES DIRECTORATE

Special Needs Support Services,
Thompson House, Sandy Lane, Newport,
Isle of Wight PO30 3NA
Tel: 01983 533 523

NEWPORT

Medina House Special School
School Lane, NEWPORT, Isle of Wight
PO30 2HS
Tel: 01983 522917
Head: Ms Julie Stewart
Category: Severe & complex needs (Coed 2-11)

St Georges School
Watergate Road, NEWPORT, Isle of Wight
PO30 1XW
Tel: 01983 524634
Head: Mrs S Holman
Category: Severe complex needs (Coed 2-11)

KENT
EDUCATION, LEARNING AND SKILLS DIRECTORATE

SEN Team, Sessions House, County Hall,
Maidstone, Kent ME14 1XQ
Tel: (East) 01227 284405 (Mid) 01233
898639 (West) 01732 525037

ASHFORD

The Wyvern School
Great Chart Bypass, ASHFORD, Kent
TN23 4ER
Tel: 01233 621302
Head: Mr David Spencer
Category: PMLD SLD CLD PD (Coed 3-19)

BROADSTAIRS

Stone Bay School
Stone Road, BROADSTAIRS, Kent
CT10 1EB
Tel: 01843 863421
Head: Mrs Helen Dando
Category: SLD AUT SLCN MLD C&I (Coed
Day & residential 11-19)

The Foreland School
Lanthorne Road, BROADSTAIRS, Kent
CT10 3NX
Tel: 01843 863891
Head: Mr Nick Howard
Category: ASD PMLD SLD PSCN (Coed 2-19)

CANTERBURY

St Nicholas' School
Holme Oak Close, Nunnery Fields,
CANTERBURY, Kent CT1 3JJ
Tel: 01227 464316
Head: Mr Daniel Lewis
Category: PMLD SLD CLD PSCN (Coed 3-19)

The Orchard School
Cambridge Road, CANTERBURY, Kent
CT1 3QQ
Tel: 01227 769220
Head: Mrs Nikki Mason
Category: MLD CLD B&L (Coed 11-16)

DARTFORD

Milestone School
Ash Road, New Ash Green, DARTFORD,
Kent DA3 8JZ
Tel: 01474 709420
Head: Mrs Margaret Fisher
Category: PMLD SLD AUT MLD PSCN
(Coed 2-19)

Rowhill School
Main Road, Longfield, DARTFORD, Kent
DA3 7PW
Tel: 01474 705377
Head: Mr Timothy South
Category: B&L AUT LD Complex needs
Behavioural difficulties (Coed Day 4-16)

DOVER

Harbour School
Elms Vale Road, DOVER, Kent CT17 9PS
Tel: 01304 201964
Head: Ms Denise Baker
Category: BESD ASD MLD B&L (Coed 4-
16)

Portal House School
Sea Street, St Margarets-at-Cliffe,
DOVER, Kent CT15 6SS
Tel: 01304 853033
Head: Mrs Rosemary Bradley
Category: BESD (Coed 11-16)

FOLKESTONE

Highview School
Moat Farm Road, FOLKESTONE, Kent
CT19 5DJ
Tel: 01303 258755
Head: Mr Neil Birch
Category: MLD CLD Complex needs
(Coed 4-17)

GRAVESEND

The Ifield School
Cedar Avenue, GRAVESEND, Kent
DA12 5JT
Tel: 01474 365485
Head: Mrs Pamela Jones
Category: CLD PMLD SLD MLD PSCN
(Coed 4-18)

HYTHE

Foxwood School
Seabrook Road, HYTHE, Kent CT21 5QJ
Tel: 01303 261155
Head: Mr Neil Birch
Category: AUT SLD (Coed 2-19)

MAIDSTONE

Bower Grove School
Fant Lane, MAIDSTONE, Kent ME16 8NL
Tel: 01622 726773
Head: Mr Trevor Phipps
Category: BESD MLD ASD B&L (Coed Day
5-16)

Five Acre Wood School
Boughton Lane, Loose Valley,
MAIDSTONE, Kent ME15 9QL
Tel: 01622 743925
Head: Ms Peggy Murphy
Category: ASD PMLD SLD PD CLD PSCN
(Coed 4-19)

MARGATE

Laleham Gap School
Northdown Park Road, MARGATE, Kent
CT9 2TP
Tel: 01843 221946
Head: Mr Keith Mileham
Category: AUT ABD PD SLCN C&I (Coed 3-
16)

St Anthony's School
St Anthony's Way, MARGATE, Kent
CT9 3RA
Tel: 01843 292015
Head: Mr Neil Rees-Davies
Category: MLD ASD LD SEBD SLCN B&L
(Coed 3-11)

SEVENOAKS

Grange Park School
Borough Green Road, Wrotham,
SEVENOAKS, Kent TN15 7RD
Tel: 01732 882111
Head: Mr Robert Wyatt
Category: AUT C&I (Coed 11-19)

SITTINGBOURNE

Meadowfield School
Swanstree Avenue, SITTINGBOURNE,
Kent ME10 4NL
Tel: 01795 477788
Head: Ms Jill Palmer
Category: CLD PMLD SLD ASD SP&LD
PSCN (Coed 4-19)

SWANLEY

Furness School
Rowhill Road, Hextable, SWANLEY, Kent
BR8 7RP
Tel: 01322 662937
Principle: Ms Jill Howson
Category: BESD (Coed Day/boarding 10-
16)

TONBRIDGE

Ridge View School
Cage Green Road, TONBRIDGE, Kent
TN10 4PT
Tel: 01732 771384
Head: Ms Jacqui Tovey
Category: PMLD SLD CLD PSCN (Coed 2-
19)

TUNBRIDGE WELLS

Broomhill Bank School
Broomhill Road, Rusthall, TUNBRIDGE
WELLS, Kent TN3 0TB
Tel: 01892 510440
Head: Ms Emma Leitch
Category: MLD SP&LD CLD AUT C&I (Girls
Boarding & day 8-19)

Oakley School
Pembury Road, TUNBRIDGE WELLS, Kent
TN2 4NE
Tel: 01892 823096
Head: Mr Gordon Tillman
Category: PMLD ASD MLD PSCN (Coed 3-
19)

WESTERHAM

Valence School
Westerham Road, WESTERHAM, Kent
TN16 1QN
Tel: 01959 562156
Head: Mr Roland Gooding
Category: PD Sensory Medical (Coed
Day/boarding 4-19)

KINGSTON UPON HULL
CITY COUNCIL

Children and Young Peoples Services, Guildhall, Alfred Gelder Street, Hull HU1 2AA
Tel: 01482 616 647

HESSLE

Bridgeview School
Ferriby Road, HESSLE HU13 0HR
Tel: 01482 640115
Head: Mrs G Garnett
Category: BESD

KINGSTON UPON HULL

Frederick Holmes School
Inglemire Lane, KINGSTON UPON HULL HU6 8JJ
Tel: 01482 804766
Head: Mrs S Garland-Grimes
Category: PH

Ganton School
294 Anlaby Park Road South, KINGSTON UPON HULL HU4 7JB
Tel: 01482 564646
Acting Head: Mr I Simpson
Category: SLD

Northcott School
Dulverton Close, Bransholme, KINGSTON UPON HULL HU7 4EL
Tel: 01482 825311
Head: Mrs G Volans
Category: Vulnerable ASD

Oakfield School
Inglemire Lane, KINGSTON UPON HULL HU6 8JH
Tel: 01482 854588
Head: Mrs R Davies
Category: BESD

Tweendykes School
Midmere Avenue, Leads Road, KINGSTON UPON HULL HU7 4PW
Tel: 01482 826508
Head: Mrs B Dobson
Category: SLD

LANCASHIRE
CHILDREN & YOUNG PEOPLE DIRECTORATE

PO Box 78, County Hall, Fishergate, Preston, Lancashire PR1 8XJ
Tel: 0845 053 0000

ACCRINGTON

Broadfield Specialist School for SEN
Fielding Lane, Oswaldtwistle, ACCRINGTON, Lancashire BB5 3BE
Tel: 01254 381782
Head: Mrs Angela Banner
Category: MLD SLD ASD (Coed 4-16)

White Ash School
Thwaites Road, Oswaldtwistle, ACCRINGTON, Lancashire BB5 4QG
Tel: 01254 235772
Head: Mrs Phillipa Conti
Category: SLD ASD PMLD (Coed 3-19)

BURNLEY

Holly Grove School
Burnley Campus, Barden Lane, BURNLEY, Lancashire BB10 1JD
Tel: 01282 682278
Head: Ms Sue Kitto
Category: SLD MLD PMLD ASD Medical needs (Coed 2-11)

Ridgewood Community High School
Eastern Avenue, BURNLEY, Lancashire BB10 2AT
Tel: 01282 682316
Head: Mrs Frances Entwhistle
Category: MSI PD LD (Coed 11-16)

The Rose School
Greenock Street, BURNLEY, Lancashire BB11 4DT
Tel: 01282 683050
Head: Ms Nicola Jennings
Category: BESD (Coed 11-16)

CARNFORTH

Bleasdale House School
27 Emesgate Lane, Silverdale, CARNFORTH, Lancashire LA5 0RG
Tel: 01524 701217
Head: Karen Dexter
Category: PMLD PH (Coed 2-19)

CHORLEY

Astley Park School
Harrington Road, CHORLEY, Lancashire PR7 1JZ
Tel: 01257 262227
Head: Mr Kieran Welsh
Category: MLD SLD ASD EBD(Coed 4-17)

Mayfield Specialist School
Gloucester Road, CHORLEY, Lancashire PR7 3HN
Tel: 01257 263063
Head: Ms Rachel Kay
Category: CLD ASD EBD (Coed 2-19)

COLNE

Pendle View Primary School
Gibfield Road, COLNE, Lancashire BB8 8JT
Tel: 01282 865011
Head: Ms Debbie Morris
Category: LD PD SLD PMLD ASD MSI (Coed 2-11)

HASLINGDEN

Tor View Community Special School
Clod Lane, HASLINGDEN, Lancashire BB4 6LR
Tel: 01706 214640
Head: Mr Andrew Squire
Category: AUT MLD SLD PMLD MSI (Coed 4-19)

KIRKHAM

Pear Tree School
29 Station Road, KIRKHAM, Lancashire PR4 2HA
Tel: 01772 683609
Head: Ms Lesley Sullivan
Category: SLD PMLD ASD (Coed 2-19)

LANCASTER

The Loyne School
Sefton Drive, LANCASTER, Lancashire LA1 2PZ
Tel: 01524 64543
Head: Mrs Carol Murphy
Category: MSI LD CLD PD AUT EPI (2-19)

Wennington Hall School
Lodge Lane, Wennington, LANCASTER, Lancashire LA2 8NS
Tel: 01524 221333
Head: Mr Joseph Prendergast
Category: SEBD (Boys Day or resident 11-16)

MORECAMBE

Morecambe Road School
Morecambe Road, MORECAMBE,
Lancashire LA3 3AB
Tel: 01524 414384
Head: Mr Paul Edmondson
Category: LD ASD BESD (Coed 3-16)

NELSON

Pendle Community High School and College
Oxford Road, NELSON, Lancashire
BB9 8LF
Tel: 01282 682240
Head: Mr Paul Wright
Category: MLD BESD ASD (Coed 11-19)

POULTON-LE-FYLDE

Brookfield School
Fouldrey Avenue, POULTON-LE-FYLDE,
Lancashire FY6 7HE
Tel: 01253 886895
Head: Mrs Jane Ware
Category: SEBD ADHD ASD SPLD (Coed 11-16)

PRESTON

Acorns Primary School
Blackpool Road, Moor Park, PRESTON,
Lancashire PR1 6AU
Tel: 01772 792681
Head: Mr Steve Artis
Category: AUT SLD PMLD (Coed 2-19)

Hillside Specialist School for Autistic Spectrum Disorders
Ribchester Road, Longridge, PRESTON,
Lancashire PR3 3XB
Tel: 01772 782205
Head: Mrs Alison Foster
Category: ASD (Coed 2-16)

Moor Hey School
Far Croft, off Leyland Road, Lostock Hall,
PRESTON, Lancashire PR5 5SS
Tel: 01772 336976
Head: Mrs Helen-Ruth McLenahan
Category: MLD CLD EBD (4-16)

Moorbrook School
Ainslie Road, Fulwood, PRESTON,
Lancashire PR2 3DB
Tel: 01772 774752
Head: Mr Mick Ironmonger
Category: SEBN (11-16)

Royal Cross Primary School
Elswick Road, Ashton-on-Ribble,
PRESTON, Lancashire PR2 1NT
Tel: 01772 729705
Head: Ms Ruth Bonney
Category: SLCN D ASD (Coed 4-11)

Sir Tom Finney Community High School
Blackpool Road, Moor Park, PRESTON,
Lancashire PR1 6AA
Tel: 01772 795749
Head: Mr Shaun Jukes
Category: PD PMLD BESD MLD (Coed 2-19)

The Coppice School
Ash Grove, Bamber Bridge, PRESTON,
Lancashire PR5 6GY
Tel: 01772 336342
Head: Mrs Liz Davies
Category: SLD PMLD CLD Medical needs (Coed 2-19)

RAWTENSTALL

Cribden House Community Special School
Haslingden Road, RAWTENSTALL,
Lancashire BB4 6RX
Tel: 01706 213048
Head: Siobhan Halligan
Category: SEBD (Coed 5-11)

SKELMERSDALE

Elm Tree Community Primary School
Elmers Wood Road, SKELMERSDALE,
Lancashire WN8 6SA
Tel: 01695 50924
Head: Mr David Lamb
Category: BESD (Coed)

Hope High School
Clay Brow, SKELMERSDALE, Lancashire
WN8 9DP
Tel: 01695 721066
Head: Mr Nick Joseph
Category: EBD (Coed 11-16)

Kingsbury Primary School
School Lane, Chapel House,
SKELMERSDALE, Lancashire WN8 8EH
Tel: 01695 722991
Head: Ms Fiona Grieveson
Category: SLD PMLD LD ASD MLD (Coed 2-11)

West Lancashire Community High School
School Lane, Chapel House,
SKELMERSDALE, Lancashire WN8 8EH
Tel: 01695 721487
Head: Ms Sue Reynolds
Category: MLD SLD PMLD AUT (Coed 11-19)

THORNTON-CLEVELEYS

Great Arley School
Holly Road, THORNTON-CLEVELEYS,
Lancashire FY5 4HH
Tel: 01253 821072
Head: Mrs Anne Marshfield
Category: MLD ASD SLD BESD (Coed Day 4-16)

Red Marsh School
Holly Road, THORNTON-CLEVELEYS,
Lancashire FY5 4HH
Tel: 01253 868451
Head: Ms Catherine Dellow
Category: SLD PMLD CLD (Coed 2-19)

LEICESTER CITY COUNCIL
EDUCATION AUTHORITY

New Walk Centre, Welford Place,
Leicester LE1 6ZG
Tel: 0116 252 7000

LEICESTER

Ash Field School
Broad Avenue, LEICESTER LE5 4PY
Tel: 0116 273 7151
Head: Mr David Bateson
Category: PH

Children's Hospital School
University Hospitals of Leicester NHS
Trust, Infirmary Square, LEICESTER
LE1 5WW
Tel: 0116 258 5330
Head: Mr George Sfougaras
Category: HS

Ellesmere College
Ellesmere Road, LEICESTER LE3 1BE
Tel: 0116 2894224
Head: Mr Andrew Large

Keyham Lodge School
Keyham Lane, LEICESTER LE5 1FG
Tel: 0116 241 6852
Head: Mr Chris Bruce
Category: EBD (Boys Secondary)

Millgate School
18A Scott Street, LEICESTER LE2 6DW
Tel: 0116 2704922
Head: Mr Chris Bruce

Nether Hall School
Netherhall Road, LEICESTER LE5 1DT
Tel: 0116 2417258
Head: Ms Erica Dennies

Oaklands School
Whitehall Road, LEICESTER LE5 6GJ
Tel: 0116 241 5921
Head: Mrs E Shaw
Category: MLD (Primary)

On-Trak Inclusion Service (linked to PRU)
495 Welford Road, LEICESTER LE2 6BN
Tel: 0116 270 6016
Head: Mr Shaun Whittingham
Category: PRU

Phoenix (PRU)
c/o Thurnby Lodge Primary School,
Dudley Avenue, LEICESTER LE5 2EG
Tel: 0116 241 9538
Team Leader: Allison Benson
Category: Primary PRU

The ARC (PRU)
c/o Holy Cross Primary School, Stonesby
Avenue, LEICESTER LE2 6TY
Tel: 0116 283 2185
Team Leader: Mrs C H Pay
Category: Primary PRU

West Gate School
Glenfield Road, LEICESTER LE3 6DN
Tel: 0116 285 6181
Head: Ms Jan Hesketh
Category: SLD MLD

Wigston Lane Educational Unit (PRU)
126 Wigston Lane, Aylestone, LEICESTER
LE2 8TN
Tel: 0116 283 6139
Head: Mr Shaun Whittingham
Category: Children Centre, PRU

LEICESTERSHIRE
COUNTY COUNCIL

Children & Young People's Service, SEN
Assessment Service, County Hall,
Leicester Road, Glenfield, Leicestershire
LE3 8RA
Tel: 0116 265 6600

COALVILLE

Forest Way School
Warren Hills Road, COALVILLE,
Leicestershire LE67 4UU
Tel: 01530 831899
Head: Mrs L Slinger
Category: SLD PMLD (2-18)

HINCKLEY

Dorothy Goodman School Hinckley
Stoke Road, HINCKLEY, Leicestershire
LE10 0EA
Tel: 01455 634582
Head: Mr Tony Smith
Category: (2-18)

LOUGHBOROUGH

Ashmount School
Beacon Road, LOUGHBOROUGH,
Leicestershire LE11 2BG
Tel: 01509 268506
Head: Mr D Thomas
Category: SLD PMLD (2-18)

Maplewell Hall School
Maplewell Road, Woodhouse Eaves,
LOUGHBOROUGH, Leicestershire
LE12 8QY
Tel: 01509 890237
Head: Mr Jason Brooks
Category: MLD AUT (10-15)

MELTON MOWBRAY

Birch Wood (Melton Area Special School)
Grange Drive, MELTON MOWBRAY,
Leicestershire LE13 1HA
Tel: 01664 483340
Head: Mr Phil Omerod
Category: MLD SLD AUT (5-19)

WIGSTON

Birkett House Community Special School
Launceston Road, WIGSTON,
Leicestershire LE18 2FZ
Tel: 0116 288 5802
Head: Mrs S Horn
Category: SLD PMLD (2-18)

The MENPHYS Centre
Launceston Road, WIGSTON,
Leicestershire LE18 2FR
Tel: 0116 288 9977
Head: Mrs Christine Silver

LINCOLNSHIRE
COUNTY COUNCIL

Special Needs Services Group, County
Offices, Newland, Lincoln, Lincolnshire
LN1 1YL
Tel: 01522 553332

BOSTON

John Fielding School
Ashlawn Drive, BOSTON, Lincolnshire
PE21 9PX
Tel: 01205 363395
Head: Mrs S Morrison
Category: SLD (2-19)

The Pilgrim School
Sibsey Road, BOSTON, Lincolnshire
PE21 9QS
Tel: 01205 445641
Head: Mrs C Seymour
Category: HS (4-16)

BOURNE

Willoughby School
South Road, BOURNE, Lincolnshire
PE10 9JE
Tel: 01778 425203
Head: Mr A Booker
Category: SLD (2-19)

GAINSBOROUGH

The Aegir Community School
Gainsborough Educational Village,
Sweyn Lane, GAINSBOROUGH,
Lincolnshire DN21 1PB
Tel: 01427 619360
Head: Ms K Gittins
Category: MLD SLD (11-19)

Warren Wood Community School
Middlefield Lane, GAINSBOROUGH,
Lincolnshire DN21 1PU
Tel: 01427 615498
Head: Ms C Cumberlidge
Category: MLD SLD (3-11)

GOSBERTON

Gosberton House School
Westhorpe Road, GOSBERTON,
Lincolnshire PE11 4EW
Tel: 01775 840250
Head: Ms L Stanton
Category: MLD (3-11)

GRANTHAM

Sandon School
Sandon Close, GRANTHAM, Lincolnshire
NG31 9AX
Tel: 01476 564994
Head: Mrs J Roddis
Category: SLD (2-19)

**The Ambergate Sports College
Specialist Education Centre**
Dysart Road, GRANTHAM, Lincolnshire
NG31 7LP
Tel: 01476 564957
Head: Mr P Bell
Category: MLD (5-16)

The Phoenix School
Great North Road, GRANTHAM,
Lincolnshire NG31 7US
Tel: 01476 574112
Head: Mr W Bush
Category: EBD (11-16)

HORNCASTLE

St Lawrence School
Bowl Alley Lane, HORNCASTLE,
Lincolnshire LN9 5EJ
Tel: 01507 522563
Head: Mr K Bruzas
Category: MLD (5-16)

LINCOLN

Queen's Park School
South Park, LINCOLN, Lincolnshire
LN5 8EW
Tel: 01522 878112
Head: Mr A Lacey
Category: SLD MLD (2-19)

St Christopher's School
Hykeham Road, LINCOLN, Lincolnshire
LN6 8AR
Tel: 01522 528378
Head: Mr D Metcalfe
Category: MLD (3-16)

St Francis School
Wickenby Crescent, Ermine Estate,
LINCOLN, Lincolnshire LN1 3TJ
Tel: 01522 526498
Head: Mrs A Hoffman
Category: PD Sensory (2-19)

The Fortuna Primary School
Kingsdown Road, Doddington Park,
LINCOLN, Lincolnshire LN6 0FB
Tel: 01522 705561
Head: Ms B Robson
Category: EBD (4-11)

The Sincil School
South Park, LINCOLN, Lincolnshire
LN5 8EL
Tel: 01522 534559
Head: Mr R Parkin
Category: EBD (11-16)

LOUTH

St Bernard's School
Wood Lane, LOUTH, Lincolnshire
LN11 8RS
Tel: 01507 603776
Head: Mrs L Mason
Category: SLD (2-19)

SLEAFORD

The Ash Villa School
Willoughby Road, Greylees, SLEAFORD,
Lincolnshire NG34 8QA
Tel: 01529 488066
Head: Mr N Barton
Category: HS (8-16)

SPALDING

The Garth School
Pinchbeck Road, SPALDING, Lincolnshire
PE11 1QF
Tel: 01775 725566
Head: Mr D Bland
Category: SLD (2-19)

The Priory School
Neville Avenue, SPALDING, Lincolnshire
PE11 2EH
Tel: 01775 724080
Head: Mr D Bland
Category: MLD (11-16)

SPILSBY

The Eresby School
Eresby Avenue, SPILSBY, Lincolnshire
PE23 5HU
Tel: 01790 752441
Head: Mrs J McPherson
Category: SLD (2-19)

The Lady Jane Franklin School
Partney Road, SPILSBY, Lincolnshire
PE23 5EJ
Tel: 01790 753902
Head: Mr C Armond
Category: EBD (11-16)

NORTH LINCOLNSHIRE
PEOPLE DIRECTORATE

SEND Team, Hewson House, PO Box 35,
Station Road, Brigg, North Lincolnshire
DN20 8XJ
Tel: 01724 297148

SCUNTHORPE

**St Hugh's Communication & Interaction
Specialist College**
Bushfield Road, SCUNTHORPE, North
Lincolnshire DN16 1NB
Tel: 01724 842960
Head: Mrs Tracy Millard
Category: MLD CLD PMLD (Coed 11-19)

St Luke's Primary School
Grange Lane North, SCUNTHORPE, North
Lincolnshire DN16 1BN
Tel: 01724 844560
Head: Dr R W Ashdown
Category: PMLD SLD MLD (Coed 3-11)

NORTH EAST LINCOLNSHIRE
DIRECTORATE OF LEARNING & CHILDREN

Municipal Offices, Town Hall Square, Grimsby DN31 1HU
Tel: 01472 313131

GRIMSBY

Humberston Park Special School
St Thomas Close, Humberston, GRIMSBY, N E Lincolnshire DN36 4HS
Tel: 01472 590645
Head: Mr Andy Zielinski
Category: SLD PMLD PD CLD MSI (Coed 3-19)

The Cambridge Park Academy
Cambridge Road, GRIMSBY, N E Lincolnshire DN34 5EB
Tel: 01472 230110
Head: Mrs Gill Kendall
Category: ASD SLCN MLD SLD (Coed 3-19)

LONDON
BARKING AND DAGENHAM
SPECIAL EDUCATIONAL NEEDS ASSESSMENT AND REVIEW TEAM

Roycraft House, 5th Floor, 15 Linton Road, Barking, Essex IG11 8HE
Tel: 020 8227 2400, *Fax:* 020 8227 3104

DAGENHAM

Trinity School
Heathway, DAGENHAM, Essex RM10 7SJ
Tel: 020 8270 1601
Head: Mr Peter McPartland
Category: SLD ASD PMLD (Coed 3-19)

LONDON
BARNET
COUNCIL

Education and Learning, North London Business Park, Oakleigh Road South, London N11 1NP
Tel: 020 8359 2000

LONDON

Mapledown Special School
Claremont Road, Golders Green, LONDON NW2 1TR
Tel: 020 8455 4111
Head: Mr S Caroll
Category: SLD CLD (Mixed 11-19)

Northway Special School
The Fairway, Mill Hill, LONDON NW7 3HS
Tel: 020 8359 5450
Head: Ms L Burgess
Category: CLD AUT (Mixed 5-11)

Oak Lodge Special School
Heath View, Off East End Road, LONDON N2 0QY
Tel: 020 8444 6711
Head: Mrs L Walker
Category: MLD ASD SCLN EBD (Mixed 11-19)

Oakleigh Special School
Oakleigh Road North, Whetstone, LONDON N20 0DH
Tel: 020 8368 5336
Head: Ms J Gridley
Category: SLD AUT PMLD (Mixed 3-11)

LONDON
LONDON BOROUGH OF BEXLEY
DIRECTORATE OF EDUCATION AND SOCIAL CARE

Hill View, Hill View Drive, Welling, Kent DA16 3RY
Tel: 020 8303 7777

BELVEDERE

Woodside School
Halt Robin Road, BELVEDERE, Kent DA17 6DW
Tel: 01322 433494
Interim Head: Audrey Chamberlain
Category: MLD (Primary/Secondary)

BEXLEY HEATH

Oakwood School
Woodside Road, BEXLEY HEATH, Kent DA7 6LB
Tel: 01322 553787
Head: Miss S Middleham
Category: BESD (Coed 11-16)

CRAYFORD

Shenstone School
Old Road, CRAYFORD, Kent DA1 4DZ
Tel: 01322 524145
Head: Mrs L Aldcroft
Category: SLD (2-11)

SIDCUP

Marlborough School
Marlborough Park Avenue, SIDCUP, Kent DA15 9DP
Tel: 020 8300 6896
Acting Head: Ms Bird
Category: SLD (11-19)

WELLING

Westbrooke School
Gipsy Road South, WELLING, Kent DA16 1JB
Tel: 020 8304 1320
Head: Mrs C Hance
Category: BESD (5-11)

LONDON
BRENT
CHILDREN & FAMILIES DEPARTMENT

Chesterfield House, 9 Park Lane, Wembley, Middlesex HA9 7RH
Tel: 020 8937 3229, *Fax:* 020 8937 3222

KENSALE RISE

Manor School
Chamberlayne Road, KENSALE RISE, London NW10 3NT
Tel: 020 8968 3160
Head: Ms Mary Adossides
Category: MLD SLD CLD ASD (Coed 4-11)

KINGSBURY

The Village School
Grove Park, KINGSBURY, London NW9 0JY
Tel: 020 8204 5396
Head: Ms Kay Johnson
Category: LD DD VIS Medical needs (Coed 2-19)

Woodfield School
Glenwood Avenue, KINGSBURY, London NW9 7LY
Tel: 020 8205 1977
Head: Ms Desi Lodge-Patch
Category: MLD BESD ASD (Coed 11-16)

NEASDEN

Phoenix Arch School
Drury Way, NEASDEN, London NW10 0NQ
Tel: 020 8451 6961
Head: Ms Jude Towell
Category: BESD LD ADHD ASD (Coed 5-11)

LONDON
BROMLEY
EDUCATION AUTHORITY

Education Offices, Civic Centre, Stockwell Close, Bromley, Kent BR1 3UH
Tel: 020 8464 3333

BECKENHAM

Riverside School ASD Centre
2 Hayne Road, BECKENHAM, kENT BR3 4HY
Tel: 0208 639 0079
Head: Mr S Solomons
Category: ASD (Coed 4-11)

CHISLEHURST

Marjorie McClure School
Hawkwood Lane, CHISLEHURST, Kent BR7 5PS
Tel: 020 8467 0174
Head: Mrs Denise James-Mason
Category: PD SLD Medical needs (4Ω-19)

ORPINGTON

Burwood School
Avalon Road, ORPINGTON, Kent BR6 9BD
Tel: 01689 821205
Head: Mr G Ingram
Category: EBD (11-16)

Riverside School
Main Road, ORPINGTON, Kent BR5 3HS
Tel: 01689 870519
Head: Mr S Solomons
Category: PMLD ASD SLD (Coed 4-19)

WEST WICKHAM

Glebe School
Hawes Lane, WEST WICKHAM, Kent BR4 9AE
Tel: 020 8777 4540
Head: Mr K Seed
Category: Complex needs SCD ASD SLD (11-19)

LONDON BOROUGH
CAMDEN
CHILDREN, SCHOOLS & FAMILIES DIRECTORATE

Special Educational Needs Team, Crowndale Centre, 218 Eversholt Street, London NW1 1BD
Tel: 020 7974 6500

LONDON

Chalcot School
Harmood Street, LONDON NW1 8DP
Tel: 020 7485 2147
Head: Ms Jeanette Lowe
Category: BESD (Coed 11-16)

Frank Barnes Primary School for Deaf Children
Jubilee Waterside Centre, 105 Camley Street, LONDON N1C 4PF
Tel: 020 7391 7040
Head: Ms Karen Simpson
Category: HI (Coed 2-11)

Great Ormond Street Hospital School
(Grant Maintained), Great Ormond Street, LONDON WC1N 3JH
Tel: 020 7813 8269
Head: Ms Jayne Franklin
Category: HS (Coed 0-19)

Royal Free Hospital School
Ward 6 West B, 6th Floor, Pond Street, LONDON NW3 2QG
Tel: 020 7472 6298
Head: Jude Chalk
Category: HS (5-16)

Swiss Cottage School Development and Research Centre
80 Avenue Road, LONDON NW8 6HX
Tel: 020 7681 8080
Head: Ms Kay Bedford
Category: LD (2-16)

LONDON
CROYDON
CHILDREN, YOUNG PEOPLE & LEARNERS

SEN Team, Taberner House, Park Lane, Croydon, Surrey CR9 3JS
Tel: 020 8726 6000 ext 62394

BECKENHAM

Beckmead School
Monks Orchard Road, BECKENHAM, Kent BR3 3BZ
Tel: 020 8777 9311
Head: Dr Jonty Clark
Category: SEBD (Coed 7-16)

CROYDON

Red Gates School
Farnborough Avenue, CROYDON, Surrey CR2 8HD
Tel: 020 8651 6540
Head: Mrs Susan Beaman
Category: SLD PMLD ASD (Coed 4-12)

St Giles School
207 Pampisford Road, CROYDON, Surrey CR2 6DF
Tel: 020 8680 2141
Head: Ms Ginny Marshall
Category: PH Complex medical needs (Coed 4-19)

PURLEY

St Nicholas School
Old Lodge Lane, PURLEY, Surrey CR8 4DN
Tel: 020 8660 4861
Head: Mr Nick Dry
Category: MLD ASD SLCN AUT (Coed 4-11)

SOUTH NORWOOD

Priory School
Tennison Road, SOUTH NORWOOD, Surrey SE25 5RR
Tel: 020 8653 8222
Head: Ms Jillian Thomas
Category: PMLD CLD (Coed 11-19)

THORNTON HEATH

Bensham Manor School
Ecclesbourne Road, THORNTON HEATH, Surrey CR7 7BN
Tel: 020 8684 0116
Head: Mr Phil Poulton
Category: MLD SEBD SLD ASD (Coed 11-16)

LONDON
EALING
EDUCATION DEPARTMENT

Special Educational Needs Administration Section, Ealing Service for Children with Additional Needs (ESCAN), Carmelita House 1st Floor, 21-22 The Mall, Ealing, London W5 2PJ
Tel: 020 8825 5533

EALING

Castlebar School
Hathaway Gardens, EALING, London W13 0DH
Tel: 020 8998 3135
Head: Mr Paul Adair
Category: MLD SLD ASD (Coed 4-11)

Springhallow School
Compton Close, Off Cavendish Avenue, EALING, London W13 0JG
Tel: 020 8998 2700
Head: Andy Balmer
Category: ASD (Coed 4-16/17)

GREENFORD

Mandeville School
Horsenden Lane North, GREENFORD, Middlesex UB6 0PA
Tel: 020 8864 4921/0911
Acting Head: Ms Denise Feasey
Category: SLD ASD PMLD (Coed 2-12)

HANWELL

St Ann's School
Springfield Road, HANWELL, London W7 3JP
Tel: 020 8567 6291
Head: Ms Gillian Carver
Category: SLD MSI PNLD SLCN Complex medical conditions (Coed 12-19)

NORTHOLT

Belvue School
Rowdell Road, NORTHOLT, London UB5 6AG
Tel: 020 8845 5766
Head: Mrs Shelagh O'Shea
Category: MLD SLD ASD (Coed 11-18)

John Chilton School
Compton Crescent, NORTHOLT, London UB5 5LD
Tel: 020 8842 1329
Head: Mr Simon Rosenberg
Category: PH/Medical (Coed 2-18)

LONDON
ENFIELD
EDUCATION & LEARNING

Education Office, Civic Centre, Silver Street, Enfield, Middlesex EN1 3XA
Tel: 020 8379 1000

EDMONTON

West Lea School
Haselbury Road, EDMONTON, London N9 9TU
Tel: 020 8807 2656
Head: Mrs Sue Tripp
Category: HA ASD PD LD (Coed 4-18)

ENFIELD

Aylands School
Keswick Drive, ENFIELD, London EN3 6NY
Tel: 01992 761229
Head: Ms Sashi Sivaloganathan
Category: EBD (Coed 7-16)

Durants School
4 Pitfield Way, ENFIELD, London EN3 5BY
Tel: 020 8804 1980
Head: Mr Peter De Rosa
Category: CLD ASD (Coed 4-19)

Russet House School
11 Autumn Close, ENFIELD, London EN1 4JA
Tel: 020 8350 0650
Head: Mrs Julie Foster
Category: AUT (Coed 3-11)

Waverley School
105 The Ride, ENFIELD, London EN3 7DL
Tel: 020 8805 1858
Head: Ms Sue Hogan
Category: PMLD SLD (Coed 3-19)

SOUTHGATE

Oaktree School
Chase Side, SOUTHGATE, London
N14 4HN
Tel: 020 8440 3100
Head: Mr Finlay Douglas
Category: Complex needs (Coed 7-19)

LONDON
ROYAL BOROUGH OF GREENWICH
CHILDREN'S SERVICES

1st Floor, The Woolwich Centre, 35
Wellington Street, Woolwich, London
SE18 6HQ
Tel: 020 8921 8945

LONDON

Charlton Park Academy
Charlton Park Road, LONDON SE7 8HX
Tel: 020 8249 6844
Head: Mark Dale-Emberton
Category: SCLD (Coed 11-19)

Moatbridge School
Eltham Palace Road, LONDON SE9 5LX
Tel: 020 8850 8081
Head: Mike Byron
Category: SEBD BESD (Boys 11-16)

Waterside School
Robert Street, Plumstead, LONDON
SE18 7NB
Tel: 020 8317 7659
Head: Susan Vernoit
Category: BESD (Coed 5-11)

Willow Dene Primary School & Assessment Nursery
Swingate Lane, Plumstead, LONDON
SE18 2JD
Tel: 020 8854 9841
Head: Michelle Bernard
Category: SLD CLD (Coed 5-11)

LONDON
HACKNEY
THE LEARNING TRUST

Hackney Technology & Learning Centre,
1 Reading Lane, London E8 1GQ
Tel: 020 8820 7000

LONDON

Clissold Park School
Tiger Way, Downs Road, LONDON E5 8QP
Tel: 0208 985 6833
Head: Shane Foley

Downsview School
Wordsworth Road, LONDON N16 8BZ
Tel: 020 8985 6833
Head: Ms Pat Quigley
Category: SLD ASD (Primary)

Horizon School
Wordsworth Road, LONDON N16 8BZ
Tel: 020 7254 8096
Headteacher: Ms Kt Khan
Category: MLD ASD (Secondary)

Ickburgh School
Ickburgh Road, LONDON E5 8AD
Tel: 020 8806 4638
Head: Mrs Shirleyanne Sullivan
Category: SLD PMLD (2-19)

Stormont House School
Mount Pleasant Lane, LONDON E5 9JG
Tel: 020 8985 4245
Head: Mr Kevin McDonnell
Category: Complex needs (Secondary)

LONDON
HAMMERSMITH & FULHAM
COUNCIL

SEN Service, Education Department,
Town Hall, King Street, Hammersmith,
London W6 9JU
Tel: 020 8753 3732

LONDON

Cambridge School
61 Bryony Road, Hammersmith, LONDON
W12 0SP
Tel: 020 8735 0980
Head: Ms Olivia Meyrick
Category: MLD (11-16)

Jack Tizard School
South Africa Road, LONDON W12 7PA
Tel: 020 8735 3590
Head: Ms Cathy Welsh
Category: SLD PMLD (Coed Day 2-19)

Queensmill School
Clancarty Road, Fulham, LONDON
SW6 3AA
Tel: 020 7384 2330
Head: Ms Jude Ragan
Category: ASD (Coed 3-19)

The Courtyard at Langford Primary
The Courtyard, Langford Primary,
Gilstead Road, LONDON SW6 2LG
Tel: 020 7736 4045
Head: Ms Anne-Louise de Burianne
Category: BESD (5-11)

Woodlane High School
Du Cane Road, LONDON W12 0TN
Tel: 020 8743 5668
Head: Mr Peter Harwood
Category: SCLN SPLD SEBD MSI Medical
difficulties (Coed 11-16)

LONDON
HARINGEY
CHILDREN & YOUNG PEOPLE'S SERVICE

Special Educational Needs (SEN), South Podiam Floor, River Park House, 225 High Road, London N22 8HQ
Tel: 020 8489 1913

MUSWELL HILL

Blanche Nevile School
Burlington Road, MUSWELL HILL, London N10 1NJ
Tel: 020 8442 2750
Head: Ms Veronica Held
Category: HI (Coed Day 3-18)

TOTTENHAM

Riverside School
Wood Green Inclusive Learning Campus, White Hart Lane, TOTTENHAM, London N22 5QJ
Tel: 020 8889 7814
Head: Mr Martin Doyle

The Brook on Broadwaters
Adams Road, TOTTENHAM, London N17 6HW
Tel: 020 8808 7120
Head: Ms Margaret Sumne
Category: (Coed Day 4-11)

WEST GREEN

The Vale School
Northumberland Park Community School, Trulock Road, WEST GREEN, London N17 0PG
Tel: 020 8801 6111
Head: Ms Sarah McLay
Category: PD (Coed Day 2-16)

LONDON
BOROUGH OF HARROW
SPECIAL SCHOOLS

Childrens Services, Pinner Road, South Harrow, Middlesex HA3 7QX
Tel: 020 8863 5544

EDGWARE

Woodlands First & Middle School
Bransgrove Road, EDGWARE, Middlesex HA8 6JP
Tel: 020 8381 2188
Head: Mr John Feltham
Category: SLD PMLD ASD (Coed 3-11)

HARROW

Kingsley High School
Whittlesea Road, HARROW, Middlesex HA3 6ND
Tel: 020 8421 3676
Head: Ms Pauline Atkins
Category: SLD PMLD (Coed 11-19)

Shaftesbury School
Headstone Lane, HARROW, Middlesex HA3 6LE
Tel: 020 8428 2482
Head: Mr Paul Williams
Category: MLD EBD ASD (Coed 11-19)

SOUTH HARROW

Alexandra School
Alexandra Avenue, SOUTH HARROW, Middlesex HA2 9DX
Tel: 020 8864 2739
Head: Mr Dennis Goldthorpe
Category: MLD EBD ASD (Coed 4-11)

LONDON BOROUGH OF HAVERING
EDUCATION AUTHORITY

Children's Services, Mercury House, Mercury Gardens, Romford, Essex RM1 3SL
Tel: 01708 434343

ROMFORD

Dycorts School
Settle Road, Harold Hill, ROMFORD, Essex RM3 9YA
Tel: 01708 343649
Head: Mr G Wroe
Category: MLD

Ravensbourne School
Neave Cres, Faringdon Ave, Harold Hill, ROMFORD, Essex RM3 8HN
Tel: 01708 341800
Head: Mrs M Cameron
Category: SLD PMLD

UPMINSTER

Corbets Tey School
Harwood Hall Lane, Corbets Tey, UPMINSTER, Essex RM14 2YQ
Tel: 01708 225888
Head: Mrs Emma Allen
Category: MLD

LONDON
HILLINGDON
EDUCATION

SEN Team, 4E/05, Civic Centre, High Street, Uxbridge, Middlesex UB8 1UW
Tel: 01895 250489

HAYES

Hedgewood Special School
Weymouth Road, HAYES, Middlesex UB4 8NF
Tel: 020 8845 6756
Head: Mr M J Goddard
Category: MLD ASD Complex moderate learning needs (Coed 5-11)

The Willows Special School
Stipularis Drive, HAYES, Middlesex
UB4 9QB
Tel: 020 8841 7176
Head: Mr Malcolm Shaw
Category: SEBD ASD ADHD Challenging
behaviour (Coed 3-11)

PINNER

Grangewood School
Fore Street, Eastcote, PINNER, Middlesex
HA5 2JQ
Tel: 01895 676401
Head: Mr J D Ayres
Category: SLD PMLD AUT (Coed 3-11)

UXBRIDGE

Meadow High School
Royal Lane, Hillingdon, UXBRIDGE,
Middlesex UB8 3QU
Tel: 01895 443310
Head: Mr R Macdonald
Category: CLD ASD Complex moderate
learning needs (Coed 11-19)

Moorcroft Special School
Bramble Close, Hillingdon, UXBRIDGE,
Middlesex UB8 3BF
Tel: 01895 437799
Head: Ms J Nutall
Category: SLD PMLD AUT (Coed 11-19)

WEST DRAYTON

Chantry Special School
Falling Lane, Yiewsley, WEST DRAYTON,
Middlesex UB7 8AB
Tel: 01895 446747
Head: Mr Mark Pearson
Category: BESD AUT ADHD (Coed 11-16)

LONDON
HOUNSLOW
CHILDREN'S SERVICES AND LIFELONG LEARNING

The Civic Centre, Lampton Road,
Hounslow TW3 4DN
Tel: 020 8583 2000

BEDFONT

Marjory Kinnon School
Hatton Road, BEDFONT, London
TW14 9QZ
Tel: 020 8890 2032
Head: Ms Denise Morton
Category: MLD AUT (5-16)

CRANFORD

The Cedars Primary School
High Street, CRANFORD, London
TW5 9RU
Tel: 020 8230 0015
Head: Mrs Lesley Julian
Category: EBD (Primary)

HANWORTH

The Lindon Bennett School
Main Street, HANWORTH, London
TW13 6ST
Tel: 020 8898 0479
Head: Mr Steve Line
Category: SLD (Primary)

ISLEWORTH

Oaklands School
Woodlands Road, ISLEWORTH, London
TW7 6JZ
Tel: 020 8560 3569
Head: Ms Anne Clinton
Category: SLD (Secondary)

LONDON
ISLINGTON
SPECIAL EDUCATIONAL NEEDS TEAM

First Floor, 222 Upper Street, London
N1 1XR
Tel: 020 7527 5518/4860

LONDON

Richard Cloudesley School
Golden Lane Campus, 101 Whitecross
Street, LONDON EC1Y 8JA
Tel: 020 7786 4800
Head: Ms Anne Corbett
Category: PD (Coed 2-19)

Samuel Rhodes School
Montem Community Campus, Hornsey
Road, LONDON N7 7QT
Tel: 020 7281 5114
Head: Ms Julie Keylock
Category: MLD ASD BESD (Coed 5-16)

The Bridge School
251 Hungerford Road, LONDON N7 9LD
Tel: 020 7619 1000
Head: Ms Penny Barratt
Category: ASD SLD PMLD (Coed 2-19)

LONDON
ROYAL BOROUGH OF KINGSTON UPON THAMES
EDUCATION AUTHORITY

Learning & Children's Services, Guildhall
2, Kingston upon Thames, Surrey
KT1 1EU
Tel: 020 8547 4615

CHESSINGTON

St Philip's School & Post 16
Harrow Close, Leatherhead Road,
CHESSINGTON, Surrey KT9 2HR
Tel: 020 8397 2672
Head: Ms Bowen
Category: MLD SLD ASD (11-19)

KINGSTON UPON THAMES

Bedelsford School
Grange Road, KINGSTON UPON THAMES,
Surrey KT1 2QZ
Tel: 020 8546 9838
Head: Ms J James
Category: PD PMLD (3-16)

SURBITON

Dysart Special School
190 Ewell Road, SURBITON, Surrey
KT6 6HL
Tel: 020 8412 2600
Head: Mr J Prior
Category: SLD ASD (5-19)

WEST DULWICH

Turney School
Turney Road, WEST DULWICH, London
SE21 8LX
Tel: 020 8670 7220
Head: Bela Handa
Category: MLD SLD CLD ASD (Coed 5-16)

WEST NORWOOD

Elm Court School
96 Elm Park, WEST NORWOOD, London
SW2 2EF
Tel: 020 8674 3412
Head: Ms Joanna Tarrant
Category: SEBN SLCN (Coed 11-16)

Brent Knoll School
Mayow Road, Forest Hill, LONDON
SE23 2XH
Tel: 020 8699 1047
Head: Mr J Sharpe
Category: AUT ASP SLCN Emotionally
Vulnerable (Coed 4-16)

Greenvale School
Waters Road, LONDON SE6 1UF
Tel: 020 8465 0740
Executive Head: Mrs A Youd
Category: SLD PMLD (Coed 11-19)

Watergate School
Lushington Road, Bellingham, LONDON
SE6 3WG
Tel: 020 8695 6555
Head: Mrs A Youd
Category: SLD PMLD (Coed 3-11)

LONDON
LAMBETH
CHILDREN & YOUNG PEOPLE'S SERVICE

International House, Canterbury
Crescent, Brixton, London SW9 7QE
Tel: 020 7926 1000

BRIXTON

Livity School
Mandrell Road, BRIXTON, London
SW2 5DW
Tel: 020 7733 0681
Head: Ms Geraldine Lee
Category: SLD PMLD ASD (Coed 2-11)

RUSKIN PARK

The Michael Tippet School
Heron Road, RUSKIN PARK, London
SE24 0HZ
Tel: 020 7326 5898
Head: Ms Jan Stogden
Category: CLD AUT PD SLD PMLD (Coed
11-19)

STOCKWELL

Lansdowne School
Argyll Close, Dalyell Road, STOCKWELL,
London SW9 9QL
Tel: 020 7737 3713
Head: Ms Linda Adams
Category: MLD SEBD ASD CLD SLD (Coed
11-16)

LONDON
LEWISHAM
CHILDREN & YOUNG PEOPLE

Special Educational Needs, 32
Kaleidoscope Child Development Centre,
Rushey Green, London SE6 4JF
Tel: 020 7138 1100

BROMLEY

Drumbeat School
Pendragon Road, Downham, BROMLEY,
Kent BR1 5LD
Tel: 020 8698 9738
Head: Dr Vivian Hinchcliffe
Category: EBD LD MLD AUT SLD Complex
needs (11-16)

DOWNHAM

New Woodlands School
49 Shroffold Road, DOWNHAM, Kent
BR1 5PD
Tel: 020 8695 2380
Head: Mr D Harper
Category: BESD (Coed 4-14)

LONDON

Abbey Manor College
40 Falmouth Close, Lee, LONDON
SE12 8PJ
Tel: 020 8297 7060
Head: Ms Liz Jones
Category: BESD (Coed 11-16)

LONDON
MERTON
DEPARTMENT OF CHILDREN, SCHOOLS AND FAMILIES

Special Educational Needs (SEN) Team,
1st Floor, Merton Civic Centre, London
Road, Morden, Surrey SM4 5DX
Tel: 020 8545 - 4810

MITCHAM

Cricket Green School
Lower Green West, MITCHAM, Surrey
CR4 3AF
Tel: 020 8640 1177
Head: Mrs Celia Dawson
Category: CLD (Coed 5-16)

Melrose School
Church Road, MITCHAM, Surrey CR4 3BE
Tel: 020 8646 2620
Head: Mr Steve Childs
Category: SEBD (Coed 11-16)

MORDEN

Perseid School
Bordesley Road, MORDEN, Surrey
SM4 5LT
Tel: 020 8648 9737
Head: Mrs Tina Harvey
Category: SCLD ASD (Coed 3-19)

LONDON
NEWHAM
LOCAL AUTHORITY

Children and Young People's Services, SEN, Newham Dockside, 1st Floor, East Wing, 1000 Dockside Road, London E16 2QU
Tel: 020 8430 2000

PLAISTOW

Eleanor Smith School
North Street, PLAISTOW, London E13 9HN
Tel: 020 8471 0018
Head: Graham Smith
Category: SEBD (5-16)

STRATFORD

John F Kennedy School
Pitchford Street, STRATFORD, London E15 4RZ
Tel: 020 8534 8544
Head: Diane Rochford
Category: SLD PMLD ASD Complex medical needs (Coed 2-19)

LONDON
REDBRIDGE
EDUCATION AUTHORITY

Lynton House, 255-259 High Road, Ilford, Essex IG1 1NN
Tel: 020 8554 5000

GOODMAYES

Newbridge School - Barley Lane Campus
258 Barley Lane, GOODMAYES, Essex IG3 8XS
Tel: 020 8599 1768
Head: Mr P Bouldstridge
Category: SLD PMLD ASD Complex medical needs (4-21)

HAINAULT

New Rush Hall School
Fencepiece Road, HAINAULT, Essex IG6 2LJ
Tel: 020 8501 3951
Head: Mr J V d'Abbro OBE
Category: SEBD (6-16)

ROMFORD

Little Heath Foundation School
Hainault Road, Little Heath, ROMFORD, Essex RM6 5RX
Tel: 020 8599 4864
Head: Mr P Johnson
Category: MLD (11-16)

Newbridge School - Gresham Drive Campus
161 Gresham Drive, Chadwell Heath, ROMFORD, Essex RM6 4TR
Tel: 020 8590 7272
Head: Mr P Bouldstridge
Category: SLD PMLD ASD Complex medical needs (4-21)

WOODFORD GREEN

Hatton School
Roding Lane South, WOODFORD GREEN, Essex IG8 8EU
Tel: 020 8551 4131
Head: Mrs Sue Blows
Category: AUT SP&LD (3-11)

LONDON
RICHMOND UPON THAMES
EDUCATION AUTHORITY

Education, Children's and Cultural Services, Civic Centre, 44 York Street, Twickenham, Middlesex TW1 3BZ
Tel: 020 8891 7906, *Fax:* 020 8891 7714

HAMPTON

Clarendon School
Hanworth Road, HAMPTON, Surrey TW12 3DH
Tel: 020 8979 1165
Head: Mr John Kipps
Category: MLD (7-16) (offsite EBD 7-11)

RICHMOND

Strathmore School
Meadlands Drive, Petersham, RICHMOND, Surrey TW10 7ED
Tel: 020 8948 0047
Head: Mr Ivan Pryce
Category: SLD PMLD (7-19)

LONDON
SOUTHWARK
SPECIAL COUNCIL

Special Education Needs, PO Box 64529, London SE1P 5LX
Tel: 020 7525 4278

BERMONDSEY

Beormund Primary School
Crosby Row, Long Lane, BERMONDSEY SE1 3PS
Tel: 020 7525 9027
Head: Mr Andrew Henderson
Category: EBD (Boys 5-11)

Cherry Garden Primary School
Macks Road, BERMONDSEY SE16 3XU
Tel: 020 7237 4050
Head: Ms Teresa Neary
Category: SLD Complex needs (Coed 2-11)

Spa School
Monnow Road, BERMONDSEY SE1 5RN
Tel: 020 7237 3714
Head: Mr Simon Eccles
Category: MLD AUT ASP SLD SCD (Coed 11-19)

LAMBETH

Evelina Hospital School (Level 3)
Evelina Children's Hospital, Westminister Bridge Road, LAMBETH SE1 7EH
Tel: 020 7188 2267
Head: Ms Manuela Beste
Category: HS (Coed 3-18)

PECKHAM

Bredinghurst School
Stuart Road, PECKHAM SE15 3AZ
Tel: 020 7639 2541
Head: Ms Colin Boxall
Category: SEBD (Boys 11-16)

Haymerle
Haymerle Road, PECKHAM SE15 6SY
Tel: 020 7639 6080
Head: Ms Liz Nolan
Category: SLD ASD Complex needs (Coed 5-11)

Highshore Secondary School
Bellenden Road, PECKHAM SE15 5BB
Tel: 020 7639 7211
Head: Ms Christine Wood
Category: DYS PD SLCN EBD Complex needs (Coed 11-19)

Tuke Secondary School
Daniels Gardens, PECKHAM SE15 6ER
Tel: 020 7639 5584
Head: Ms Heidi Tully
Category: SLD PMLD ASD (Coed 11-19)

LONDON
SUTTON
CHILDREN, YOUNG PEOPLE AND LEARNING SERVICES

The Grove, Carshalton, Surrey SM5 3AL
Tel: 020 8770 5000

CARSHALTON

Wandle Valley School
Welbeck Road, CARSHALTON, Surrey SM5 1LP
Tel: 020 8648 1365
Head: Mr D L Bone
Category: SEBD (Coed 5-16)

WALLINGTON

Carew Manor School
Church Road, WALLINGTON, Surrey SM6 7NH
Tel: 020 8647 8349
Acting Head: Mr John Prior
Category: MLD ASD (Coed 7-16)

Sherwood Park School
Streeters Lane, WALLINGTON, Surrey SM6 7NP
Tel: 020 8773 9930
Head: Mrs Ann Nanasi
Category: SLD PMLD (Coed 2-19)

LONDON
TOWER HAMLETS
EDUCATION AUTHORITY

SEN Service, 3rd Floor, Mulberry Place, 5 Clove Crescent, London E14 2BG
Tel: 020 7364 4880

BETHNAL GREEN

Beatrice Tate School
St Jude's Road, BETHNAL GREEN, London E2 9RW
Tel: 020 7739 6249
Head: Mr A Black
Category: PMLD SLD (Coed Day 11-19)

BOW

Cherry Trees School
68 Campbell Road, BOW, London E3 4EA
Tel: 020 8983 4344
Head: Mr A Fletcher
Category: SEBD (Boys Day 5-11)

Phoenix School
49 Bow Road, BOW, London E3 2AD
Tel: 020 8980 4740
Head: Mr S Harris
Category: ASD (Coed Day 3-19)

BROMLEY-BY-BOW

Ian Mikardo High School
60 William Guy Gardens, Talwin Street, BROMLEY-BY-BOW, London E3 3LF
Tel: 020 3069 0760
Head: Ms C Lillis
Category: SEBD (Boys Day 11-16)

LIMEHOUSE

Stephen Hawking School
Brunton Place, LIMEHOUSE, London E14 7LL
Tel: 020 7423 9848
Head: Dr Matthew Rayner
Category: PMLD (Coed Day 2-11)

SEAFORD (East Sussex)

Bowden House School
Firle Road, SEAFORD (East Sussex) BN25 2JB
Tel: 01323 893138
Head: Mr G Crook
Category: BESD (Boys Boarding 9-16)

LONDON
WALTHAM FOREST
CHILDREN AND YOUNG PEOPLE SERVICES

Silver Birch House, Uplands Business Park, Blackhorse Lane, Walthamstow, London E17 5SD
Tel: 020 8496 3000

HALE END

Joseph Clarke School
Vincent Road, Highams Park, HALE END, London E4 9PP
Tel: 020 8523 4833
Head: Peter Falconbridge
Category: VIS Complex needs (Coed 2-18)

LEYTON

Belmont Park School
101 Leyton Green Road, LEYTON, London E10 6DB
Tel: 0208 556 0006
Head: Ms Julia Mainwaring
Category: Challenging behaviour (Coed 11-16)

WALTHAM FOREST

Whitefield School & Centre
Macdonald Road, WALTHAM FOREST, London E17 4AZ
Tel: 020 8531 3426
Head: Ms Elaine Colquhoun
Category: LD MSI SP&LD (Coed 2-19)

WALTHAMSTOW

William Morris School
Folly Lane, WALTHAMSTOW, London E17 5NT
Tel: 020 8503 2225
Head: Mr Alan Campbell
Category: MLD SLD PMLD (Coed 11-16)

WOODFORD GREEN

Brookfield House School
Alders Avenue, WOODFORD GREEN, Essex IG8 9PY
Tel: 020 8527 2464
Head: Mr Gary Pocock
Category: HI PD Complex medical needs (Coed 2-16)

LONDON
WANDSWORTH
EDUCATION AUTHORITY

Special Needs Assessment Section, The Town Hall, High Street, Wandsworth, London SW18 2PU
Tel: 020 8871 8061

BALHAM

Oak Lodge School
101 Nightingale Lane, BALHAM, London SW12 8NA
Tel: 020 8673 3453
Head: Ms Shanee Buxton
Category: D (Coed, Day/boarding 11-19)

BROADSTAIRS

Bradstow School
Dumpton Park Drive, BROADSTAIRS, Kent CT10 1BY
Tel: 01843 862123
Head: Ms Sarah Dunn
Category: PD AUT Challenging behaviour (Coed 5-19)

EARLSFIELD

Garratt Park School
Waldron Road, EARLSFIELD, London SW18 3BT
Tel: 020 8946 5769
Head: Mrs I Parkes
Category: MLD SP&LD (Coed 11-18)

PUTNEY

Paddock Primary School
St Margaret's Crescent, PUTNEY, London SW15 6HL
Tel: 020 8788 5648
Head: Ms Sarah Santos
Category: ASD MLD SLD (Coed 3-11)

ROEHAMPTON

Greenmead School
St Margaret's Crescent, ROEHAMPTON, London SW15 6HL
Tel: 020 8789 1466
Head: Ms Gail Weir
Category: PD PMLD (Coed 3-11)

Paddock Secondary School
Priory Lane, ROEHAMPTON, London SW15 5RT
Tel: 020 8878 1521
Head: Ms P Walpole
Category: SCLD ASD with SLD (Coed 11-19)

SOUTHFIELDS

Linden Lodge
61 Princes Way, SOUTHFIELDS, London SW19 6JB
Tel: 020 8788 0107
Head: Mr Roger Legate
Category: VIS PMLD MSI (Coed 3-11)

TOOTING

Nightingale School
Beechcroft Road, TOOTING, London SW17 7DF
Tel: 020 8874 9096
Head: Mr Mike Chivers
Category: BESD (Boys 11-19)

LONDON
CITY OF WESTMINSTER
CHILDREN'S SERVICE AUTHORITY

SEN Team, 1st Floor, 4 Frampton Street, London NW8 8LF
Tel: 020 7641 5348, *Fax:* 020 7641 7609

LONDON

College Park School
C/o Westminster Kingsway College, Castle Lane, LONDON SW1E 6DR
Tel: 020 7976 5593
Head: Regan Watkinson
Category: MLD (Coed 5-19)

Queen Elizabeth II Jubilee School
Kennet Road, LONDON W9 3LG
Tel: 020 7641 5825
Acting Head: Mr Scott Pickard
Category: SLD (Coed 5-19)

LUTON
BOROUGH COUNCIL

The SEN Assessment Team, Unity House, 111 Stuart Street, Luton LU1 5NP
Tel: 01582 548132

LUTON

Lady Zia Werner School
Ashcroft Road, LUTON, Bedfordshire LU2 9AY
Tel: 01582 728705
Head: Mrs D May
Category: SLD PMLD (Yr 1-6 & Early Years)

Richmond Hill School
Sunridge Avenue, LUTON, Bedfordshire LU2 7JL
Tel: 01582 721019
Head: Mrs J Miller
Category: SLD PMLD (Primary Yr 1-6)

Woodlands Secondary School
Northwell Drive, LUTON, Bedfordshire LU3 3SP
Tel: 01582 572880
Head: Mrs Jill Miller
Category: SLD PMLD (11-19)

GREATER MANCHESTER
BOLTON
CHILDREN'S SERVICES OFFICES

Paderborn House, Civic Centre, Bolton BL1 1AU
Tel: 01204 332121

BOLTON

Firwood School
Crompton Way, BOLTON BL2 3AF
Tel: 01204 333044
Head: Dr Jonathan Steele
Category: SLD PMLD ASD (Coed 11-19)

Ladywood School
Masefield Road, Little Lever, BOLTON
BL3 1NG
Tel: 01204 333400
Head: Mrs Sally McFarlane
Category: MLD with Complex needs incl
ASD PD MSI (Coed 4-11)

Rumworth School
Armadale Road, Ladybridge, BOLTON
BL3 4TP
Tel: 01204 333600
Head: Mr Bill Bradbury
Category: MLD with Complex needs incl
ASD PD MSI (Coed 11-19)

Thomasson Memorial School
Devonshire Road, BOLTON BL1 4PJ
Tel: 01204 333118
Head: Mr Bill Wilson
Category: D HI (Coed 4-11)

FARNWORTH

Green Fold School
Highfield Road, FARNWORTH BL4 0RA
Tel: 01204 335883
Head: Mrs Jane Grecic
Category: SLD ASD PMLD (Coed 4-11)

HORWICH

Lever Park School
Stocks Park Drive, HORWICH BL6 6DE
Tel: 01204 332666
Head: Mr Colin Roscoe
Category: SEBD (Coed 11-16)

GREATER MANCHESTER
BURY
CHILDREN'S SERVICES

SEN Team, Seedfield Site, Parkinson
Street, Bury, Lancashire BL9 6NY
Tel: 01612 535692

BURY

Elms Bank Specialist Arts College
Ripon Avenue, Whitefield, BURY M45 8PJ
Tel: 0161 766 1597
Head: Mrs E J Parkinson
Category: LD (Coed 11-19)

Millwood Primary Special
School Street, Radcliffe, BURY M26 3BW
Tel: 0161 724 2266
Head: Ms H Chadwick
Category: SLD PMLD ASD AUT Complex
needs (Coed 2-11)

PRESTWICH

**Cloughside College (Hospital Special
School)**
Bury New Road, PRESTWICH M25 3BL
Tel: 0161 772 4625
Head: Mrs M Cullen
Category: HS (Coed 14-19)

RAMSBOTTOM

Pupil Learning Centre
New Summerseat House, Summerseat
Lane, RAMSBOTTOM BL0 9UD
Tel: 01204 885277
Head: Mrs K Chantrey

GREATER MANCHESTER
MANCHESTER
LOCAL AUTHORITY

Children's Services, 1st Floor, Universal
Square, Devonshire Street North,
Manchester, Lancashire M12 6JH
Tel: 0161 245 7439, *Fax:* 0161 274 7084

CONGLETON

Buglawton Hall School
Buxton Road, CONGLETON, Cheshire
CW12 3PQ
Tel: 01260 274492
Head: Ms Lynette Edwards
Category: BESD (Residential Boys 8-16)

MANCHESTER

Ashgate Primary School
Crossacres Road, Peel Hall,
Wythenshawe, MANCHESTER M22 5DR
Tel: 0161 219 6642
Head: Ms Dianne Wolstenholme
Category: SLD (5-11)

Camberwell Park School
Bank House Road, Blackley,
MANCHESTER M9 8LT
Tel: 0161 740 1897
Head: Mrs Mary Isherwood
Category: SLD (2-11)

Castlefield Campus
Jackson Crescent, Hulme, MANCHESTER
M15 5AL
Tel: 0161 234 5670
Head: Mr Alan Braven
Category: (14-16)

Grange School
Matthews Lane, MANCHESTER M12 4GR
Tel: 0161 231 2590
Head: Mr Keith Cox
Category: ASD (4-19)

Lancasterian School
Elizabeth Slinger Road, West Didsbury,
MANCHESTER M20 2XA
Tel: 0161 445 0123
Head: Mrs Katie Cass
Category: PD (2-16)

**Manchester Hospital Schools & Home
Teaching Service**
3rd Floor, Royal Manchester Children's
Hospital, MANCHESTER M13 9WL
Tel: 0161 701 0684
Head of Service: Mrs Sandra Hibbert
Category: HS

Meade Hill School
Chain Road, Blackley, MANCHESTER
M9 6GN
Tel: 0161 234 3925
Head: Mr George Campbell
Category: BESD (11-16)

Melland High School
50 Wembley Road, Gorton,
MANCHESTER M18 7DT
Tel: 0161 223 9915
Head: Mrs Judith O'Kane
Category: SLD (11-19)

North Ridge High School
Higher Blackley Educational Village,
Alworth Road, MANCHESTER M9 0RP
Tel: 0161 234 3588
Head: Mrs Bernice Kostick
Category: MLD (11-19)

Piper Hill High School
Firbank Road, Newall Green,
MANCHESTER M23 2YS
Tel: 0161 436 3009
Head: Ms Linda Jones
Category: SLD (11-19)

Rodney House School
388 Slade Lane, Burnage, MANCHESTER
M19 2HT
Tel: 0161 224 2774
Head: Ms Nuala Finegan
Category: ASD (2-5)

Southern Cross School
Barlow Hall Road, Chorlton,
MANCHESTER M21 7JJ
Tel: 0161 881 2695
Head: Miss Jackie Sale
Category: BESD (11-16)

The Birches School
Newholme Road, West Didsbury,
MANCHESTER M20 2XZ
Tel: 0161 448 8895
Head: Mr Andrew Pitts
Category: SLD (2-11)

GREATER MANCHESTER
OLDHAM
EDUCATION & CULTURAL SERVICES

Civic Centre, West Street, Oldham,
Greater Manchester OL1 1UT
Tel: 0161 770 3000

CHADDERTON

Kingfisher Community Special School
Foxdenton Lane, CHADDERTON OL9 9QR
Tel: 0161 770 5910
Head: Mrs Anne Redmond
Category: PD MLD SLD

OLDHAM

New Bridge Learning Centre
St Martins Road, OLDHAM OL8 2PZ
Tel: 0161 620 0231
Head: Mr Graham Quinn

New Bridge School
Roman Road, Hollinwood, OLDHAM,
Greater Manchester OL8 3PH
Tel: 0161 770 6999
Head: Mr Graham Quinn
Category: SLD MLD PD HI VIS

Spring Brook
Spring Brook, Heron Street, OLDHAM,
Greater Manchester OL8 4JD
Tel: 0161 770 5007
Head: Mrs Janet Jones
Category: EBD

GREATER MANCHESTER
ROCHDALE
METROPOLITAN BOROUGH COUNCIL

Support for Learning Service, PO Box
70, Municipal Offices, Smith Street,
Rochdale OL16 1YD
Tel: 01706 647474, *Fax:* 01706 925033

MIDDLETON

Newlands School
Waverley Road, MIDDLETON M24 6JG
Tel: 0161 655 0220
Head: Mrs D Rogers
Category: Generic Primary Special School
(3-11)

ROCHDALE

Brownhill Learning Community
Heights Lane, ROCHDALE OL12 0PZ
Tel: 0300 303 8384
Head: Mrs K Connolly
Category: EBD (10-16)

Redwood School
Hudson's Walk, ROCHDALE OL11 5EF
Tel: 01706 750815
Head: Mr S Pidgeon
Category: Generic Secondary Special
School (11-19)

Springside School
Albert Royds Street, ROCHDALE
OL16 2SU
Tel: 01706 764451
Head: Ms E Templeman
Category: Generic Primary Special School
(3-11)

GREATER MANCHESTER
SALFORD
CHILDREN'S SERVICES DIRECTORATE

Inclusive Learning Services, 1st Floor,
Burrows House, 10 Priestley Road,
Wardley Industrial Estate, Worsley
M28 2LY
Tel: 0161 607 1671

ECCLES

Chatsworth High School
Chatsworth Road, Ellesmere Park,
ECCLES M30 9DY
Tel: 0161 921 1405
Head: Martin Hanbury
Category: SLD PMLD ASD (Coed 11-19)

New Park High School
Green Lane, ECCLES M30 0RW
Tel: 0161 921 2000
Head: Ms A Bever-Warren
Category: SEBD LD (Coed 11-16)

Oakwood High School
Chatsworth Road, Ellesmere Park,
ECCLES M30 9DY
Tel: 0161 786 1920
Head: Ms Amanda Nicolson
Category: MLD HI VIS SEBD Complex
needs (Coed 11-16)

SWINTON

Springwood Primary School
Barton Road, SWINTON M27 5LP
Tel: 0161 778 0022
Head: Ms Lesley Roberts
Category: ASD MLD SLD PMLD (Coed 2-
11)

GREATER MANCHESTER
STOCKPORT
CHILDREN & YOUNG PEOPLE'S DIRECTORATE

Stopford House, Picadilly, Stockport
SK1 3XE
Tel: 0161 474 3870, *Fax:* 0161 474 3896

STOCKPORT

Castle Hill School
Lapwing Lane, Brinnington, STOCKPORT
SK5 8LF
Tel: 0161 494 6439
Head: Mr John Law
Category: EBD GLD CLD (Coed 11-16)

Heaton School
St James Road, Heaton Moor,
STOCKPORT SK4 4RE
Tel: 0161 432 1931
Head: Ms Elizabeth Seers
Category: SLD PMLD (Coed 10-19)

Lisburne School
Half Moon Lane, Offerton, STOCKPORT
SK2 5LB
Tel: 0161 483 5045
Head: Ms Samantha Benson
Category: CLD (Coed 4-11)

Oakgrove School
Matlock Road, Heald Green, STOCKPORT
SK8 3BU
Tel: 0161 437 4956
Head: Mr Rob Metcalfe
Category: SEBD (Coed 5-11)

Valley School
Whitehaven Road, Bramhall, STOCKPORT
SK7 1EN
Tel: 0161 439 7343
Head: Mrs Cath Goodlet
Category: PMLD ASD SLD (Coed 2-11)

Windlehurst School
Windlehurst Road, Hawk Green, Marple,
STOCKPORT SK6 7HZ
Tel: 0161 427 4788
Head: Ms Lesley Abercromby
Category: EBD (Coed 11-16)

GREATER MANCHESTER
TAMESIDE
SERVICES FOR CHILDREN AND YOUNG PEOPLE

Council Offices, Wellington Road,
Ashton-under-Lyne, Tameside OL6 6DL
Tel: 0161 342 8355, *Fax:* 0161 342 3260

ASHTON-UNDER LYNE

Samuel Laycock School
Broadoak Road, ASHTON-UNDER LYNE,
Tameside OL6 8RF
Tel: 0161 344 1992
Head: Mrs C Humble
Category: MLD (Secondary)

AUDENSHAW

Hawthorns School
Sunnyside Moss Campus, Lumb Lane,
AUDENSHAW, Tameside M34 5SF
Tel: 0161 370 1312
Head: Mrs M Thompson
Category: MLD (Primary)

DUKINFIELD

Cromwell School
Yew Tree Lane, DUKINFIELD, Tameside
SK16 5BJ
Tel: 0161 338 9730
Head: Mr A Foord
Category: SLD PMLD (Secondary)

Oakdale School
Cheetham Hill Road, DUKINFIELD,
Tameside SK16 5LD
Tel: 0161 367 9299
Head: Ms Linda Lester
Category: SLD PMLD (Primary)

White Bridge College
Globe Lane, DUKINFIELD, Tameside
SK16 4UJ
Tel: 0161 214 8484
Head: Mr P Hartman
Category: BESD (Secondary)

HYDE

Thomas Ashton School
Bennett Street, HYDE, Tameside
SK14 1SS
Tel: 0161 368 6208
Head: Mr R A Elms
Category: BESD (Primary)

GREATER MANCHESTER
TRAFFORD
FAMILY INFORMATION SERVICE

C/O, Davyhulme Library, Hayeswater
Road, Davyhulme, Manchester M41 7BL
Tel: 0161 912 1053

ALTRINCHAM

Brentwood Special School
Brentwood Avenue, Timperley,
ALTRINCHAM, Cheshire WA14 1SR
Tel: 0844 842 9060
Head: Mrs Hilary Moon
Category: AUT SLD (Coed 11-19)

Pictor Special School
Grove Lane, Timperley, ALTRINCHAM,
Cheshire WA15 6PH
Tel: 0161 912 3082
Head: Mrs J Spruce
Category: PD MLD SPLD SLCN AUT (Coed 2-11)

FLIXTON

Delamere Special School
Irlam Road, FLIXTON, Greater Manchester
M41 6AP
Tel: 0161 747 5893
Head: Mrs S Nichols
Category: AUT SLD (Coed 2-11)

Woodsend Education Centre
Lydney Road, FLIXTON, Manchester
M41 8RN
Tel: 0161 912 4766
Category: (Coed 5-16)

SALE

Cherry Manor Education Centre
Cherry Lane, SALE, Cheshire M33 4GY
Tel: 0161 912 5214

Manor High School
Manor Avenue, SALE, Cheshire M33 5JX
Tel: 0161 976 1553
Head: Mr N Eltringam
Category: AUT EBD MLD (Coed 11-18)

STRETFORD

Longford Park Special School
74 Cromwell Road, STRETFORD, Greater
Manchester M32 8QJ
Tel: 0161 912 1895
Head: Mrs B Owens
Category: MLD (Coed 5-11)

URMSTON

Egerton High Special School
Kingsway Park, URMSTON, Greater
Manchester M1 7FZ
Tel: 0161 749 7094
Head: Mrs E Scroggie
Category: EBD (Coed 5-16)

GREATER MANCHESTER
WIGAN
CHILDREN AND YOUNG PEOPLE'S SERVICES

Access & Inclusion Team, Progress
House, Westwood Park Drive, Wigan,
Greater Manchester WN3 4HH
Tel: 01942 486145

ATHERTON

New Greenhall School
Green Hall Close, ATHERTON, Greater
Manchester M46 9HP
Tel: 01942 883928
Head: Ms E Loftus
Category: PD CLD AUT (Coed 2-14)

WIGAN

Landgate School
Landgate Lane, Bryn, WIGAN WN4 0EP
Tel: 01942 776688
Head: Ms J Sharps
Category: AUT SP&LD (Coed 4-19)

Newbridge Learning Community School
Moss Lane, Platt Bridge, WIGAN WN2 3TL
Tel: 01942 776020
Head: Mrs E Kucharski

Oakfield High School
Long Lane, Hindley Green, WIGAN
WN2 4XA
Tel: 01942 776142
Head: Mrs C Taylor
Category: MLD SLD PD SEBD (Coed 11-19)

Wigan Hope School
Kelvin Grove, Marus Bridge, WIGAN
WN3 6SP
Tel: 01942 824150
Head: Mr J P R Dahlstrom
Category: ASD SLD PMLD (Coed 2-19)

Willow Grove Primary School
Willow Grove, Ashton-in-Makerfield,
WIGAN WN4 8XF
Tel: 01942 727717
Head: Ms V Pearson
Category: SEBD (Coed 5-11)

MEDWAY
CHILDREN'S SERVICES

Gun Wharf, Dock Road, Chatham
ME4 4TR
Tel: 01634 306000

CHATHAM

Bradfields School
Churchill Avenue, CHATHAM, Kent
ME5 0LB
Tel: 01634 683990
Head: Mr Kim Johnson
Category: MLD SLD ASD (Coed 11-18)

GILLINGHAM

Danecourt Community Special
Hotel Road, Watling Street, GILLINGHAM,
Kent ME8 6AA
Tel: 01634 232589
Head: Mr John Somers
Category: MLD CLD (Coed 4-11)

Rivermead School
Forge Lane, GILLINGHAM, Kent ME7 1UG
Tel: 01634 338348
Head: Ms Susan Rogers
Category: Complex emotional needs
(Coed 11-16)

STROOD

Abbey Court
Rede Court Road, STROOD, Kent
ME2 3SP
Tel: 01634 338220
Head: Ms Karen Joy
Category: SLD (Coed 4-18)

MERSEYSIDE
KNOWSLEY
CHILDREN & FAMILY SERVICES

SEN Team, The Cordingley Building,
Scotchbarn Lane, Prescot, Merseyside
L35 7JD
Tel: 0151 443 5145

HALEWOOD

Highfield School
Baileys Lane, HALEWOOD, Merseyside
L26 0TY
Tel: 0151 288 8930
Acting Head: Ms Pam Kilham
Category: SEBD (Coed 6-16)

Knowsley Southern Primary Support Centre
Arncliffe Road, HALEWOOD, Merseyside
L25 9QE
Tel: 0151 288 8950
Executive Headteacher: Mr Ian Chisnall
Category: MLD AUT SEBD SP&LD (Coed 4-11)

HUYTON

Alt Bridge Secondary Support Centre
Wellcroft Road, HUYTON, Merseyside
L36 7TA
Tel: 0151 477 8310
Head: Mr Barry Kerwin
Category: MLD SPLD CLD ASD SLD PD
(Coed 11-16)

Knowsley Central Primary Support Centre
Mossbrow Road, HUYTON, Merseyside
L36 7SY
Tel: 0151 477 8450
Head: Mrs Patricia Thomas
Category: CLD SEBD (Coed 2-11)

KIRKBY

Knowsley Northern Primary Support Centre
Bramcote Walk, Northwood, KIRKBY,
Knowsley L33 9UR
Tel: 0151 477 8140
Head: Mrs Amanda Nicholson
Category: ASD SEBD PD LD CLD SLD
(Coed 3-11)

Newstead School
Bracknell Avenue, Southdene, KIRKBY,
Knowsley L32 9PW
Tel: 0151 477 8382
Head: Mr Mike Marshall
Category: PRU (Coed 11-18)

Springfield Elms Federation at Bluebell Park
Cawthorne Walk, Southdene, KIRKBY,
Merseyside L32 3XP
Tel: 0151 477 8350
Head: Mr John Parkes
Category: PD PMLD SLD MLD (Coed 2-19)

MERSEYSIDE
LIVERPOOL
CITY COUNCIL

Children's Services (Education),
Municipal Buildings, Dale Street,
Liverpool L2 2DH
Tel: 0151 233 3000

LIVERPOOL

Abbot's Lea School
Beaconsfield Road, Woolton, LIVERPOOL,
Merseyside L25 6EE
Tel: 0151 428 1161
Head: Mrs Margaret Lucas
Category: AUT (Coed 5-19)

Bank View High School
Sherwoods Lane, Fazakerley, LIVERPOOL,
Merseyside L10 1LW
Tel: 0151 525 3451
Head: Mr Ian Wright
Category: CLD (Coed 11-18)

Clifford Holroyde School
Thingwall Lane, LIVERPOOL, Merseyside
L14 7NX
Tel: 0151 228 9500
Head: Ms Elaine Dwyer
Category: EBD (Coed 7-16)

Ernest Cookson School
54 Bankfield Road, West Derby,
LIVERPOOL, Merseyside L13 0BQ
Tel: 0151 220 1874
Head: Mr S Roberts
Category: EBD (Boys 5-16)

Hope School
Naylorsfield Drive, LIVERPOOL,
Merseyside L27 0YD
Tel: 0151 498 4055
Head: Mr Rohit Naik
Category: EBD (Boys 5-16)

Millstead Special Needs Primary
Old Mill Lane, Wavertree, LIVERPOOL,
Merseyside L15 8LW
Tel: 0151 722 0974
Head: Mrs Shirley Jones
Category: SLD (Coed 2-11)

Palmerston School
Beaconsfield Road, Woolton, LIVERPOOL,
Merseyside L25 6EE
Tel: 0151 428 2128
Head: Mrs Alison Burbage
Category: SLD (Coed 11-19)

Princes Primary School
Selborne Street, LIVERPOOL, Merseyside
L8 1YQ
Tel: 0151 709 2602
Head: Mrs Kathy Brent
Category: SLD (Coed 2-11)

Redbridge High School
Sherwoods Lane, Fazakerley, LIVERPOOL,
Merseyside L10 1LW
Tel: 0151 525 5733
Head: Mr Paul Cronin
Category: SLD (Coed 11-19)

Sandfield Park School
Sandfield Walk, West Derby, LIVERPOOL,
Merseyside L12 1LH
Tel: 0151 228 0324
Head: Mr J M Hudson
Category: PD HS (Coed 11-19)

MERSEYSIDE
SEFTON

Children, Schools & Families, Town Hall,
Bootle, Merseyside L20 7AE
Tel: 0151 934 3250

BOOTLE

Rowan Park School
Sterrix Lane, BOOTLE, Merseyside
L21 0DB
Tel: 0151 222 4894
Head: Ms K Lynskey
Category: SLD (Coed 3-18)

CROSBY

Crosby High School
De Villiers Avenue, CROSBY, Merseyside
L23 2TH
Tel: 0151 924 3671
Head: Mrs T Oxton-Grant
Category: MLD (Coed 11-16)

Newfield Special School
Edge Lane, CROSBY, Merseyside L23 4TG
Tel: 0151 934 2991
Head: Mrs J Starkey
Category: BESD (Coed 5-17)

SOUTHPORT

Merefield Special School
Westminster Drive, SOUTHPORT,
Merseyside PR8 2QZ
Tel: 01704 577163
Head: Mrs S Clare
Category: SLD (Coed 3-16)

Presfield High School and Specialist College
Preston New Road, SOUTHPORT,
Merseyside PR9 8PA
Tel: 01704 227831
Head: Mrs G Roberts
Category: ASD (Coed 11-16)

MERSEYSIDE
ST HELENS
COMMUNITY, EDUCATION & LEISURE SERVICES DEPARTMENT

Additional Educational Needs Service,
Contact Centre, Wesley House, St
Helens, Merseyside WA10 1HF
Tel: 01744 676789, *Fax:* 01744 676895

NEWTON-LE-WILLOWS

Mill Green School
Mill Lane, NEWTON-LE-WILLOWS,
Merseyside WA12 8BG
Tel: 01744 678760
Head: Mr Colin Myers
Category: SLD CLD PMLD ASD (Coed 6-19)

Penkford School
Wharf Road, NEWTON-LE-WILLOWS,
Merseyside WA12 9XZ
Tel: 01744 678745
Head: Ms Julie Johnson
Category: SEBD (9-16)

ST HELENS

Lansbury Bridge School
Lansbury Avenue, Parr, ST HELENS,
Merseyside WA9 1TB
Tel: 01744 678579
Head: Mr Bob Brownlow
Category: CLD PD MLD ASD (Coed 3-16)

MERSEYSIDE
WIRRAL
CHILDREN & YOUNG PEOPLE'S DEPARTMENT

Hamilton Building, Conway Street,
Birkenhead CH41 4FD
Tel: 0151 606 2000

BIRKENHEAD

Kilgarth School
Cavendish Street, BIRKENHEAD,
Merseyside CH41 8BA
Tel: 0151 652 8071
Head: Miss J Dawson
Category: EBD ADHD (Boys 11-16)

PRENTON

The Observatory School
Bidston Village Road, Bidston, PRENTON,
Merseyside CH43 7QT
Tel: 0151 652 7093
Head: Mrs Elaine Idris
Category: SEBD LD (Coed 11-16)

THINGWALL

Stanley School
Pensby Road, THINGWALL, Merseyside
CH61 7UG
Tel: 0151 648 3171
Head: Mr A B Newman
Category: SLD AUT CLD (Coed 2-11)

WALLASEY

Clare Mount Specialist Sports College
Fender Lane, Moreton, WALLASEY,
Merseyside CH46 9PA
Tel: 0151 606 9440
Head: Ms S Allen
Category: MLD (Coed 11-19)

Elleray Park School
Elleray Park Road, WALLASEY,
Merseyside CH45 0LH
Tel: 0151 639 3594
Head: Ms M Morris
Category: CLD SLD PD AUT PMLD (Coed 2-11)

Foxfield School
Douglas Drive, Moreton, WALLASEY,
Merseyside CH46 6BT
Tel: 0151 677 8555
Head: Mr Andre Baird
Category: ADHD SLD ASD PD (Coed 11-19)

Orrets Meadow School
Chapelhill Road, Moreton, WALLASEY,
Merseyside CH46 9QQ
Tel: 0151 678 8070
Head: Mrs Carolyn Duncan
Category: SPLD SP&LD LD AUT ASD EBD (Coed 7-11)

Wirral Hospitals Schools
Solar Campus, 235 Leasowe Road,
WALLASEY, Merseyside CH45 8LW
Tel: 0151 637 6310
Head: Mr D Kitchen
Category: HS (Coed 2-19)

WIRRAL

Gilbrook School
Glebe Hey Road, Woodchurch, WIRRAL,
Merseyside CH49 8HE
Tel: 0151 522 3900
Head: Mr R Richardson
Category: EBD DYS (Coed 4-12)

Hayfield School
Manor Drive, Upton, WIRRAL, Merseyside
CH49 4LN
Tel: 0151 677 9303
Head: Ms S Lowy
Category: MLD CLD ASD (Coed 4-11)

Meadowside School
Pool Lane, Woodchurch, WIRRAL,
Merseyside CH49 5LA
Tel: 0151 678 7711
Head: Mrs P Wareing
Category: CLD SLD (Coed 11-19)

The Lyndale School
Lyndale Avenue, Eastham, WIRRAL,
Merseyside CH62 8DE
Tel: 0151 327 3682
Head: Mrs P L Stewart
Category: CLD SLD MLD PMLD (Coed 2-11)

MIDDLESBROUGH
EDUCATION AND LEARNING

SEN Team, Middlesborough Teaching &
Learning Centre, Tranmere Avenue, Town
Farm, Middlesbrough TS3 8PB
Tel: 01642 245432

MIDDLESBROUGH

Beverley School
Saltersgill Avenue, MIDDLESBROUGH,
Cleveland TS4 3JS
Tel: 01642 811350
Head: Mrs Bernadette Knill
Category: AUT (Coed 3-19)

Holmwood School
Saltersgill Avenue, Easterside,
MIDDLESBROUGH, Cleveland TS4 3PT
Tel: 01642 819157
Head: Mr J Appleyard
Category: EBD (Coed 4-11)

Priory Woods School
Tothill Avenue, Netherfields,
MIDDLESBROUGH, Cleveland TS3 0RH
Tel: 01642 770541
Head: Mrs Bernadette Knill
Category: SLD PMLD (Coed 4-19)

MILTON KEYNES
CHILDREN AND FAMILIES SERVICE

Saxon Court, 502 Avebury Boulevard, Milton Keynes MK9 3HS
Tel: 01908 691691, *Fax:* 01908 252727

MILTON KEYNES

Romans Field School
Shenley Road, Bletchley, MILTON KEYNES, Buckinghamshire MK3 7AW
Tel: 01908 376011
Head: Mr Paul Morton
Category: SEBD (Coed Day/boarding 5-12)

Slated Row School
Old Wolverton Road, Wolverton, MILTON KEYNES, Buckinghamshire MK12 5NJ
Tel: 01908 316017
Head: Ms Liz Bull
Category: MLD Complex needs (Coed Day 4-19)

Stephenson Academy
Crosslands, Stantonbury, MILTON KEYNES, Buckinghamshire MK14 6AX
Tel: 01908 889400
Head: Mr Neil Barrett
Category: EBD (Boys Day/boarding 12-16)

The Redway School
Farmborough, Netherfield, MILTON KEYNES, Buckinghamshire MK6 4HG
Tel: 01908 206400
Head: Ms Ruth Sylvester
Category: PMLD CLD SCD (Coed Day 2-19)

The Walnuts School
Admiral Drive, Hazeley, MILTON KEYNES, Buckinghamshire MK8 0PU
Tel: 01908 563885
Head: Mr Nick Jackman
Category: ASD SCD (Coed Day/boarding 4-19)

White Spire School
Rickley Lane, Bletchley, MILTON KEYNES, Buckinghamshire MK3 6EW
Tel: 01908 373266
Head: Ms Maria Penicud
Category: MLD (Coed Day & boarding 5-19)

NORFOLK
CHILDREN'S SERVICES

County Hall, Martineau Lane, Norwich, Norfolk NR1 2DH
Tel: 0344 800 8020

ATTLEBOROUGH

Chapel Road School
Chapel Road, ATTLEBOROUGH, Norfolk NR17 2DS
Tel: 01953 453116
Head: Mrs K Heap
Category: SLD ASD PMLD (Coed 3-19)

CROMER

Sidestrand Hall School
Cromer Road, Sidestrand, CROMER, Norfolk NR27 0NH
Tel: 01263 578144
Head: Mrs Sarah Macro
Category: MLD (Coed 3-19)

DEREHAM

Fred Nicholson School
Westfield Road, DEREHAM, Norfolk NR19 1JB
Tel: 01362 693915
Head: Mrs Alison Kahn
Category: MLD SEBD SLD ASD (Coed 3-19)

GREAT YARMOUTH

John Grant School
Saint George's Drive, Caister-on-Sea, GREAT YARMOUTH, Norfolk NR30 5QW
Tel: 01493 720158
Head: Ms Pam Ashworth
Category: SLD ASD PMLD (Coed 3-19)

KING'S LYNN

Churchill Park School
Winston Churchill Drive, KING'S LYNN, Norfolk PE30 4RP
Tel: 01553 763679
Head: Mrs Diane Whitham
Category: Complex Needs (Day 3-19)

NORWICH

Eaton Hall Specialist Academy
Pettus Road, NORWICH, Norfolk NR4 7BU
Tel: 01603 457480
Head: Miss V Moore
Category: EBD (Coed 7-16)

Hall School
St Faith's Road, Old Catton, NORWICH, Norfolk NR6 7AD
Tel: 01603 466467
Head: Mr Keith McKenzie
Category: CLD (Coed 3-19)

Harford Manor School
43 Ipswich Road, NORWICH, Norfolk NR2 2LN
Tel: 01603 451809
Head: Mr Paul Eteson
Category: ASD PMLD SLD (Coed 3-19)

The Clare School
South Park Avenue, NORWICH, Norfolk NR4 7AU
Tel: 01603 454199
Head: Mr N Smith
Category: PH MSI LD Complex medical needs (Coed 3-19)

The Parkside School
College Road, NORWICH, Norfolk NR2 3JA
Tel: 01603 441126
Head: Mr Barry Payne
Category: SLD AUT EBD MLD MSI PD (Coed 3-19)

SHERINGHAM

Woodfields Special School
Holt Road, SHERINGHAM, Norfolk NR26 8ND
Tel: 01263 820520
Acting Headteacher: Ms Carol Evans
Category: CLD (Coed 3-19)

NORTHAMPTONSHIRE
COUNTY COUNCIL

CYPS, John Dryden House, 8-10 The Lakes, Northampton NN4 7YD
Tel: 01604 364077

CORBY

Maplefields School
Tower Hill Road, CORBY, Northamptonshire NN18 0TH
Tel: 01536 424090
Head: Mrs Lynda Morgan
Category: BESD (3-19)

KETTERING

Isebrook SEN College
Eastleigh Road, KETTERING, Northamptonshire NN15 6PT
Tel: 01536 500030
Head: Mrs Denise Williams
Category: MLD ASD SLD SP&LD PH (11-19)

Kingsley School
Churchill Way, KETTERING, Northamptonshire NN15 5DP
Tel: 01536 316880
Head: Mr Tomas O'Duibhir
Category: PMLD SLD ASD (3-11)

Wren Spinney Community Special School
Westover Road, KETTERING, Northamptonshire NN15 7LB
Tel: 01536 481939
Head: Mrs Deborah Withers
Category: SLD PMLD ASD MSI (11-19)

NORTHAMPTON

Billing Brook Special School
Penistone Road, NORTHAMPTON, Northamptonshire NN3 8EZ
Tel: 01604 773910
Head: Mrs Caroline Grant
Category: MLD ASD SLD SPLD PH (3-19)

Fairfields School
Trinity Avenue, NORTHAMPTON, Northamptonshire NN2 6JN
Tel: 01604 714777
Head: Dr Corallie Murray
Category: PMLD PH MSI SLD ASD (3-11)

Greenfields School and Sports College
Prentice Court, Lings Way, Goldings, NORTHAMPTON, Northamptonshire NN3 8XS
Tel: 01604 741960
Head: Mrs Lisa-Marie Atack
Category: PMLD SLD ASD MSI (11-19)

Kings Meadow School
Manning Road, Moulton Leys, NORTHAMPTON, Northamptonshire NN3 7AR
Tel: 01604 673730
Head: Mrs Karen Lewis
Category: BESD (3-11)

Northgate School Arts College
Queens Park Parade, NORTHAMPTON, Northamptonshire NN2 6LR
Tel: 01604 714098
Head: Miss Sheralee Webb
Category: MLD SLD ASD (11-19)

TIFFIELD

The Gateway School
St Johns Road, TIFFIELD, Northamptonshire NN12 8AA
Tel: 01604 878977
Head: Mr David Lloyd
Category: BESD (11-19)

WELLINGBOROUGH

Friars School
Friar's Close, WELLINGBOROUGH, Northamptonshire NN8 2LA
Tel: 01933 304950
Head: Mrs Suzzanne Ijewsky
Category: MLD SLD ASD (11-19)

Rowan Gate Primary School
Finedon Road, WELLINGBOROUGH, Northamptonshire NN8 4NS
Tel: 01933 304970
Head: Mrs Laura Clarke
Category: PMLD ASD (3-11)

NORTHUMBERLAND
STRATEGY, PLANNING & PERFORMANCE

Family Services Directorate, SEN Team, County Hall, Morpeth, Northumberland NE61 2EF
Tel: 0845 600 6400, *Fax:* 01670 511 413

ALNWICK

Barndale House School
Howling Lane, ALNWICK, Northumberland NE66 1DQ
Tel: 01665 602541
Head: Mr Colin Bradshaw
Category: SLD

BERWICK UPON TWEED

The Grove Special School
Grove Gardens, Tweedmouth, BERWICK UPON TWEED, Northumberland TD15 2EN
Tel: 01289 306390
Head: Mrs Elizabeth Brown
Category: SLD

BLYTH

The Dales
Cowpen Road, BLYTH, Northumberland NE24 4RE
Tel: 01670 352556
Head: Mr Hugh Steele
Category: MLD CLD PH EBD

CHOPPINGTON

Cleaswell Hill School
School Avenue, Guide Post, CHOPPINGTON, Northumberland NE62 5DJ
Tel: 01670 823182
Head: Mr Kevin Burdis
Category: MLD

CRAMLINGTON

Atkinson House School
North Terrace, Seghill, CRAMLINGTON, Northumberland NE23 7EB
Tel: 0191 2980838
Head: Mr Derek Cogle
Category: EBD

Cramlington Hillcrest School
East View Avenue, CRAMLINGTON,
Northumberland NE23 1DY
Tel: 01670 713632
Head: Mr Colin Gibson
Category: MLD

HEXHAM

Hexham Priory School
Corbridge Road, HEXHAM,
Northumberland NE46 1UY
Tel: 01434 605021
Head: Mr Michael Thompson
Category: SLD

MORPETH

**Collingwood School & Media Arts
College**
Stobhillgate, MORPETH, Northumberland
NE61 2HA
Tel: 01670 516374
Head: Mr Richard Jones
Category: MLD CLD AUT SP&LD PH
Emotionally fragile Specific medical
conditions

NOTTINGHAM
CITY COUNCIL

The SEN Team, Glenbrook Management
Centre, Wigman Road, Bilborough,
Nottingham NG8 4PD
Tel: 0115 915 5555

NOTTINGHAM

Nethergate Special School
Swansdowne Road, NOTTINGHAM
NG11 8HX
Tel: 0115 9152959
Head: Mrs Tracey Ydlibi
Category: MLD

Oak Fields School and Sports College
Wigman Road, Bilborough, NOTTINGHAM
NG8 3HW
Tel: 0115 915 3265
Head: Mr David Stewart

Rosehill Special School
St Matthias Road, St Ann's,
NOTTINGHAM NG3 2FE
Tel: 0115 9155815
Head: Mr Andy Sloane
Category: AUT

Westbury School
Chingford Road, Bilborough,
NOTTINGHAM NG8 3BT
Tel: 0115 9155858
Exec Head: Mr John Dyson
Category: EBD

Woodlands Special School
Beechdale Road, Aspley, NOTTINGHAM
NG8 3EZ
Tel: 0115 9155734
Exec Head: Mr John Dyson
Category: MLD

NOTTINGHAMSHIRE
CHILDREN & YOUNG
PEOPLE'S SERVICE

County Hall, Loughborough Road, West
Bridgford, Nottingham, Nottinghamshire
NG2 7QP
Tel: 0300 500 80 80

COTGRAVE

Ash Lea School
Owthorpe Road, COTGRAVE,
Nottinghamshire NG12 3PA
Tel: 0115 989 2744
Head: Mrs D Wigley
Category: SLD (Coed Day 3-16)

KIRKBY-IN-ASHFIELD

Bracken Hill School
Chartwell Road, KIRKBY-IN-ASHFIELD,
Nottinghamshire NG17 7HZ
Tel: 01623 477268
Head: Mr R McCrossen
Category: SLD MLD (Coed Day 3-16)

MANSFIELD

Beech Hill School
Fairholme Drive, MANSFIELD,
Nottinghamshire NG19 6DX
Tel: 01623 626008
Head: Mr M Sutton
Category: MLD (Coed Day 3-16)

Fountaindale School
Nottingham Road, MANSFIELD,
Nottinghamshire NG18 5BA
Tel: 01623 792671
Head: Mr M Dengel
Category: PD (Coed Boarding 3-16)

Redgate School
Somersall Street, MANSFIELD,
Nottinghamshire NG19 6EL
Tel: 01623 455944
Head: Mr Hugh Daybell
Category: MLD (Coed Day 3-16)

Yeoman Park School
Park Hall Road, Mansfield Woodhouse,
MANSFIELD, Nottinghamshire NG19 8PS
Tel: 01623 459540
Head: Mr P Betts
Category: SLD (Coed Day 3-16)

NEWARK

Newark Orchard School
Appleton Gate, NEWARK,
Nottinghamshire NG24 1JR
Tel: 01636 682255
Head: Ms Margot Tyers
Category: SLD MLD (Coed 3-16)

NOTTINGHAM

Carlton Digby School
Digby Avenue, Mapperley, NOTTINGHAM
NG3 6DS
Tel: 0115 956 8289
Head: Mrs G Clifton
Category: SLD (Coed 3-16)

Derrymount School
Churchmoor Lane, Arnold, NOTTINGHAM
NG5 8HN
Tel: 0115 953 4015
Head: Ms K McIntyre
Category: MLD (Coed 3-16)

Foxwood Academy
Derby Road, Bramcote Hills, Beeston,
NOTTINGHAM NG9 3GF
Tel: 0115 917 7202
Head: Mr C Humphreys
Category: MLD (Coed 3-16)

RETFORD

St Giles School
Babworth Road, RETFORD,
Nottinghamshire DN22 7NJ
Tel: 01777 703683
Head: Mrs Hilary Short
Category: MLD SLD (Coed 3-16)

OXFORDSHIRE
CHILDREN, EDUCATION & FAMILIES

SEN Team, Knights Court, 21 Between Towns Road, Cowley, Oxford OX4 3LX
Tel: 01865 815275

ABINGDON

Kingfisher School
Radley Road, ABINGDON, Oxfordshire OX14 3RR
Tel: 01235 555512
Head: Adrienne Martin
Category: SLD PMLD (Coed 2-19)

BANBURY

Frank Wise School
Hornbeam Close, BANBURY, Oxfordshire OX16 9RL
Tel: 01295 263520
Head: Mr Sean O'Sullivan
Category: SLD PMLD (Coed 2-19)

BICESTER

Bardwell School
Hendon Place, Sunderland Drive, BICESTER, Oxfordshire OX26 4RZ
Tel: 01869 242182
Head: John Riches
Category: SLD PMLD MSI SP&LD CLD (Coed 2-19)

OXFORD

ISIS Academy
Iffley Turn, OXFORD OX4 4DU
Tel: 01865 747606
Head: Mrs Kay Willett
Category: BESD Complex MLD (Coed 11-19)

John Watson School
Littleworth Road, Wheatley, OXFORD OX33 1NN
Tel: 01865 452725
Head: Mrs Sally Withey
Category: SLD PMLD (Coed 2-19)

Mabel Prichard School
Cuddesdon Way, OXFORD OX4 6SB
Tel: 01865 777878
Head: Miss Jane Wallington
Category: SLD PMLD (Coed 2-19)

Northern House School
South Parade, OXFORD OX2 7JN
Tel: 01865 557004
Head: Mr Ian Barker
Category: BESD (5-11)

Northfield School
Knights Road, Blackbird Leys, OXFORD OX4 6DQ
Tel: 01865 771703
Head: Mr Mark Blencowe
Category: BESD (Day/residential weekday boarding 11-18)

Oxfordshire Hospital School
The Harlow Centre, Raymund Road, Old Marston, OXFORD OX3 0SW
Tel: 01865 253177
Head: Mr Dave Matthews
Category: HS (Coed 3-18)

Woodeaton Manor School
Woodeaton, OXFORD OX3 9TS
Tel: 01865 558722
Head: Mrs Anne Pearce
Category: BESD (Day/residential weekday boarding 11-18)

SONNING COMMON

Bishopswood Special School
Grove Road, SONNING COMMON, Oxfordshire RG4 9RJ
Tel: 0118 972 4311
Head: Stephen Passey
Category: SLD PMLD (Coed 2-16)

WANTAGE

Fitzwaryn School
Denchworth Road, WANTAGE, Oxfordshire OX12 9ET
Tel: 01235 764504
Head: Stephanie Coneboy
Category: SLD Complex MLD PMLD (Coed 3-19)

WITNEY

Springfield School
The Bronze Barrow, Cedar Drive, Madley Park, WITNEY, Oxfordshire OX28 1AR
Tel: 01993 703963
Head: Mrs Emma Lawley
Category: SLD (Coed 2-16)

PETERBOROUGH
CHILDREN'S SERVICES

1st Foor, Bayard Place, Broadway, Peterborough PE1 1AY
Tel: 01733 864180, *Fax:* 0870 2384083

PETERBOROUGH

Heltwate School
North Bretton, PETERBOROUGH, Cambridgeshire PE3 8RL
Tel: 01733 262878
Head: Ms Debbie Hasman
Category: MLD SLD AUT PD SCD (Coed 4-16)

Marshfields School
Eastern Close, Eastern Avenue, PETERBOROUGH, Cambridgeshire PE1 4PP
Tel: 01733 568058
Head: Mrs Janet James
Category: MLD SCD SEBD SLD (Coed 11-19)

Nenegate School
Park Lane, Eastfield, PETERBOROUGH, Cambridgeshire PE1 5GZ
Tel: 01733 349438
Head: Ms Anna Besley
Category: EBD (Coed 11-16)

Phoenix School
Clayton, Orton Goldhay, PETERBOROUGH, Cambridgeshire PE2 5SD
Tel: 01733 391666/391800
Head: Mr Phil Pike
Category: SLD PMLD PD SCN ASD MSI (Coed 2-19)

PLYMOUTH
DEPARTMENT FOR EDUCATION, LEARNER AND FAMILY SUPPORT

PLYMOUTH

Brook Green Centre for Learning
Bodmin Road, Whitleigh, PLYMOUTH, Devon PL5 4DZ
Tel: 01752 773875
Head: Mr C Edwards
Category: MLD BESD (11-16)

Cann Bridge Special School
Miller Way, Estover, PLYMOUTH, Devon PL6 8UN
Tel: 01752 207909
Head: Mr Michael Loveman
Category: SLD (Day/boarding 3-18)

Courtlands School
Widey Lane, Crownhill, PLYMOUTH, Devon PL6 5JS
Tel: 01752 776848
Head: Mr Lee Earnshaw
Category: MLD BESD (4-11)

Longcause Community Special School
Plympton, PLYMOUTH, Devon PL7 1JB
Tel: 01752 336881
Head: Mrs Anne Thorne
Category: MLD AUT (5-16)

Mill Ford Community Special School
Rochford Crescent, Ernesettle, PLYMOUTH, Devon PL5 2PY
Tel: 01752 300270
Head: Mrs Claire Wills
Category: SLD PMLD AUT (3-19)

Mount Tamar School
Row Lane, St Budeaux, PLYMOUTH, Devon PL5 2EF
Tel: 01752 365128
Head: Mr B Storry
Category: BESD ASD (5-16)

Woodlands
Wood View Drive, Tamerton Foliot Road, Whitleigh, PLYMOUTH, Devon PL6 5ES
Tel: 01752 300101
Head: Mrs A Hemmers
Category: PD PMLD MED (2-18)

BOROUGH OF POOLE
CHILDREN & YOUNG PEOPLE'S INTEGRATED SERVICES

Borough of Poole, The Dolphin Centre, Poole, Dorset BH15 1SA
Tel: 01202 262277

POOLE

Longspee School
Learoyd Road, Canford Heath, POOLE, Dorset BH17 8PJ
Tel: 01202 380266
Acting Head: Mr Stewart Bullen
Category: BESD (5-14)

Montacute School (Academy Status)
3 Canford Heath Road, POOLE, Dorset BH17 9NG
Tel: 01202 693239
Head: Mr Andrew Mears
Category: PMLD SLD CLD PH Medical needs (3-19)

Winchelsea Special School
Guernsey Road, Parkstone, POOLE, Dorset BH12 4LL
Tel: 01202 746240
Head: Mr Sean Pavitt
Category: ADHD ASD ASP MLD (3-16)

PORTSMOUTH
DIRECTORATE OF CHILDREN, FAMILIES AND LEARNING

SEN team, Floor 2 Core 1, Civic Offices, Guildhall Square, Portsmouth, Hampshire PO1 2EA
Tel: 023 9284 1238

PORTSMOUTH

Cliffdale Primary School
Battenburg Avenue, North End, PORTSMOUTH, Hampshire PO2 0SN
Tel: 023 9266 2601
Head: Ms Alison Beane
Category: MLD PD SLCN (Coed 4-11)

Mary Rose School
Gisors Road, Southsea, PORTSMOUTH, Hampshire PO4 8GT
Tel: 023 9285 2330
Head: Ms Alison Beane
Category: SLDCLD PD MLD (Coed 2-19)

Redwood Park School
Wembley Grove, Cosham, PORTSMOUTH, Hampshire PO6 2RY
Tel: 023 9237 7500
Head: Mr Tony Cox
Category: MLD SP&LD ASD (Coed 11-16)

READING
DIRECTORATE OF EDUCATION AND CHILDREN'S SERVICES

SEN Team, Civic Centre, Reading RG1 7AE
Tel: 0118 937 2674

READING

Phoenix College
40 Christchurch Road, READING, Berkshire RG2 7AY
Tel: 0118 937 5524
Head: Mrs Ekie Lansdown-Bridge
Category: BESD ADHD (Coed 11-16)

The Avenue Special School
Conwy Close, Tilehurst, READING, Berkshire RG30 4BZ
Tel: 0118 937 5554
Head: Mrs S Bourne
Category: CLD (Coed 2-19)

The Holy Brook Special School
145 Ashampstead Road, Southcote, READING, Berkshire RG30 3LT
Tel: 0118 937 5489
Head: Mr Lee Smith

REDCAR AND CLEVELAND
CHILDREN'S SERVICES

SEN Service, Seafield House,
Kirkleatham Street, Redcar TS10 1SP
Tel: 01642 444104

MIDDLESBROUGH

Pathways Special School
Tennyson Avenue, Grangetown,
MIDDLESBROUGH TS6 7NP
Tel: 01642 779292
Head: Mr S O'Gara
Category: SEBD (Coed Day 7-15)

REDCAR

Kirkleatham Hall School
Kirkleatham Village, REDCAR, Cleveland
TS10 4QR
Tel: 01642 483009
Head: Mrs K Robson
Category: PMLD ASD Complex needs
(Coed Day 4-19)

SALTBURN-BY-SEA

KTS Academy
Marshall Drive, Brotton, SALTBURN-BY-SEA, Cleveland TS12 2UW
Tel: 01287 677265
Head: Mr K Thompson
Category: SLD PMLD BESD ASD PD
SP&LD (Coed day 2-19)

RUTLAND
INCLUSION SERVICE

Catmose, Oakham, Rutland LE15 6HP
Tel: 01572 722577

OAKHAM

The Parks School
Burley Road, OAKHAM, Rutland LE15 6GY
Tel: 01572 722404
Head: Mrs J Gibson
Category: AUT MLD PMLD SP&LD VIS
SEBD (Coed 2-5)

SHROPSHIRE
SEN TEAM

Shropshire Council, The Shirehall, Abbey
Foregate, Shrewsbury, Shropshire
SY2 6ND
Tel: 01743 254395

SHREWSBURY

Severndale School
Hearne Way, Monkmoor, SHREWSBURY,
Shropshire SY2 5SL
Tel: 01743 281600
Head: Mr Christopher Davies
Category: SLD PD (Coed Day 2-19)

Woodlands School
The Woodlands Centre, Tilley Green,
Wem, SHREWSBURY, Shropshire SY4 5PJ
Tel: 01939 232372
Head: Mr R Wilson
Category: EBD (Coed 11-16)

SLOUGH
SLOUGH BOROUGH COUNCIL

Service for Children with Learning
Difficulties & Disabilities, St Martin's
Place, 51 Bath Road, Slough, Berkshire
SL1 3UF
Tel: 01753 475111

SLOUGH

Arbour Vale School
Farnham Road, SLOUGH, Berkshire
SL2 3AE
Tel: 01753 515560
Head: Mrs Debbie Richards
Category: SLD ASD MLD (Coed 2-19)

Haybrook College/Millside School
112 Burnham Lane, SLOUGH, Berkshire
SL1 6LZ
Tel: 01628 696077/696079
Head: Ms Helen Huntley
Category: BESD (Boys 11-16)

Littledown School
Queen's Road, SLOUGH, Berkshire
SL1 3QW
Tel: 01753 521734
Head: Jo Matthews
Category: BESD (Coed 5-11)

SOMERSET
CHILDREN AND YOUNG PEOPLE'S SERVICES

County Hall, Taunton, Somerset TA1 4DY
Tel: 0845 345 9122

BRIDGWATER

Penrose School
Albert Street, Willow Brook,
BRIDGWATER, Somerset TA6 7ET
Tel: 01278 423660
Head: Mrs E Hayward
Category: CLD ASD SLD (4-10 and Post-16)

Robert Blake Science College
Hamp Avenue, BRIDGWATER, Somerset
TA6 6AW
Tel: 01278 456243
Head: Mrs Ann Winter
Category: AUT EBD CLD (Coed Day 4-16)

FROME

Critchill School
Nunney Road, FROME, Somerset
BA11 4LB
Tel: 01373 464148
Head: Mr Mark Armstrong
Category: SLD MLD CLD (Coed Day 4-16)

STREET

Avalon Special School
Brooks Road, STREET, Somerset
BA16 0PS
Tel: 01458 443081
Head: Mrs Alison Murkin
Category: SLD MLD PMLD ASD (Coed Day 3-16)

TAUNTON

Selworthy School
Selworthy Road, TAUNTON, Somerset
TA2 8HD
Tel: 01823 284970
Head: Ms Karen Milton
Category: SLD PMLD MLD ASD BESD
(Coed Day 4-19)

**Sky College (formerly The Priory
School)**
Pickeridge Close, TAUNTON, Somerset
TA2 7HW
Tel: 01823 275569
Executive Head: Mr Richard Berry
Category: EBD (Boys Boarding 11-16)

YEOVIL

Fairmead School
Mudford Road, YEOVIL, Somerset
BA21 4NZ
Tel: 01935 421295
Head: Miss Diana Denman
Category: MLD SEBD AUT SLD (Coed Day
4-16)

Fiveways Special School
Victoria Road, YEOVIL, Somerset
BA21 5AZ
Tel: 01935 476227
Head: Mr M Collis
Category: SLD PMLD ASD (Coed Day 4-
19)

NORTH SOMERSET
CHILDREN AND YOUNG
PEOPLE'S SERVICES

Special Educational Needs Team, Town
Hall, Room 119, Weston-Super-Mare,
North Somerset BS23 1UJ
Tel: 01275 888297

NAILSEA

Ravenswood School
Pound Lane, NAILSEA, North Somerset
BS48 2NN
Tel: 01275 854134
Head: Mrs P Clark
Category: CLD SLD (3-19)

WESTON-SUPER-MARE

Baytree School
The Campus, Highlands Lane, WESTON-
SUPER-MARE, North Somerset BS24 7DX
Tel: 01934 427555
Head: Mrs F Richings
Category: SLD (3-19)

Westhaven School
Ellesmere Road, Uphill, WESTON-SUPER-
MARE, North Somerset BS23 4UT
Tel: 01934 632171
Head: Mrs C Hill
Category: CLD (7-16)

SOUTHAMPTON
CITY COUNCIL

SEN Team, 4th Floor (South), Marland
House, (off Civic Centre Road),
Southampton, Hampshire SO14 7PQ
Tel: 023 8083 3270

SOUTHAMPTON

Great Oaks School
Vermont Close, SOUTHAMPTON,
Hampshire SO16 7LT
Tel: 023 8076 7660
Head: Mr Andy Evans
Category: MLD AUT ASP SLD (11-18)

Springwell School
Hinkler Road, Thornhill, SOUTHAMPTON,
Hampshire SO19 6DH
Tel: 023 8044 5981
Head: Jackie Partridge
Category: CLD SP&LD AUT SLD
Challenging behaviour (4-11)

The Cedar School
Redbridge Lane, SOUTHAMPTON,
Hampshire SO16 0NX
Tel: 023 8073 4205
Head: Jonathan Howells
Category: PD (3-16)

The Polygon School
Handel Terrace, SOUTHAMPTON,
Hampshire SO15 2FH
Tel: 023 8063 6776
Head: Anne Hendon-John
Category: EBD (Boys 11-16)

Vermont School
Vermont Close, SOUTHAMPTON,
Hampshire SO16 7LT
Tel: 023 8076 7988
Head: Barry Smith
Category: EBD (Boys 5-11)

SOUTHEND-ON-SEA
BOROUGH COUNCIL

Children's Services, Civic Centre, Victoria
Avenue, Southend-on-Sea, Essex
SS2 6ER
Tel: 01702 215007

LEIGH-ON-SEA

The St Christopher School
Mountdale Gardens, LEIGH-ON-SEA,
Essex SS9 4AW
Tel: 01702 524193
Head: Mrs Jackie Mullan
Category: SEBD AUT ADHD (Coed Day 3-
11) ADHD AUT (Coed 11-16)

SOUTHEND-ON-SEA

Kingsdown Special School
Snakes Lane, SOUTHEND-ON-SEA, Essex
SS2 6XT
Tel: 01702 527486
Head: Ms Margaret Rimmer
Category: PNI PD SLD PMLD (Coed Day 3-
14)

Priory Special School
Burr Hill Chase, SOUTHEND-ON-SEA,
Essex SS2 6PE
Tel: 01702 347490
Head: Ms Elizabeth Baines
Category: SEBD (Coed Day 11-16)

St Nicholas School
Philpott Avenue, SOUTHEND-ON-SEA,
Essex SS2 4RL
Tel: 01702 462322
Head: Mrs June Mitchell
Category: SEBD AUT MLD (Coed Day 11-
16)

WESTCLIFF-ON-SEA

Lancaster Special School
Prittlewell Chase, WESTCLIFF-ON-SEA,
Essex SS0 0RT
Tel: 01702 342543
Head: Ms Melanie Hall
Category: PNI PD SLD PMLD (Coed Day
14-19)

STAFFORDSHIRE
CHILDREN & LIFELONG
LEARNING DIRECTORATE

Tipping Street, Stafford, Staffordshire
ST16 2DH
Tel: 0800 1313126

BURNTWOOD

Chasetown Community School
Church Street, Chasetown,
BURNTWOOD, Staffordshire WS7 3QL
Tel: 01543 686315
Head: Dr Linda James
Category: SEBD (Coed Day 4-11)

BURTON UPON TRENT

The Fountains High School
Bitham Lane, Stretton, BURTON UPON
TRENT, Staffordshire DE13 0HB
Tel: 01283 239161
Head: Mrs Melsa Buxton
Category: MLD SLD PMLD AUT (Coed Day
11-19)

The Fountains Primary School
Bitham Lane, Stretton, BURTON UPON
TRENT, Staffordshire DE13 0HB
Tel: 01283 239700
Head: Mrs Melsa Buxton
Category: SLD PMLD MLD AUT (Coed Day
2-11)

CANNOCK

Hednesford Valley High School
Stanley Road, Hednesford, CANNOCK,
Staffordshire WS12 4JS
Tel: 01543 423714
Head: Mrs Anita Rattan
Category: MLD ASD SLD PMLD (Coed Day
10-18)

Sherbrook Primary School
Brunswick Road, CANNOCK,
Staffordshire WS11 5SF
Tel: 01543 510216
Head: Mrs Sarah Ashley
Category: SLD ASD MLD PMLD (Coed Day
2-11)

LEEK

**Horton Lodge Community Special
School and Key Learning Centre**
Reacliffe Road, Rudyard, LEEK,
Staffordshire ST13 8RB
Tel: 01538 306214
Head: Mr Charlie Rivers
Category: PD MSI SP&LD (Coed
Day/boarding 2-11)

Meadows Special School
Springfield Road, LEEK, Staffordshire
ST13 6EU
Tel: 01538 483036
Head: Mr Christopher Best
Category: MLD ASD (Coed Day 11-16)

Springfield Community Special School
Springfield Road, LEEK, Staffordshire
ST13 6LQ
Tel: 01538 383558
Head: Mr Charlie Rivers
Category: SLD PMLD ASD (Coed Day 3-
19)

LICHFIELD

Queen's Croft High School
Birmingham Road, LICHFIELD,
Staffordshire WS13 6PJ
Tel: 01543 510669
Head: Mr John Edwards
Category: MLD (Coed Day 10-19)

Rocklands School
Purcell Avenue, LICHFIELD, Staffordshire
WS13 7PH
Tel: 01543 510760
Head: Ms Sandra Swift
Category: ASD MLD PMLD SLD (Coed Day
2-11)

**Saxon Hill Community Special School
and PDSS**
Kings Hill Road, LICHFIELD, Staffordshire
WS14 9DE
Tel: 01543 414892
Head: Mr Ronald Thickett
Category: PD (Coed Day 2-19)

NEWCASTLE UNDER LYME

Blackfriars Special School
Priory Road, NEWCASTLE UNDER LYME,
Staffordshire ST5 2TF
Tel: 01782 297780
Head: Mr James Kane
Category: PD LD MSI (Coed Day 5-19)

Merryfields School
Hoon Avenue, NEWCASTLE UNDER LYME,
Staffordshire ST5 9NY
Tel: 01782 296076
Head: Mrs Sarah Poyner
Category: MLD PMLD PD AUT (Coed Day
2-11)

The Coppice School
Abbots Way, Westlands, NEWCASTLE
UNDER LYME, Staffordshire ST5 2EY
Tel: 01782 297490
Head: Mr James Kane
Category: MLD PMLD SEBD SLD ASD
(Coed Day 11-19)

STAFFORD

Greenhall Nursery
Second Avenue, Holmcroft, STAFFORD,
Staffordshire ST16 1PS
Tel: 01785 246159
Head: Mrs Karen Milligan
Category: MSI ASD SP&LD (Coed Day 2-
5)

Marshlands Special School
Lansdowne Way, Wildwood, STAFFORD,
Staffordshire ST17 4RD
Tel: 01785 356385
Head: Mrs Kim Ellis
Category: SLD (Coed Day 2-11)

**Walton Hall Community Special School,
a Specialist Arts Centre**
Stafford Road, Walton, STAFFORD,
Staffordshire ST21 6JR
Tel: 01785 850420
Head: Mr Duncan Gorwood
Category: LD (Coed Day/boarding 11-19)

STOKE ON TRENT

**Cicely Haughton Community Special
School**
Westwood Manor, Wetley Rocks, STOKE
ON TRENT, Staffordshire ST9 0BX
Tel: 01782 550202
Head: Mr Leonard Phillips
Category: BESD (Boys Boarding 5-11)

TAMWORTH

Two Rivers High School
Deltic, off Silver Link Road, Glascote,
TAMWORTH, Staffordshire B77 2HJ
Tel: 01827 475690
Head: Mr Anthony Dooley
Category: MLD MSI SLD ASD EBD PMLD
(Coed Day 11-18)

Two Rivers Primary School
Quince, Amington Heath, TAMWORTH,
Staffordshire B77 4EN
Tel: 01827 475740
Head: Mr Anthony Dooley
Category: SLD MSI EBD MLD ASD PMLD
(Coed Day 2-11)

UTTOXETER

Loxley Hall School
Stafford Road, Loxley, UTTOXETER,
Staffordshire ST14 8RS
Tel: 01889 256390
Head: Mr Richard Redgate
Category: EBD (Boys Boarding 11-16)

WOLVERHAMPTON

Cherry Trees School
Giggetty Lane, Wombourne,
WOLVERHAMPTON, West Midlands
WV5 0AX
Tel: 01902 894484
Head: Mr Paul Elliot
Category: SLD MLD ASD(Coed Day 2-11)

Wightwick Hall School
Tinacre Hill, Wightwick,
WOLVERHAMPTON, West Midlands
WV6 8DA
Tel: 01902 761889
Head: Mr Paul Elliot
Category: MLD AUT (Coed Boarding 11-19)

STOCKTON-ON-TEES
BOROUGH COUNCIL

Special Educational Needs (SEN),
Municipal Buildings, Church Road,
Stockton-on-Tees TS18 1LD
Tel: 01642 524813

BILLINGHAM

Ash Trees School
Bowes Road, BILLINGHAM, Stockton-on-Tees TS23 2BU
Tel: 01642 563712
Head: Mrs Pauline Banks
Category: SLD PMLD AUT (Coed 4-11)

STOCKTON-ON-TEES

Abbey Hill School Technology College
Ketton Road, Hardwick Green,
STOCKTON-ON-TEES TS19 8BU
Tel: 01642 677113
Head: Mrs Claire Devine
Category: SLD PMLD AUT (Coed 11-19)

THORNABY

Westlands School
Eltham Crescent, THORNABY, Stockton-on-Tees TS17 9RA
Tel: 01642 883030
Head: Mr Edward Fearnside
Category: BESD (Coed Residential 4-16)

STOKE-ON-TRENT
SEND SERVICES

The Mount Education Support Centre,
Mount Avenue, Penkhull, Stoke-on-Trent, Staffordshire ST4 7JU
Tel: 01782 232538

BLYTHE BRIDGE

Portland School and Specialist College
Uttoxeter Road, BLYTHE BRIDGE,
Staffordshire ST11 9JG
Tel: 01782 392071
Head: Mrs Angela Hardstaff
Category: MLD SEBD (Coed Day 3-16)

FENTON

Kemball Special School
Duke Street, FENTON, Stoke-on-Trent
ST4 3NR
Tel: 01782 234879
Head: Mrs Elizabeth Spooner
Category: PMLD SLD ASD CLD (Coed Day 2-19)

STOKE-ON-TRENT

Abbey Hill School and Performing Arts College
Greasley Road, Bucknall, STOKE-ON-TRENT, Staffordshire ST2 8LG
Tel: 01782 234727
Head: Mr Philip Kidman
Category: MLD AUT (Coed Day 2-18)

TUNSTALL

Heathfield Special School
Chell Heath Road, Chell Heath,
TUNSTALL, Stoke-on-Trent ST6 6PD
Tel: 01782 234494
Head: Ms Catherine Lewis
Category: SLD (Coed Day 2-16)

Middlehurst Special School
Turnhurst Road, Chell, TUNSTALL, Stoke-on-Trent ST6 6NQ
Tel: 01782 234612/234494
Head: Mr Jonathon May
Category: MLD (Coed Day 5-16)

SUFFOLK
COUNTY COUNCIL

Endeavour House, 8 Russell Road,
Ipswich, Suffolk IP1 2BX
Tel: 08456 066 067

BURY ST EDMUNDS (West)

Priory School
Mount Road, BURY ST EDMUNDS (West),
Suffolk IP32 7BH
Tel: 01284 761934
Headteacher: Mr R MacKenzie
Category: MLD (Coed Day & boarding 7-16)

Riverwalk School
South Close, BURY ST EDMUNDS (West),
Suffolk IP33 3JZ
Tel: 01284 764280
Headteacher: Mrs A Finch
Category: SLD (Coed Day 2-19)

IPSWICH (South)

Beacon Hill School
Stone Lodge Lane West, IPSWICH
(South), Suffolk IP2 9HW
Tel: 01473 601175
Head: Ms Carolyn Davis
Category: MLD ASD (Coed Day 5-16)

The Bridge School Primary Campus
Heath Road, IPSWICH (South), Suffolk
IP4 5SN
Tel: 01473 725508
Head: Mr O Doran
Category: SLD (Coed Day 3-11)

The Bridge School Secondary Campus
Sprites Lane, Belstead, IPSWICH (South),
Suffolk IP8 3ND
Tel: 01473 556200
Head: Mr O Doran
Category: SLD (Coed Day 11-16)

Thomas Wolsey School
Defoe Road, IPSWICH (South), Suffolk
IP1 6SG
Tel: 01473 467600
Head: Mrs Nancy McArdle
Category: PD/Comunication (Coed Day 3-16)

LOWESTOFT (North)

The Ashley School Academy Trust
Ashley Downs, LOWESTOFT (North),
Suffolk NR32 4EU
Tel: 01502 565439
Head: Mrs L Dupen
Category: MLD (Coed Day & boarding 7-16)

Warren School
Clarkes Lane, LOWESTOFT (North),
Suffolk NR33 8HT
Tel: 01502 561893
Head: Mrs D Moxon
Category: SLD (Coed Day 3-19)

SUDBURY (West)

Hillside Special School
Hitchcock Place, SUDBURY (West),
Suffolk CO10 1NN
Tel: 01787 372808
Head: Mrs S Upson
Category: SLD (Coed day 3-19)

SURREY
EDUCATION AUTHORITY

Contact Centre, County Hall, Penrhyn
Road, Kingston upon Thames, Surrey
KT1 2DW
Tel: 03456 009009

ADDLESTONE

Philip Southcote School
Addlestone Moor, ADDLESTONE, Surrey
KT15 2QH
Tel: 01932 562326
Head Teacher: Mr R W Horton
Category: LD (11-16)

CAMBERLEY

Carwarden House Community School
118 Upper Chobham Road, CAMBERLEY,
Surrey GU15 1EJ
Tel: 01276 709080
Head Teacher: Mr J O'Brien
Category: LD (11-19)

Portesbery School
Portesbery Road, CAMBERLEY, Surrey
GU15 3SZ
Tel: 01276 63078
Head Teacher: Mr M Sartin
Category: SLD (2-19)

CATERHAM

Clifton Hill School
Chaldon Road, CATERHAM, Surrey
CR3 5PH
Tel: 01883 347740
Head Teacher: Ms Andrea Ashton-Coulton
Category: SLD (11-19)

Sunnydown School
Portley House, 152 Whyteleafe Road,
CATERHAM, Surrey CR3 5ED
Tel: 01883 342281
Head Teacher: Mr T M Armstrong
Category: Aspergers/ASD (Boarding &
day 11-16)

CHOBHAM

Wishmore Cross School
Alpha Road, CHOBHAM, Surrey
GU24 8NE
Tel: 01276 857555
Acting Head Teacher: Mr J Donnelly
Category: BESD (Boarding & day 11-16)

DORKING

Starhurst School
Chart Lane South, DORKING, Surrey
RH5 4DB
Tel: 01306 883763
Head Teacher: Mr J Watson
Category: BESD (Boarding & day 11-16)

FARNHAM

The Abbey School
Menin Way, FARNHAM, Surrey GU9 8DY
Tel: 01252 725059
Head Teacher: Mr C J Gardiner
Category: LD (11-16)

The Ridgeway Community School
Frensham Road, FARNHAM, Surrey
GU9 8HB
Tel: 01252 724562
Head Teacher: Mr D Morgan
Category: SLD (2-19)

GUILDFORD

Gosden House School
Horsham Road, Bramley, GUILDFORD,
Surrey GU5 0AH
Tel: 01483 892008
Head Teacher: Mr J David
Category: LD (Boarding & day 5-16)

Pond Meadow School
Larch Avenue, GUILDFORD, Surrey
GU1 1DR
Tel: 01483 532239
Head Teacher: Mr D J Monk
Category: SLD (2-19)

Wey House School
Horsham Road, Bramley, GUILDFORD,
Surrey GU5 0BJ
Tel: 01483 898130
Head Teacher: Ms D Smith
Category: BESD (Day only 7-11)

LEATHERHEAD

West Hill School
Kingston Road, LEATHERHEAD, Surrey
KT22 7PW
Tel: 01372 814714
Head Teacher: Mrs J V Nettleton
Category: LD (11-16)

Woodlands School
Fortyfoot Road, LEATHERHEAD, Surrey
KT22 8RY
Tel: 01372 377922
Head Teacher: Ms A Knight
Category: SLD (Day 2-19)

OXTED

Limpsfield Grange School
89 Bluehouse Lane, Limpsfield, OXTED,
Surrey RH8 0RZ
Tel: 01883 713928
Head Teacher: Mrs S Williams-Wild
Category: ELD (Boarding & day 11-16)

REDHILL

St Nicholas School
Taynton Drive, Merstham, REDHILL,
Surrey RH1 3PU
Tel: 01737 215488
Head Teacher: Mr C Anderson
Category: BESD LD (Boarding & day 11-16)

Woodfield School
Sunstone Grove, Merstham, REDHILL,
Surrey RH1 3PR
Tel: 01737 642623
Head Teacher: Mrs S Lawrence
Category: LD (11-19)

REIGATE

Brooklands School
27 Wray Park Road, REIGATE, Surrey
RH2 0DF
Tel: 01737 249941
Head Teacher: Mr M Bryant
Category: SLD (2-11)

SHEPPERTON

Manor Mead School
Laleham Road, SHEPPERTON, Middlesex
TW17 8EL
Tel: 01932 241834
Head Teacher: Mrs L F Neal
Category: SLD (2-11)

WALTON-ON-THAMES

Walton Leigh School
Queens Road, WALTON-ON-THAMES,
Surrey KT12 5AB
Tel: 01932 223243
Head Teacher: Mrs L Mardell
Category: SLD (11-19)

WOKING

Freemantles School
Smarts Heath Road, Mayford Green,
WOKING, Surrey GU22 0AN
Tel: 01483 545680
Head Teacher: Mr J Price
Category: ASD (4-19)

The Park School
Onslow Crescent, WOKING, Surrey
GU22 7AT
Tel: 01483 772057
Head Teacher: Mrs K Eastwood
Category: LD (11-16)

WORCESTER PARK

Linden Bridge School
Grafton Road, WORCESTER PARK, Surrey
KT4 7JW
Tel: 020 8330 3009
Head Teacher: Mrs R Watt
Category: ASD (Residential & day 4-19)

EAST SUSSEX
CHILDREN'S SERVICES AUTHORITY

SEN Team, PO Box 4, County Hall, St
Anne's Crescent, Lewes, East Sussex
BN7 1SG
Tel: 01273 481230

BEXHILL-ON-SEA

Glyne Gap School
Hastings Road, BEXHILL-ON-SEA, East
Sussex TN40 2PU
Tel: 01424 217720
Head: Mr J A Hassell
Category: CLD/ASD (2-19)

CROWBOROUGH

Grove Park School - Pre-School & Primary School
Church Road, CROWBOROUGH, East
Sussex TN6 1BN
Tel: 01892 663018
Category: CLD/ASD

Grove Park School - Secondary & Post 16
Beacon Community College, East
Beeches Road, CROWBOROUGH, East
Sussex TN6 2AS
Tel: 01892 663018
Category: CLD/ASD

EASTBOURNE

Hazel Court Special School
The Causeway School, Larkspur Drive,
EASTBOURNE, East Sussex BN23 8EJ
Tel: 01323 465720
Head: Mr P Gordon
Category: CLD/ASD (11-19)

South Downs Community Special School (West Site)
Beechy Avenue, EASTBOURNE, East
Sussex BN20 8NU
Tel: 01323 730302
Head: Mr R Palladino
Category: ACLD (4-11)

The Lindfield School
Lindfield Road, EASTBOURNE, East
Sussex BN22 0BQ
Tel: 01323 502988
Category: ACLD (11-16)

HASTINGS

Torfield School
Croft Road, HASTINGS, East Sussex
TN34 3JT
Tel: 01424 428228
Head: Ms J Mockford
Category: ACLD (4-11)

HEATHFIELD

St Mary's School
Maynards Green, Horam, HEATHFIELD,
East Sussex TN21 0BT
Tel: 01435 812278
Category: LD EBSD (Boys Day/residential
9-16)

SEAFORD

Cuckmere House School
Eastbourne Road, SEAFORD, East Sussex
BN25 4BA
Tel: 01323 893319
Executive Head: Mr F Stanford
Category: SEBD (Day/residential 4-16)

ST LEONARDS-ON-SEA

New Horizons School
Beauchamp Road, ST LEONARDS-ON-
SEA, East Sussex TN38 9JU
Tel: 01424 858020
Head: Miss S Hopkins
Category: SEBD (7-16)

Saxon Mount School
Edinburgh Road, ST LEONARDS-ON-SEA,
East Sussex TN38 8HH
Tel: 01424 426303
Head: Mr R Preece
Category: ACLD (11-16)

WEST SUSSEX
CHILDREN & YOUNG PEOPLE'S SERVICES

County Hall, West Street, Chichester,
West Sussex PO19 1RQ
Tel: 0845 075 1007

BURGESS HILL

**Woodlands Meed Special Educational
Needs School**
Chanctonbury Road, BURGESS HILL,
West Sussex RH15 9EY
Tel: 01444 244133
Head: Ms G Perry
Category: LD (Coed 2-19)

CHICHESTER

Fordwater School
Summersdale Road, CHICHESTER, West
Sussex PO19 6PP
Tel: 01243 782475
Head: Mrs S Meekings
Category: SLD (Coed 2-19)

Littlegreen School
Compton, CHICHESTER, West Sussex
PO18 9NW
Tel: 023 9263 1259
Head: Mr R Hatherley
Category: SEBD (Boys 7-16)

St Anthony's School
Woodlands Lane, CHICHESTER, West
Sussex PO19 5PA
Tel: 01243 785965
Head: Ms H Ball
Category: MLD (Coed 4-16)

CRAWLEY

Manor Green College
Lady Margaret Road, Ifield, CRAWLEY,
West Sussex RH11 0DX
Tel: 01293 520351
Head: Mr G Robson
Category: LD (Coed 11-19)

Manor Green Primary School
Lady Margaret Road, Ifield, CRAWLEY,
West Sussex RH11 0DB
Tel: 01293 526873
Head: Mr D Reid
Category: LD (Coed 2-11)

HORSHAM

Queen Elizabeth II Silver Jubilee School
Compton's Lane, HORSHAM, West
Sussex RH13 5NW
Tel: 01403 266215
Head: Mrs L K Dyer
Category: SLD AUT PMLD (Coed 2-19)

LITTLEHAMPTON

Cornfield School
Cornfield Close, Worthing Road,
LITTLEHAMPTON, West Sussex BN17 6HY
Tel: 01903 731277
Head: Ms M Davis
Category: SEBD (Coed 7-16)

SHOREHAM-BY-SEA

Herons Dale School
Hawkins Crescent, SHOREHAM-BY-SEA,
West Sussex BN43 6TN
Tel: 01273 596904
Head: Ms T Stepney
Category: LD (Coed 4-11)

WORTHING

Oak Grove College
The Boulevard, WORTHING, West Sussex
BN13 1JX
Tel: 01903 708870
Head: Mr P Potter
Category: LD (Coed 11-19)

Palatine Primary School
Palatine Road, WORTHING, West Sussex
BN12 6JP
Tel: 01903 242835
Head: Mrs C Goldsmith
Category: LD (Coed 3-11)

SWINDON
BOROUGH COUNCIL

SWINDON

Brimble Hill School
Tadpole Lane, Redhouse, SWINDON,
Wiltshire SN25 2NB
Tel: 01793 493900
Head: Mrs Alison Paul
Category: SLD (2-11)

Chalet School
Liden Drive, Liden, SWINDON, Wiltshire
SN3 6EX
Tel: 01793 534537
Head: Ms Katherine Bryan
Category: CLD including ASD (2-11)

Crowdys Hill School
Jefferies Avenue, Cricklade Road,
SWINDON, Wiltshire SN2 7HJ
Tel: 01793 332400
Head: Mrs M Clarke
Category: CLD & other difficulties (11-16)

Nyland Campus
Nyland Road, Nythe, SWINDON, Wiltshire
SN3 3RD
Tel: 01793 535023
Executive Headteacher: Ms Lauren
Connor
Category: BESD (Primary)

St Luke's School
Cricklade Road, SWINDON, Wiltshire
SN2 7AS
Tel: 01793 705566
Head: Mrs Jane Cordes
Category: BESD (11-16)

Stratton Education Centre
St Philips Road, Upper Stratton,
SWINDON, Wiltshire SN2 7QP
Tel: 01793 828941
Head: Mr Richard Marshall
Category: (Coed 2-11)

Uplands School
The Learning Campus, Tadpole Lane,
Redhouse, SWINDON, Wiltshire
SN25 2NB
Tel: 01793 493910
Head: Mrs Jackie Smith
Category: SLD (11-19)

TELFORD & WREKIN
SPECIAL EDUCATIOINAL NEEDS

Darby House, 2nd Floor C Wing, Lawn
Central, Telford TF3 4JA
Tel: 01952 385399

TELFORD

Haughton School
Queen Street, Madeley, TELFORD,
Shropshire TF7 4BW
Tel: 01952 387540
Head: Mrs Gill Knox
Category: MLD ASD SLD SP&LD BESD
(Coed 5-11)

Mount Gilbert School
Hinkshay Road, Dawley, TELFORD,
Shropshire TF4 3PP
Tel: 01952 387670
Head: Mrs Lisa Lyon
Category: SEBD SPLD AUT (Coed 11-16)

Southall School
Off Rowan Avenue, Dawley, TELFORD,
Shropshire TF4 3PN
Tel: 01952 387600
Head: Mrs Jo Burdon
Category: MLD ASD SEBD (Coed 11-16)

The Bridge School
Hadley Learning Community, Waterloo
Road, Hadley, TELFORD, Shropshire
TF1 5NU
Tel: 01952 387108
Head: Mrs Heather Davies
Category: SLD PMLD (Coed 2-19)

THURROCK
COUNCIL

SEN Services, Education Dept, PO Box
118, Grays, Essex RM17 6GF
Tel: 01375 652652

GRAYS

Beacon Hill School (Post 16 Provision)
Buxton Road, GRAYS, Essex RM16 2WU
Tel: 01375 898656
Head: Mr R Milligan
Category: SLD PNI PMLD (Coed 16-19)

Treetops School
Buxton Road, GRAYS, Essex RM16 2XN
Tel: 01375 372723
Head: Mr Paul Smith
Category: MLD ASD (Coed 3-16)

Treetops School (6th Form)
Buxton Road, GRAYS, Essex RM16 2XN
Tel: 01375 372723
Head: Mr Paul Smith

SOUTH OCKENDON

Beacon Hill School (Main Site)
Erriff Drive, SOUTH OCKENDON, Essex
RM15 5AY
Tel: 01708 852006
Head: Mr Richard Milligan
Category: PNI PMLD SLD (Coed 3-16)

TORBAY
COUNCIL

SEN Team, 4th Floor South, Tor Hill
House, c/o Torquay Town Hall, Castle
Circus, Torquay, Devon TQ1 3DR
Tel: 01803 208274

PAIGNTON

Torbay School
170B Torquay Road, Preston, PAIGNTON,
Devon TQ3 2AL
Tel: 01803 665522
Head: Mr James Evans
Category: BESD (9-16)

TORQUAY

**Combe Pafford Business & Enterprise
School**
Steps Lane, Watcombe, TORQUAY, Devon
TQ2 8NL
Tel: 01803 327902
Head: Mr M E Lock
Category: MLD PH AUT (7-16)

Mayfield School
Moor Lane, Watcombe, TORQUAY, Devon
TQ2 8NH
Tel: 01803 328375
Head: Mrs J M Palmer
Category: SLD PMLD PH AUT (3-19)

TYNE & WEAR
GATESHEAD
COUNCIL

Learning and Schools, Civic Centre, Regent Street, Gateshead, Tyne & Wear NE8 1HH
Tel: 0191 433 3000

GATESHEAD

Dryden School
Shotley Gardens, Low Fell, GATESHEAD, Tyne & Wear NE9 5UR
Tel: 0191 420 3811
Head: Mrs R Harrison
Category: SLD (Coed 11-19)

Eslington Primary School
Hazel Road, GATESHEAD, Tyne & Wear NE8 2EP
Tel: 0191 433 4131
Head: Mrs M Richards
Category: EBD (Coed 5-11)

Furrowfield School
Whitehills Drive, Felling, GATESHEAD, Tyne & Wear NE10 9RZ
Tel: 0191 4954700
Head: Mr S Thursby
Category: EBD (Boys 11-16)

Hill Top School
Wealcroft, Felling, GATESHEAD, Tyne & Wear NE10 8LT
Tel: 0191 469 2462
Head: Mrs R Harrison
Category: MLD AUT (Coed 11-16)

The Cedars Academy
Ivy Lane, Low Fell, GATESHEAD, Tyne & Wear NE9 6QD
Tel: 0191 4874595
Head: Mrs J Fraser
Category: PD (Coed 2-16)

NEWCASTLE UPON TYNE

Gibside School
Burnthouse Lane, Whickham, NEWCASTLE UPON TYNE, Tyne & Wear NE16 5AT
Tel: 0191 441 0123
Head: Mrs J Higgin
Category: SLD MLD AUT (Coed 4-11)

NEWCASTLE UPON TYNE
CHILDREN'S SERVICES DIRECTORATE

Civic Centre, Barras Bridge, Newcastle upon Tyne, Tyne & Wear NE1 8PU
Tel: 0191 211 5312, *Fax:* 0191 277 4983

NEWCASTLE UPON TYNE

Deneview school
Freeman Road, South Gosforth, NEWCASTLE UPON TYNE, Tyne & Wear NE3 1SZ
Tel: 0191 298 6950
Head: Mr B Curley

Hadrian School
Bertram Crescent, NEWCASTLE UPON TYNE, Tyne & Wear NE15 6PY
Tel: 0191 273 4440
Head: Mr Christopher Rollings
Category: PMLD SLD (Coed Day 2-11)

Newcastle Bridges School
C/o Kenton College, Drayton Road, Kenton, NEWCASTLE UPON TYNE, Tyne & Wear NE3 3RU
Tel: 0191 826 7086
Head: Mrs Margaret Dover
Category: HS (Coed 2-19)

Sir Charles Parson School
Westbourne Avenue, NEWCASTLE UPON TYNE, Tyne & Wear NE6 4ED
Tel: 0191 295 2280
Head: Mr Nicholas Sharing
Category: SLD PD PMLD (Coed Day 11-19)

Thomas Bewick School
Linhope Road, West Denton, NEWCASTLE UPON TYNE, Tyne & Wear NE5 2LW
Tel: 0191 229 6020
Acting Head: Ms Diane Scott
Category: AUT (Coed Day/boarding 3-19)

Trinity School
Condercum Road, NEWCASTLE UPON TYNE, Tyne & Wear NE4 8XJ
Tel: 0191 298 6950
Executive Head: Mr B Curley
Category: SEBD (Coed Day 7-16)

TYNE & WEAR
SUNDERLAND
CHILDREN'S SERVICES

SEN and Accessibility Team, Sunderland Customer Service Centre, Bunny Hill, Hylton Lane, Sunderland, Tyne & Wear SR5 4BW
Tel: 0191 561 2235, *Fax:* 0191 566 1423

SUNDERLAND

Barbara Priestman School & Technology College
Meadowside, SUNDERLAND, Tyne & Wear SR2 7QN
Tel: 0191 553 6000
Head: Mrs C Barker
Category: PD (Coed Day 11-19)

Castlegreen Community School
Craigshaw Road, Hylton Castle, SUNDERLAND, Tyne & Wear SR5 3NF
Tel: 0191 553 5335
Head: Mr I Reed
Category: SEBD (Coed Day 11-18)

Maplewood School
Redcar Road, SUNDERLAND, Tyne & Wear SR5 5PA
Tel: 0191 553 5587
Head: Mr Gary Mellefont
Category: EBD (Coed Day 5-11)

North View School
St Lukes Road, SUNDERLAND, Tyne & Wear SR4 0HB
Tel: 0191 534 8813
Head: Mr G Mellefont
Category: EBD (5-11)

Portland Academy
Weymouth Road, Chapelgarth, SUNDERLAND, Tyne & Wear SR3 2NQ
Tel: 0191 553 6050
Head: Mrs M Carson
Category: SLD (Coed Day 11-19)

Springwell Dene School
Swindon Road, SUNDERLAND, Tyne & Wear SR3 4EE
Tel: 0191 553 6067
Head: Mr G Shillinglaw
Category: EBD (Coed Day 11-16)

Sunningdale School
Shaftoe Road, SUNDERLAND, Tyne &
Wear SR3 4HA
Tel: 0191 553 5880
Head: Mrs C Wright
Category: PMLD SLD (Coed Day 2-11)

WASHINGTON

Columbia Grange School
Oxclose Road, WASHINGTON, Tyne &
Wear NE38 7NY
Tel: 0191 219 3860
Head: Mrs K Elliott
Category: SLD AUT (Coed Day 2-11)

TYNE & WEAR
NORTH TYNESIDE
CHILDREN, YOUNG PEOPLE AND LEARNING

0-25 Integrated Disability and Additional
Needs Service, Riverside Centre, Minton
Lane, North Shields, Tyne & Wear
NE29 6DQ
Tel: 0191 6438684/5

LONGBENTON

Benton Dene School
Hailsham Avenue, LONGBENTON, Tyne &
Wear NE12 8FD
Tel: 0191 643 2730
Head: Mrs L J Turner
Category: MLD ASD (Coed 5-11+)

NORTH SHIELDS

Southlands School
Beach Road, Tynemouth, NORTH
SHIELDS, Tyne & Wear NE30 2QR
Tel: 0191 200 6348
Head: Mr D Erskine
Category: MLD BESD (Coed 11-16+)

WALLSEND

**Beacon Hill School and Specialist
College for Business and Enterprise**
Rising Sun Cottages, High Farm,
WALLSEND, Tyne & Wear NE28 9LJ
Tel: 0191 643 3000
Head: Mrs H Jones
Category: ASD SLD PMLD (Coed 2-16)

Silverdale School
Langdale Gardens, WALLSEND, Tyne &
Wear NE28 0HG
Tel: 0191 200 5982
Head: Mr P Gannon
Category: BESD (Coed 7-16)

WHITLEY BAY

Woodlawn School
Drumoyne Gardens, Monkseaton,
WHITLEY BAY, Tyne & Wear NE25 9DL
Tel: 0191 200 8729
Head: Mr Simon Ripley
Category: PD MSI Medical needs (Coed
2-16)

TYNE & WEAR
SOUTH TYNESIDE

Pupil Services, Town Hall and Civic
Offices, Westoe Road, South Shields,
Tyne & Wear NE33 2RL
Tel: 0191 424 7808

HEBBURN

Hebburn Lakes Primary School
Campbell Park Road, HEBBURN, Tyne &
Wear NE31 2QY
Tel: 0191 4839122
Head: Mr A S Watson
Category: BESD LD Complex medical
needs

Keelman's Way School
Campbell Park Road, HEBBURN, Tyne &
Wear NE31 1QY
Tel: 0191 489 7480
Head: Mrs Paula Selby
Category: PMLD SLD (Coed Day 2-19)

JARROW

Epinay Business & Enterprise School
Clervaux Terrace, JARROW, Tyne & Wear
NE32 5UP
Tel: 0191 489 8949
Head: Mrs Hilary Harrison
Category: MLD EBD (Coed 5-17)

Fellgate Autistic Unit
Oxford Way, Fellgate Estate, JARROW,
Tyne & Wear NE32 4XA
Tel: 0191 489 4801
Head: Miss C Wilson
Category: AUT (Coed 3-11)

**Hedworthfield Language Development
Unit**
Linkway, Hedworth Estate, JARROW, Tyne
& Wear NE32 4QF
Tel: 0191 537 3373
Head: Mrs T Lawton
Category: SP&LD (Coed)

Jarrow School
Field Terrace, JARROW, Tyne & Wear
NE32 5PR
Tel: 0191 489 3225
Head: Ms J Gillies
Category: HI ASD

Simonside Primary School
Glasgow Road, JARROW, Tyne & Wear
NE32 4AU
Tel: 0191 489 8315
Head: Mr J Purvis
Category: HI

SOUTH SHIELDS

Ashley Child Development Centre
Temple Park Road, SOUTH SHIELDS, Tyne
& Wear NE34 0QA
Tel: 0191 4564977
Head: Mrs D Todd
Category: Other Early Years

Bamburgh School
Horsley Hill Community Campus, SOUTH
SHIELDS, Tyne & Wear NE34 7TD
Tel: 0191 427 4330
Head: Mr Peter Nord
Category: PD MED VIS HI MLD (Coed Day
2-17)

**Harton Speech and Language and ASD
Resource Bases**
c/o Harton Technology College, Lisle
Road, SOUTH SHIELDS, Tyne & Wear
NE34 6DL
Tel: 0191 4564226
Head: Mr K A Gibson
Category: Speech and language ASD

Park View School
Temple Park Road, SOUTH SHIELDS, Tyne
& Wear NE34 0QA
Tel: 0191 4541568
Head: Mrs Angela Noble
Category: BESD (Coed Day 11-16)

WARRINGTON
CHILDREN & YOUNG PEOPLE

The Pupil Assessment Support Team, 3rd Floor, New Town House, Buttermarket Street, Warrington WA1 2NJ
Tel: 01925 443322

WARRINGTON

Fox Wood School
Chatfield Drive, Birchwood, WARRINGTON, Cheshire WA3 6QW
Tel: 01925 851393
Head: Mrs Karen Nicholls
Category: SLD (Coed Day 4-19)

Grappenhall Hall School
Church Lane, Grappenhall, WARRINGTON, Cheshire WA4 3EU
Tel: 01925 263895
Head: Mr Michael Frost
Category: EBD MLD (Coed Boarding 5-19)

Green Lane Community Special School
Green Lane, Padgate, WARRINGTON, Cheshire WA1 4JL
Tel: 01925 480128
Head: Mr P King
Category: MLD CLD (Coed Day 4-16)

WARWICKSHIRE
CHILDREN, YOUNG PEOPLE & FAMILIES DIRECTORATE

Parent Partnership Service, Saltisford Office Park, Ansell Way, Warwick, Warwickshire CV34 4UL
Tel: 02476 588464

ASH GREEN

Exhall Grange School & Science College
Easter Way, ASH GREEN, Warwickshire CV7 9HP
Tel: 024 7636 4200
Head: Mrs Christine Marshall
Category: VIS PD Med (Coed Day 2-19)

COLESHILL

Woodlands School
Packington Lane, COLESHILL, West Midlands B46 3JE
Tel: 01675 463590
Head: Mr Iain Paterson
Category: Generic SLD VIS HI AUT MSI PD MLD PMLD (Coed Day 2-19)

HENLEY-IN-ARDEN

River House School
Stratford Road, HENLEY-IN-ARDEN, West Midlands B95 6AD
Tel: 01564 792514
Head: Mr Michael Turner
Category: SEBD (Boys Day 11-16)

NUNEATON

Oak Wood Primary School
Morris Drive, NUNEATON, Warwickshire CV11 4QH
Tel: 02476 740907
Deputy Head: Ms Christine Stokoe
Category: Generic SLD MLD VIS HI AUT MSI PD PMLD (Coed Day 2-11)

Oak Wood Secondary School
Morris Drive, NUNEATON, Warwickshire CV11 4QH
Tel: 02476 740901
Head: Mr Kevin Latham
Category: Generic SLD MLD VIS HI AUT MSI PD PMLD (Coed Day 11-16)

RUGBY

Brooke School
Overslade Lane, RUGBY, Warwickshire CV22 6DY
Tel: 01788 812324
Head: Mr Christopher Pollitt
Category: Generic SLD VIS HI AUT MSI PD MLD PMLD (Coed Day 2-19)

STRATFORD-UPON-AVON

Welcombe Hills School
Blue Cap Road, STRATFORD-UPON-AVON, Warwickshire CV37 6TQ
Tel: 01789 266845
Head: Mrs Judith Humphry
Category: Generic SLD VIS HI AUT MSI PD MLD PMLD (Coed Day 2-19)

WARWICK

Ridgeway School
Deansway, WARWICK, Warwickshire CV34 5DF
Tel: 01926 491987
Head: Mrs Karen Gannon
Category: Generic SLD VIS HI AUT MSI PD MLD PMLD (Coed Day 3-11)

Round Oak School & Support Service
Brittain Lane, off Myton Road, WARWICK, Warwickshire CV34 6DX
Tel: 01926 423311
Head: Mrs Fiona Naylor
Category: Generic SLD VIS HI AUT MSI PD MLD PMLD (Coed Day 11-19)

WEST MIDLANDS
BIRMINGHAM
CHILDREN, YOUNG PEOPLE & FAMILIES

Council House Extension, Margaret Street, Birmingham B3 3BU
Tel: 0121 303 2590, *Fax:* 0121 303 1318

EDGBASTON

Baskerville School
Fellows Lane, Harborne, EDGBASTON, Birmingham B17 9TS
Tel: 0121 427 3191
Head: Mrs Rosemary Adams
Category: ASD (Coed boarding 11-19)

ERDINGTON

Queensbury School
Wood End Road, ERDINGTON, Birmingham B24 8BL
Tel: 0121 373 5731
Head: Mrs Veronica Jenkins
Category: MLD AUT SLD (Coed Day 11-19)

The Bridge School
290 Reservoir Road, ERDINGTON, Birmingham B23 6DE
Tel: 0121 464 8265
Head: Mr Adrian Coleman
Category: ASD PMLD AUT (Coed Boarding 2-11)

Wilson Stuart School
Perry Common Road, ERDINGTON,
Birmingham B23 7AT
Tel: 0121 373 4475
Head: Mr Stephen Hughes
Category: PD (Coed Day 2-19)

HALL GREEN

Fox Hollies School
Highbury Campus, Queensbridge Road,
Moseley, HALL GREEN, Birmingham
B13 8QB
Tel: 0121 464 6566
Head: Mr Paul Roberts
Category: SLD PD CLD MSI (Coed Day 11-19)

Uffculme School
Queensbridge Road, Moseley, HALL
GREEN, Birmingham B13 8QB
Tel: 0121 464 5250
Head: Mr Alex MacDonald
Category: ASD (Coed day 3-11)

HODGE HILL

Beaufort School
Stechford Road, HODGE HILL,
Birmingham B34 6BJ
Tel: 0121 675 8500
Head: Ms Fiona Woolford
Category: SLD AUT PMLD (Coed Day 2-11)

Braidwood School
Bromford Road, HODGE HILL,
Birmingham B36 8AF
Tel: 0121 464 5558
Head: Mrs Karen Saywood
Category: D HI ASD MLD (Coed Day 11-19)

Hallmoor School
Hallmoor Road, Kitts Green, HODGE HILL,
Birmingham B33 9QY
Tel: 0121 783 3972
Head: Mrs Susan Charvis
Category: MLD MSI SP&LD (Coed Day 5-19)

The Pines Special School
Dreghorn Road, Castle Bromwich,
HODGE HILL, Birmingham B36 8LL
Tel: 0121 464 6136
Head: Mrs Susan Brandwood
Category: SP&LD ASD (Coed Day 2-11)

LADYWOOD

Calthorpe School & Sports College
Darwin Street, Highgate, LADYWOOD,
Birmingham B12 0TP
Tel: 0121 773 4637
Head: Mr Graham Hardy
Category: SLD MLD CLD PD MSI AUT
(Coed Day 2-19)

James Brindley Hospital School
Bell Barn Road, Edgbaston, LADYWOOD,
Birmingham B15 2AF
Tel: 0121 666 6409
Head: Mrs Nicky Penny
Category: HS (Coed Day 2-19)

NORTHFIELD

Longwill Primary School for Deaf Children
Bell Hill, NORTHFIELD, Birmingham
B31 1LD
Tel: 0121 475 3923
Head: Mrs Barbara Day
Category: HI D (Coed Day 2-12)

Victoria School and Specialist Arts College
Bell Hill, NORTHFIELD, Birmingham
B31 1LD
Tel: 0121 476 9478
Head: Mrs Justine Sims
Category: PD (Coed Day 2-19)

PERRY BARR

Hamilton School
Hamilton Road, Handsworth, PERRY
BARR, Birmingham B21 8AH
Tel: 0121 464 1676
Head: Mr Alex MacDonald
Category: ASD SP&LD (Coed Day 4-11)

Mayfield School
Heathfield Road, Handsworth, PERRY
BARR, Birmingham B19 1HJ
Tel: 0121 464 3354
Head: Mr Paul Jenkins
Category: SLD PMLD (Coed Day 3-19)

Oscott Manor School
Old Oscott Hill, Kingstanding, PERRY
BARR, Birmingham B44 9SP
Tel: 0121 360 8222
Head: Ms Joy Hardwick
Category: PMLD ASD MLD (Coed Day 11-19)

Priestley Smith School
Beeches Road, Great Barr, PERRY BARR,
Birmingham B42 2PY
Tel: 0121 325 3900
Head: Mrs Helen Porter
Category: VIS (Coed Day 2-17)

REDDITCH

Skilts School
Gorcott Hill, REDDITCH, West Midlands
B98 9ET
Tel: 01527 853851
Head: Mr Charles Herriotts
Category: EBD (Coed Boarding 5-12)

SELLY OAK

Cherry Oak School
60 Frederick Road, SELLY OAK,
Birmingham B29 6PB
Tel: 0121 464 2037
Head: Mrs Justine Sims
Category: SLD PMLD (Coed Day 3-11)

Lindsworth School
Monyhull Hall Road, Kings Norton, SELLY
OAK, Birmingham B30 3QA
Tel: 0121 693 5363
Head: Mr David McMahon
Category: SEBD (Coed Boarding 11-16)

Selly Oak Trust School
Oak Tree Lane, SELLY OAK, Birmingham
B29 6HZ
Tel: 0121 472 0876
Head: Mr Chris Field
Category: MLD (Coed Day 11-19)

The Dame Ellen Pinsent School
Ardencote Road, SELLY OAK, Birmingham
B13 0RW
Tel: 0121 675 2487
Head: Ms Debbie Allen
Category: ASD EBD SP&LD HI (Coed day 4-11)

SOLIHULL

Springfield House Community Special School
Kenilworth Road, Knowle, SOLIHULL,
West Midlands B93 0AJ
Tel: 01564 772772
Head: Mrs Janet Collins
Category: SEBD (Coed Boarding 5-11)

SUTTON COLDFIELD

Langley School
Trinity Road, SUTTON COLDFIELD, West
Midlands B75 6TJ
Tel: 0121 675 2929
Head: Mrs Fiona Woolford
Category: MLD ASD (Coed Day 3-11)

The Bridge School
Longmoor Campus, Coppice View Road,
SUTTON COLDFIELD, Birmingham
B73 6UE
Tel: 0121 353 7833
Head: Mr Adrian Coleman
Category: PMLD AUT ASD (Coed 2-11)

YARDLEY

Brays School
Brays Road, Sheldon, YARDLEY,
Birmingham B26 1NS
Tel: 0121 743 5730
Head: Mrs Jane Edgerton
Category: PD SLD EBD CLD MSI (Coed 2-11)

WEST MIDLANDS
COVENTRY
EDUCATION AUTHORITY

SEN & Inclusion, Civic Centre 2, Little
Park Street, Coventry, West Midlands
CV1 5RS
Tel: 024 7683 1624

COVENTRY

Alice Stevens Secondary School
Ashington Grove, COVENTRY, West
Midlands CV3 4DE
Tel: 024 7630 3776
Head: Mr Stephen Garside
Category: MLD (Coed Day 11-19)

Baginton Fields Secondary School
Sedgemoor Road, COVENTRY, West
Midlands CV3 4EA
Tel: 024 7630 3854
Head: Mr Simon Grant
Category: SLD (Coed Day 11-19)

Castle Wood
Deedmore Road, COVENTRY, West
Midlands CV2 1EQ
Tel: 024 7670 9060
Head: Mrs Yvonne McCall
Category: Broad spectrum (Coed Day 3-11)

Corley Centre
Church Lane, Fillongley, COVENTRY, West
Midlands CV7 8AZ
Tel: 01676 540218
Head: Ms Lisa Batch
Category: Complex SCD (Coed 11-19)

Sherbourne Fields Primary & Secondary School
Rowington Close, Off Kingsbury Road,
COVENTRY, West Midlands CV6 1PS
Tel: 024 7659 1501
Head: Mr David Southeard
Category: PD (Coed Day 2-19)

Three Spires Primary School
Kingsbury Road, COVENTRY, West
Midlands CV6 1PJ
Tel: 024 7659 4952
Head: Ms Amanda Clugston
Category: MLD (Coed Day 3-11)

Tiverton Primary
Rowington Close, Off Kingsbury Road,
COVENTRY, West Midlands CV6 1PS
Tel: 024 7659 4954
Head: Mrs Carolyn Claridge
Category: SLD (Coed Day 3-11)

Woodfield School
Stoneleigh Road Primary Site,
COVENTRY, West Midlands CV4 7AB
Tel: 024 7641 8755
Head: Mr Mick Chilvers
Category: ESBD (Coed Day 5-11)

Woodfield School
Hawthorn Lane Secondary Site,
COVENTRY, West Midlands CV4 9PB
Tel: 024 7646 2335
Head: Mr Mick Chilvers
Category: EBD (Boys Day 11-16)

WEST MIDLANDS
DUDLEY
CHILDREN'S SERVICES

Westox House, 1 Trinity Road, Dudley,
West Midlands DY1 1JQ
Tel: 01384 814225

COSELEY

Rosewood School
Bell Street, Russells Hall Estate,
COSELEY, West Midlands WV14 8XJ
Tel: 01384 816800
Head: Mr D Kirk
Category: EBD (11-16)

DUDLEY

Old Park School
Thorns Road, Brierley Hill, DUDLEY, West
Midlands DY5 2JY
Tel: 01384 818905
Head: Mrs G Cartwright
Category: SLD (3-19)

The Brier School
Bromley Lane, Kingswinford, DUDLEY,
West Midlands DY6 8QN
Tel: 01384 816000
Head: Mr Russell Hinton
Category: MLD (5-16)

The Sutton School & Specialist College
Scotts Green Close, Russells Hall Estate,
DUDLEY, West Midlands DY1 2DU
Tel: 01384 818670
Head: Mr D Bishop-Rowe
Category: MLD (11-16)

The Woodsetton School
Tipton Road, Woodsetton, DUDLEY, West
Midlands DY3 1BY
Tel: 01384 818265
Head: Mr P A Rhind-Tutt
Category: MLD (4-11)

HALESOWEN

Halesbury School
Feldon Lane, HALESOWEN, West
Midlands B62 9DR
Tel: 01384 818630
Head: Mrs Judi Kings
Category: MLD (4-16)

STOURBRIDGE

Pens Meadow School
Ridge Hill, Brierley Hill Road, Wordsley,
STOURBRIDGE, West Midlands DY8 5ST
Tel: 01384 818945
Head: Mrs Marie Bissell
Category: SLD (3-19)

WEST MIDLANDS
SANDWELL
CHILDREN & FAMILIES SERVICES

Special Education Needs Service, PO
Box 16230, Sandwell Council House,
Freeth Street, Oldbury, West Midlands
B69 4EX
Tel: 0121 569 8240

LICHFIELD

Shenstone Lodge School
Birmingham Road, Shenstone,
LICHFIELD, Staffordshire WS14 0LB
Tel: 01543 480369
Head: Mr Steve Butt
Category: EBD (Coed Day 4-16)

OLDBURY

The Meadows Sports College
Dudley Road East, OLDBURY, West
Midlands B69 3BU
Tel: 0121 569 7080
Head: Mr G Phillips
Category: PMLD (Coed Day 11-19)

The Orchard School
Causeway Green Road, OLDBURY, West
Midlands B68 8LD
Tel: 0121 569 7040
Head: Mrs H Atkins
Category: PMLD(Coed Day 2-11)

WEST BROMWICH

The Westminster School
Westminster Road, WEST BROMWICH,
West Midlands B71 2JN
Tel: 0121 588 2421
Head: Mrs D Williams
Category: MLD (Coed Day 11-19)

WEST MIDLANDS
SOLIHULL
EDUCATION AUTHORITY

Statutory Assessment & Review Team
People Directorate, PO Box 20, Council
House, Solihull, West Midlands B91 9OU
Tel: 0121 704 6690

BIRMINGHAM

Forest Oak School
Windward Way, Smith's Wood,
BIRMINGHAM, West Midlands B36 0UE
Tel: 0121 717 0088
Head: Mrs A Mordey
Category: MLD (Coed Day 4-18)

Merstone School
Windward Way, Smith's Wood,
BIRMINGHAM, West Midlands B36 0UE
Tel: 0121 717 1040
Head: Mrs A Mordey
Category: SLD (Coed Day 2-19)

Oaklands
Lanchester Way, Castle Bromwich,
BIRMINGHAM, West Midlands B36 9LF
Tel: 0121 748 9760
Head: Ms D Bailey
Category: EBD (Coed Day 11-16)

SOLIHULL

Hazel Oak School
Hazel Oak Road, Shirley, SOLIHULL, West
Midlands B90 2AZ
Tel: 0121 744 4162
Head: Ms D Jenkins
Category: MLD (Coed Day 4-18)

Reynalds Cross School
Kineton Green Road, SOLIHULL, West
Midlands B92 7ER
Tel: 0121 707 3012
Head: Mrs Jane Davenport
Category: SLD (Coed Day 2-19)

WEST MIDLANDS
WALSALL
PARENT PARTNERSHIP SERVICE

Blakenhall Village Centre, Thames Road,
Blakenhall, Walsall, West Midlands
WS3 1LZ
Tel: 01922 650330

WALSALL

Castle Business & Enterprise College
Odell Road, Leamore, WALSALL, West
Midlands WS3 2ED
Tel: 01922 710129
Head: Mrs Christine Fraser
Category: MLD (Coed Day 4-19)

Elmwood School
King George Crescent, Rushall, WALSALL,
West Midlands WS4 1EG
Tel: 01922 721081
Head: Mr Simon Hubbard
Category: EBD (Coed Day 11-16)

Mary Elliot Special School
Leamore Lane, WALSALL, West Midlands
WS2 7NR
Tel: 01922 490190
Head: Mrs Elizabeth Jordan
Category: SLD PMLD AUT (Coed day 11-19)

Oakwood School
Druids Walk, Walsall Wood, WALSALL,
West Midlands WS9 9JS
Tel: 01543 452040
Head: Mrs Kay Mills
Category: SLD CLD PMLD ASD
Challenging behaviour (Coed Day 3-11)

Old Hall Special School
Bentley Lane, WALSALL, West Midlands
WS2 7LU
Tel: 01902 368045
Head: Mr Nigel Smith
Category: SLD PMLD AUT (Coed day 3-11)

Phoenix Primary
Odell Road, Leamore, WALSALL, West
Midlands WS3 2ED
Tel: 01922 712834
Acting Head: Mrs Dawn Evans
Category: EBD (Coed Day 4-11)

The Jane Lane School - A College for Cognition and Learning
Churchill Road, Bentley, WALSALL, West Midlands WS2 0JH
Tel: 01922 721161
Head: Mrs Heather Lomas
Category: MLD (Coed Day 5-19)

WEST MIDLANDS
WOLVERHAMPTON
COMMUNITIES DIRECTORATE- HEALTH, WELLBEING AND DISABILITIES

Special Educational Needs Statutory Assessment & Review Team (SEN-START), Civic Centre, St Peter's Square, Wolverhampton, West Midlands WV1 1RT
Tel: 01902 555873

WOLVERHAMPTON

Broadmeadow Nursery School
Lansdowne Road, WOLVERHAMPTON, West Midlands WV1 4AL
Tel: 01902 558330
Head: Miss K Warrington
Category: SLD ASD PMLD (Coed Day 2-6)

Green Park School
The Willows, Green Park Avenue, Bilston, WOLVERHAMPTON, West Midlands WV14 6EH
Tel: 01902 556429
Head: Mrs L Dawney
Category: PMLD SLD (Coed Day 4-19)

New Park School
Cromer Gardens, Whitmore Reans, WOLVERHAMPTON, West Midlands WV6 0UB
Tel: 01902 551564
Head: Mrs S Humphreyson
Category: BESD ADHD (Coed Day 8-16)

Penn Fields School
Boundary Way, Penn, WOLVERHAMPTON, West Midlands WV4 4NT
Tel: 01902 558640
Head: Miss E Stanley
Category: MLD SLD ASD (Coed Day 4-19)

Penn Hall School
Vicarage Road, Penn, WOLVERHAMPTON, West Midlands WV4 5HP
Tel: 01902 558355
Head: Mr D Parry
Category: PD SLD MLD (Coed Day 3-19)

Tettenhall Wood School
Regis Road, Tettenhall, WOLVERHAMPTON, West Midlands WV6 8XG
Tel: 01902 556519
Head: Mr M Mahoney
Category: ASD (Coed Day 5-19)

Westcroft School Sports & Vocational College
Greenacres Avenue, Underhill, WOLVERHAMPTON, West Midlands WV10 8NZ
Tel: 01902 558350
Head: Ms A Brown
Category: CLD (Coed Day 4-16)

WILTSHIRE
CHILDREN & EDUCATION DEPARTMENT

Central SEN Services, County Hall, Bythesea Road, Trowbridge, Wiltshire BA14 8JN
Tel: 01225 718095

CHIPPENHAM

St Nicholas School
Malmesbury Road, CHIPPENHAM, Wiltshire SN15 1QF
Tel: 01249 650435
Head: Mrs Jill Owen
Category: SLD PMLD (Coed Day 3-19)

DEVIZES

Downland School
Downlands Road, DEVIZES, Wiltshire SN10 5EF
Tel: 01380 724193
Head: Phil Beaumont
Category: BESD SPLD (Boys Boarding 11-16)

Rowdeford School
Rowde, DEVIZES, Wiltshire SN10 2QQ
Tel: 01380 850309
Head: Mrs Ingrid Lancaster-Gaye
Category: MLD (Coed Boarding 11-16)

SALISBURY

Exeter House Special School
Somerset Road, SALISBURY, Wiltshire SP1 3BL
Tel: 01722 334168
Headteacher: Mr Andrew Mears
Category: SLD PMLD SPLD Del (Coed Day 2-19)

TROWBRIDGE

Larkrise School
Ashton Street, TROWBRIDGE, Wiltshire BA14 7EB
Tel: 01225 761434
Head: Mrs C Goodwin
Category: SLD MLD (Coed Day 3-19)

WINDSOR AND MAIDENHEAD
CHILDREN & YOUNG PEOPLE LEARNING & CARE DIRECTORATE

Royal Borough of Windsor & Maidenhead Town Hall, St Ives Road, Maidenhead, Berkshire SL6 1RF
Tel: 01628 683800

MAIDENHEAD

Manor Green School
Elizabeth Hawkes Way, MAIDENHEAD, Berkshire SL6 3EQ
Tel: 01628 513800
Head: Ms Ania Hildrey
Category: SLD PMLD ASD MLD (Coed 2-19)

WOKINGHAM
CHILDREN'S SERVICES

Special Education, Civic Offices, Shute End, Wokingham, Berkshire RG40 1BN
Tel: 0118 974 6216

WOKINGHAM

Addington School
Woodlands Avenue, Woodley, WOKINGHAM, Berkshire RG5 3EU
Tel: 0118 966 9073
Head: Mrs L Meek
Category: SLD PMLD ASD MLD (Coed 2-19)

Southfield School
Gipsy Lane, WOKINGHAM, Berkshire RG40 2HR
Tel: 0118 977 1293
Head: Mr Dominic Geraghty
Category: BESD (Coed 11-16)

WORCESTERSHIRE
CHILDREN'S SERVICES DIRECTORATE

PO Box 73, Worcester WR5 2YA
Tel: 01905 822700

BROMSGROVE

Chadsgrove School & Specialist Sports College
Meadow Road, Catshill, BROMSGROVE, Worcestershire B61 0JL
Tel: 01527 871511
Head: Mrs D Rattley
Category: PD PMLD MSI LD (2-19)

Rigby Hall School
19 Rigby Lane, Astonfields, BROMSGROVE, Worcestershire B60 2EP
Tel: 01527 875475
Head: Ms C Pitts
Category: SLD MLD ASD (3-19)

EVESHAM

Vale of Evesham School
Four Pools Lane, EVESHAM, Worcestershire WR11 1BN
Tel: 01386 443367
Head: Mrs A Starr
Category: SLD MLD PMLD ASD (4-19)

KIDDERMINSTER

Wyre Forest School
Comberton Road, KIDDERMINSTER, Worcestershire DY10 3DX
Tel: 01562 823156
Head: Mr Mick Russell
Category: MLD SLD ASD BESD (Coed 7-16)

REDDITCH

Pitcheroak School
Willow Way, REDDITCH, Worcestershire B97 6PQ
Tel: 01527 65576
Head: Mr S Freer
Category: SLD MLD AUT (2-19)

The Kingfisher School
Clifton Close, Matchborough, REDDITCH, Worcestershire B98 0HF
Tel: 01527 502486
Head: Mr Ian Taylor
Category: BESD (Coed 7-16)

WORCESTER

Fort Royal Community Primary School
Wylds Lane, WORCESTER WR5 1DR
Tel: 01905 355525
Head: Mrs Jane Long
Category: MLD PD SLD (2-11)

Regency High School
Windermere Drive, Warndon, WORCESTER WR4 9JL
Tel: 01905 454828
Head: Mr F W Steel
Category: PD MLD SLD (11-19)

Riversides School
Thorneloe Road, WORCESTER WR1 3HZ
Tel: 01905 21261
Head: Mr P Bayly
Category: BESD (Coed 7-16)

CITY OF YORK
COUNCIL

SEN Services, West Offices, Station Rise, York YO1 6GA
Tel: 01904 554302

YORK

Applefields School
Bad Bargain Lane, YORK YO31 0LW
Tel: 01904 553900
Head: Mr G Gilmore
Category: MLD AUT SLD PMLD

Hob Moor Oaks School
Hob Moor Children's Centre, Green Lane, Acomb, YORK YO24 4PS
Tel: 01904 555000
Head Teacher: Mrs Susan Coulter
Category: MLD AUT SLD PMLD

EAST RIDING OF YORKSHIRE
COUNCIL

Children, Family & Adult Services, County Hall, Beverley, East Riding of Yorkshire HU17 9BA
Tel: 01482 392162, *Fax:* 01482 392213

BROUGH

St Anne's School
St Helen's Drive, Welton, BROUGH, East Riding of Yorkshire HU15 1NR
Tel: 01482 667379
Head: Mrs L Davies
Category: SLD

DRIFFIELD

Driffield King's Mill School
Victoria Road, DRIFFIELD, East Riding of Yorkshire YO25 6UG
Tel: 01377 253375
Head: Ms S Young
Category: SLD

GOOLE

Riverside School
Ainsty Street, GOOLE, East Riding of
Yorkshire DN14 5JS
Tel: 01405 763925
Head: Mr R Barcynski
Category: MLD and other complex needs

NORTH YORKSHIRE
EDUCATION AUTHORITY

Access and Inclusion, SEN Team, South
Block, County Hall, Northallerton, North
Yorkshire DL7 8AE
Tel: 01609 532240

BEDALE

Mowbray School
Masham Road, BEDALE, North Yorkshire
DL8 2SD
Tel: 01677 422446
Head: Mr J Tearle
Category: MLD SP&LD (2-16)

HARROGATE

Foremost School
Menwith Hill Road, HARROGATE, North
Yorkshire HG3 2RA
Tel: 01423 779232
Head: Mr A Dawson
Category: BESD (Boys 11-16)

Pupil Referral Service
59 Grove Road, HARROGATE, North
Yorkshire HG1 5EP
Tel: 01423 536111
Head: Ms S Campbell
Category: PRU

Springwater School
High Street, Starbeck, HARROGATE,
North Yorkshire HG2 7LW
Tel: 01423 883214
Head: Mrs Y Limb
Category: SLD PMLD (2-19)

KIRKBYMOORSIDE

Welburn Hall School
, KIRKBYMOORSIDE, York YO62 7HQ
Tel: 01751 431218
Head: Mrs H Smith
Category: PHLD (8-18)

KNARESBOROUGH

The Forest School
Park Lane, KNARESBOROUGH, North
Yorkshire HG5 0DG
Tel: 01423 864583
Head: Mr P Hewitt
Category: MLD (2-16)

NORTHALLERTON

**Hambleton and Richmondshire Pupil
Referral Service**
East Road, NORTHALLERTON, North
Yorkshire DL6 1SZ
Tel: 0845 034 9588
Head: Mrs F Dodgson
Category: PRU

The Dales School
Morton-on-Swale, NORTHALLERTON,
North Yorkshire DL7 9QW
Tel: 01609 772932
Head: Mrs H Barton
Category: SLD PMLD (2-19)

SCARBOROUGH

Brompton Hall School
Brompton-by-Sawdon, SCARBOROUGH,
North Yorkshire YO13 9DB
Tel: 01723 859121
Head: Mr M Mihkelson
Category: BESD (Boys 8-16)

Pupil Referral Service
Valley Bridge Parade, SCARBOROUGH,
North Yorkshire YO11 2PG
Tel: 01723 368059
Head: Mr K Rooney
Category: PRU

Springhead School
Barry's Lane, Seamer Road,
SCARBOROUGH, North Yorkshire
YO12 4HA
Tel: 01723 367829
Head: Mrs C D Wilson
Category: SLD PMLD (2-19)

The Woodlands School
Woodlands Drive, SCARBOROUGH, North
Yorkshire YO12 6QN
Tel: 01723 373260
Head: Mrs A Fearn
Category: MLD (2-16)

SELBY

Selby Pupil Referral Service
Raincliffe Street, SELBY, North Yorkshire
YO8 4AN
Head: Mr L Bell
Category: PRU

SKIPTON

Brooklands School
Burnside Avenue, SKIPTON, North
Yorkshire BD23 2DB
Tel: 01756 794028
Head: Mrs D Sansom
Category: MLD SLD PMLD (2-19)

**North and South Craven Pupil Referral
Service**
Keighley Road, SKIPTON, North Yorkshire
BD23 2QS
Tel: 01609 798196
Head: Mr D Hannah
Category: PRU

SOUTH YORKSHIRE
BARNSLEY
DIRECTORATE FOR
CHILDREN, YOUNG
PEOPLE & FAMILIES

PO Box 634, Barnsley, South Yorkshire
S70 9GG
Tel: 01226 773689

BARNSLEY

Greenacre School
Keresforth Hill Road, BARNSLEY, South
Yorkshire S70 6RG
Tel: 01226 287165
Head: Mrs Susan Hayter
Category: SLD CLD PMLD MSI AUT (Coed
Day 2-19)

Springwell Community Special School
St Helen's Boulevard, BARNSLEY, South
Yorkshire S71 2AY
Tel: 01226 291133
Head: Mrs Josie Thirkell

SOUTH YORKSHIRE
DONCASTER
COUNCIL

Special Educational Needs Service, Civic Office, Waterdale, Doncaster DN1 3BU
Tel: 01302 737209

DONCASTER

Coppice School
Ash Hill Road, Hatfield, DONCASTER, South Yorkshire DN7 6JH
Tel: 01302 844883
Head: Mrs L Jarred
Category: SLD ASD BESD (Coed Day 3-19)

Heatherwood School
Leger Way, DONCASTER, South Yorkshire DN2 6HQ
Tel: 01302 322044
Head: Mrs C Bagshaw
Category: SLD PD (Coed Day 3-19)

North Ridge Community School
Tenter Balk Lane, Adwick le Street, DONCASTER, South Yorkshire DN6 7EF
Tel: 01302 720790
Headteacher: Mr M J Wright
Category: SLD (Coed Day 3-19)

Pennine View School
Old Road, Conisbrough, DONCASTER, South Yorkshire DN12 3LR
Tel: 01709 864978
Head: Mr G Davies
Category: MLD (Coed Day 7-16)

Stone Hill School
Barnsley Road, Scawsby, DONCASTER, South Yorkshire DN5 7UB
Tel: 01302 800090
Headteacher: Mr S Leone
Category: MLD (Coed 7-16)

SOUTH YORKSHIRE
ROTHERHAM
SCHOOL ADMISSIONS, ORGANISATION AND SEN ASSESSMENT SERVICE

Wing A, 1st Floor, Riverside House, Main Street, Rotherham, South Yorkshire S60 1AE
Tel: (01709) 822660, *Fax:* (01709) 371444

MEXBOROUGH

Milton School
Storey Street, Swinton, MEXBOROUGH, South Yorkshire S64 8QG
Tel: 01709 570246
Head: Brenda Hughes
Category: MLD

Milton Special School
Storey Street, Swinton, MEXBOROUGH, South Yorkshire S64 8QG
Tel: 01709 570246
Head: Mrs Brenda Hughes

ROTHERHAM

Abbey School
Little Common Lane, Kimberworth, ROTHERHAM, South Yorkshire S61 2RA
Tel: 01709 740074
Head: Mrs Rachel Stirland
Category: MLD

Hilltop School
Larch Road, Maltby, ROTHERHAM, South Yorkshire S66 8AZ
Tel: 01709 813386
Executive Head: Mr N Whittaker
Category: SLD

Kelford School
Oakdale Road, Kimberworth, ROTHERHAM, South Yorkshire S61 2NU
Tel: 01709 512088
Head: Mr N Whittaker
Category: SLD

Newman School
East Bawtry Road, Whiston, ROTHERHAM, South Yorkshire S60 3LX
Tel: 01709 828262
Acting Head: Mrs M O'Hara
Category: PH Medical needs

The Willows School
Locksley Drive, Thurcroft, ROTHERHAM, South Yorkshire S66 9NT
Tel: 01709 542539
Head: Mrs A Sanderson
Category: MLD

SOUTH YORKSHIRE
SHEFFIELD
CHILDREN, YOUNG PEOPLE AND FAMILIES

Inclusion and Learning Services, SEN Assessment and Placement Team, 3rd Floor, Howden House, Union Street, Sheffield S1 2SH
Tel: 0114 2736394

SHEFFIELD

Becton School
Becton Centre for Children and Young People, Sevenairs Road, SHEFFIELD, South Yorkshire S20 1NZ
Tel: 0114 3053121
Head: Mrs W Dudley
Category: Mental health difficulties (Admissions managed by Sheffield Children's NHS Trust)

Bents Green Secondary School
Ringinglow Road, SHEFFIELD, South Yorkshire S11 7TB
Tel: 0114 2363545
Head: Mrs Jan Wiggins
Category: AUT, Communication Needs (Day & residential)

Heritage Park Community School
Norfolk Park Road, SHEFFIELD, South Yorkshire S2 2RU
Tel: 0114 2796850
Acting Executive Headteacher: Mr T Middleton
Category: BESD (KS 2/3/4)

Holgate Meadows Community School
Lindsay Road, SHEFFIELD, South Yorkshire S5 7WE
Tel: 0114 245 6305
Head: Mr T Middleton
Category: BESD (KS 2/3/4)

Mossbrook Special School
Bochum Parkway, SHEFFIELD, South
Yorkshire S8 8JR
Tel: 0114 2372768
Head: Mrs M Brough
Category: SLCN (Primary Day/residential)

Norfolk Park Primary School
Park Grange Road, SHEFFIELD, South
Yorkshire S2 3QF
Tel: 0114 2726165
Head: Mrs Jane Vickers
Category: PMLD (Primary)

Seven Hills School
Granville Road, SHEFFIELD, South
Yorkshire S2 2RJ
Tel: 0114 2743560
Head: Mrs C Scott
Category: LD, Complex Needs

Talbot Specialist School
Lees Hall Road, SHEFFIELD, South
Yorkshire S8 9JP
Tel: 0114 2507394
Head: Mrs J Smith
Category: LD, Complex Needs

The Rowan Primary School
4 Durvale Court, Furniss Avenue,
SHEFFIELD, South Yorkshire S17 3PT
Tel: 0114 2350479
Head: Mrs A Young
Category: Communication difficulties
(Primary)

**Woolley Wood Community Primary
School**
Chaucer Road, SHEFFIELD, South
Yorkshire S5 9QN
Tel: 0114 2321278
Head: Mr Dean Linkhorn
Category: PMLD/SLD

WEST YORKSHIRE
CALDERDALE
CHILDREN & YOUNG PEOPLE'S SERVICES

SEN Team, Heath Training and
Development Centre, Free School Lane,
Halifax, West Yorkshire HX1 2PT
Tel: 01422 394141, *Fax:* 01422 364899

BRIGHOUSE

Highbury School
Lower Edge Road, Rastrick, BRIGHOUSE,
West Yorkshire HD6 3LD
Tel: 01484 716319
Head: Ms Debbie Sweet
Category: All (3-11)

HALIFAX

Ravenscliffe High School
Skircoat Green, HALIFAX, West Yorkshire
HX3 0RZ
Tel: 01422 358621
Head: Mr Martin Moorman
Category: All (11-18)

Wood Bank School
Dene View, Luddendenfoot, HALIFAX,
West Yorkshire HX2 6PB
Tel: 01422 884170
Head: Mrs Jane D Ingham
Category: All (4-11)

WEST YORKSHIRE
KIRKLEES
DIRECTORATE FOR CHILDREN & YOUNG PEOPLE

SEN Assessment and Commissioning
Team, Civic Centre 1, High Street,
Huddersfield, West Yorkshire HD1 2NF
Tel: 01484 225057

BATLEY

Fairfield School
White Lee Road, BATLEY, West Yorkshire
WF17 8AS
Tel: 01924 326103
Head: Mr Richard Ware
Category: SLD (Coed Day 3-19)

DEWSBURY

Ravenshall School
Ravensthorpe Road, Thornhill Lees,
DEWSBURY, West Yorkshire WF12 9EE
Tel: 01924 325234
Head: Mrs Jeanette Tate
Category: MLD (Coed Day 5-16)

HOLMFIRTH

Lydgate School
Kirkroyds Lane, New Mill, HOLMFIRTH,
West Yorkshire HD9 1LS
Tel: 01484 222484
Head: Mrs Nicola Rogers
Category: MLD (Coed Day 5-16)

HUDDERSFIELD

Castle Hill School
Newsome Road South, Newsome,
HUDDERSFIELD, West Yorkshire HD4 6JL
Tel: 01484 226659
Head: Mrs Gill Robinson
Category: SLD AUT PMLD (Coed Day 3-
19)

Longley School
Dog Kennel Bank, HUDDERSFIELD, West
Yorkshire HD5 8JE
Tel: 01484 223937
Head: Mr Philip Gibbins
Category: MLD AUT EBD (Coed Day 5-16)

Nortonthorpe Hall School (Residential & Day)
Busker Lane, Scissett, HUDDERSFIELD, West Yorkshire HD8 9JU
Tel: 01484 222921
Head: Mr Dennis Shields
Category: EBD (Coed Residential & day 7-16)

WEST YORKSHIRE
LEEDS
INCLUSION SERVICES

Adam's Court, Kildare Terrace, Leeds, West Yorkshire LS12 1DB
Tel: 0113 395 1100, *Fax:* 0133 395 1099

LEEDS

BESD SILC - Elmete Central
Elmete Lane, Roundhay, LEEDS, West Yorkshire LS8 2LJ
Tel: 0113 265 5457
Head: Mark Barnett
Category: BESD (Coed 11-19)

East SILC - John Jamieson (main site)
Hollin Hill Drive, Oakwood, LEEDS, West Yorkshire LS8 2PW
Tel: 0113 293 0236
Head: Ms Diane Reynard
Category: Complex physical, learning and care needs (Coed 2-19)

North East SILC - West Oaks (main site)
Westwood Way, Boston Spa, Wetherby, LEEDS, West Yorkshire LS23 6DX
Tel: 01937 844 772
Head: Mr Andrew Hodkinson
Category: Complex physical, learning and care needs (Coed 2-19)

North West SILC - Pennyfields (main site)
Tongue Lane, LEEDS, West Yorkshire LS6 4QD
Tel: 0113 336 8270
Head: Mr Michael Purches
Category: Complex physical, learning and care needs (Coed 2-19)

South SILC - Broomfield (main site)
Broom Place, Belle Isle, LEEDS, West Yorkshire LS10 3JP
Tel: 0113 277 1603
Head: Mr John Fryer
Category: Complex physical, learning and care needs (Coed 2-19)

West SILC - Milestone (main site)
4 Town Street, Stanningley, Pudsey, LEEDS, West Yorkshire LS28 6HL
Tel: 0113 386 2450
Head: Ms M Wilman
Category: Complex physical, learning and care needs (Coed 2-19)

WEST YORKSHIRE
WAKEFIELD
EDUCATION WELFARE SERVICE

Room 229, Chantry House, Wakefield WF1 1ZS
Tel: 01924 305674

BARNSLEY

High Well School
High Well Hill Lane, South Hiendley, BARNSLEY, West Yorkshire S72 9DF
Tel: 01226 718613
Head: Miss Vanessa Jukes
Category: EBD (Coed 11-16)

CASTLEFORD

Wakefield Pathways School
Poplar Avenue, Townville, CASTLEFORD, West Yorkshire WF10 3QJ
Tel: 01977 723085
Head: Anne Lawton
Category: MLD (Coed 4-11)

OSSETT

Highfield School
Gawthorpe Lane, Gawthorpe, OSSETT, West Yorkshire WF5 9BS
Tel: 01924 302980
Head: Mr Alan Spalding
Category: MLD (Coed 11-16)

PONTEFRACT

Oakfield Park School
Barnsley Road, Ackworth, PONTEFRACT, West Yorkshire WF7 7DT
Tel: 01977 723145
Head: Ms W E Fereday
Category: SLD PMLD (Coed 11-19)

WAKEFIELD

Kingsland School
Aberford Road, Stanley, WAKEFIELD, West Yorkshire WF3 4BA
Tel: 01924 303100
Head: Miss Paula Trow
Category: SLD PMLD (Coed 3-11)

Pinderfields Hospital School (The Wrenthorpe Centre)
22 Barr Lane, Imperial Avenue, WAKEFIELD, West Yorkshire WF2 0LW
Tel: 01924 303695
Head: Mrs Helen M Ferguson
Category: HS PMLD (Coed 2-19)

GUERNSEY
THE EDUCATION DEPARTMENT

PO Box 32, Grange Road, St Peter Port, Guernsey GY1 3AU
Tel: 01481 733000

FOREST

Le Rondin School and Centre
Rue des Landes, FOREST, Guernsey GY8 0DP
Tel: 01481 268300
Head: Mrs P Sullivan
Category: MLD SLD PMLD (3-11)

ST SAMPSON'S

Le Murier School
Rue de Dol, ST SAMPSON'S, Guernsey GY2 4DA
Tel: 01481 246660
Head: Mr J Teehan
Category: MLD PMLD SLD (Coed 11-16)

JERSEY
EDUCATION, SPORT AND CULTURE

Special Needs Service, Heath and Social Services Department, Overdale Campus, Jersey JE2 3UH
Tel: 01534 443500

ST HELIER

Mont a l'Abbe School
La Grande Route de St Jean, La Pouquelaye, ST HELIER, Jersey JE2 3FN
Tel: 01534 875801
Head: Ms Sharon Eddie
Category: LD (3-19)

ST SAVIOUR

D'Hautree House
St Saviour's Hill, ST SAVIOUR, Jersey JE2 7LF
Tel: 01534 618042
Category: SEBD (Coed 11-16)

The Alternative Curriculum
Oakside Centre, La Grande Route de St Martin, Five Oaks, ST SAVIOUR, Jersey JE2 7GS
Tel: 01534 872840
Category: EBD

NORTHERN IRELAND

BELFAST
EDUCATION AND LIBRARY BOARD

40 Academy Street, Belfast, Northern Ireland BT1 2NQ
Tel: 028 9056 4000

BELFAST

Belfast Hospital School
Royal Belfast Hospital School for Sick Children, Falls Road, BELFAST, Co Antrim BT12 6BE
Tel: 02890 633498
Head: Ms Michele Godfrey
Category: HS (Coed 4-19)

Cedar Lodge School
24 Lansdowne Park North, BELFAST, Co Antrim BT15 4AE
Tel: 028 9077 7292
Head: Mrs Geraldine Bunting
Category: EPI ASD ADHD Medical needs (Coed 4-16)

Clarawood School
Clarawood Park, BELFAST, Co Antrim BT5 6FR
Tel: 028 9047 2736
Head: Mrs Joanne Brown
Category: SEBD (Coed 8-12)

Adamís Court8˜%

Fleming Fulton School
35 Upper Malone Road, BELFAST, Co Antrim BT9 6TY
Tel: 028 9061 1917
Acting Head: Mr Eddie McGlinchey
Category: PH MLD (Coed 3-19)

Glenveagh Special School
Harberton Park, BELFAST, Co Antrim BT9 6TX
Tel: 028 9066 9907
Head: Mrs Fionnuala Leneghan
Category: SLD (Coed 8-19)

Greenwood House Assessment Centre
Greenwood Avenue, Upper Newtownards Road, BELFAST, Co Antrim BT4 3JJ
Tel: 028 9047 1000
Head: Mrs S Sterling
Category: SP&LD MLD EBD SLD Medical needs (Coed 4-7)

Harberton Special School
Haberton Park, BELFAST, Co Antrim BT9 6TX
Tel: 028 9038 1525
Head: Mr M McGlade
Category: AUT ASP SP&LD EBD Medical needs (Coed 4-11)

Loughshore Educational Resource Centr
889 Shore Road, BELFAST, Co Antrim BT36 7DH
Tel: 028 9077 3062
Head: Mrs G Cameron

Mitchell House School
1A Marmont, 405 Holywood Road, BELFAST, Co Antrim BT4 2GT
Tel: 028 9076 0292
Head: Mrs Karen Hancock
Category: PD MSI (Coed 3-18)

Oakwood Assessment Centre
Harberton Park, BELFAST, Co Antrim BT9 6TX
Tel: 028 9060 5116
Head: Mrs Tish McCann
Category: SLD PMLD ASD (Coed 3-8)

Park Education Resource Centre
145 Ravenhill Road, BELFAST, Co Antrim BT6 8GH
Tel: 028 9045 0513
Head: Ms M Wilson
Category: MLD (Coed 11-16)

St Gerard's Education Resource Centre
12 Upper Springfield Road, BELFAST, Co Antrim BT12 7QP
Tel: 028 9032 5249
Head: Mrs Siobhan McIntaggart
Category: MLD (Coed 4-16)

St Teresa's Speech & Language Centre
Glen Road, BELFAST, Co Antrim BT11 8BL
Tel: 028 9061 1943
Teacher in Charge: Miss N Campbell

St Vincent's Centre
6 Willowfield Drive, BELFAST, Co Antrim BT6 8HN
Tel: 028 9046 1444
Teacher in Charge: Mr J McAuley

NORTH EASTERN
EDUCATION AND LIBRARY BOARD

SEN, 182 Galgorm Road, Ballymena, Co Antrim, Northern Ireland BT42 1HN
Tel: 028 2565 2560

ANTRIM

Riverside School
Fennel Road, ANTRIM, Co Antrim BT41 4PB
Tel: 028 9442 8946
Head: Mrs R Rankin
Category: SLD

BALLYMENA

Castletower School
91 Fry's Road, BALLYMENA, Co Antrim BT43 7EN
Tel: 028 2564 8263
Acting Head: Mr David McCan

COLERAINE

Sandelford Special School
4 Rugby Avenue, COLERAINE, Co
Londonderry BT52 1JL
Tel: 028 7034 3062
Head: Mrs S Tennant
Category: SLD

MAGHERAFELT

Kilronan School
46 Ballyronan Road, MAGHERAFELT, Co
Londonderry BT45 6EN
Tel: 028 7963 2168
Head: Mrs Alison Millar
Category: SLD

NEWTOWNABBEY

Hillcroft Special School
Manse Way, NEWTOWNABBEY, Co Antrim
BT36 5UW
Tel: 028 9083 7488
Category: SLD

Jordanstown Special School
85 Jordanstown Road, NEWTOWNABBEY,
Co Antrim BT37 0QE
Tel: 028 9086 3541
Head: Mrs Ann Magee
Category: HI VIS (Coed 4-19)

Rosstulla Special School
2 Jordanstown Road, NEWTOWNABBEY,
Co Antrim BT37 0QF
Tel: 028 9086 2743
Head: Mrs F Burke
Category: MLD (Coed 5-16)

SOUTH EASTERN
EDUCATION AND LIBRARY BOARD

SEN, Grahamsbridge Road, Dundonald,
Belfast, Northern Ireland BT16 2HS
Tel: 028 90 566200

BANGOR

Clifton Special School
292A Old Belfast Road, BANGOR, Co
Down BT19 1RH
Tel: 028 9127 0210
Head: Ms S Anderson
Category: SLD

Lakewood Special School
96 Newtownards Road, BANGOR, Co
Down BT19 1GZ
Tel: 028 9145 6227
Head: Mr Jon Bleakney

BELFAST

Longstone Special School
Millar's Lane, Dundonald, BELFAST, Co
Down BT16 0DA
Tel: 028 9048 0071
Head: Mr T Howard
Category: MLD

Tor Bank Special School
5 Dunlady Road, BELFAST, Co Down
BT16 1TT
Tel: 028 9048 4147
Head: Mr C Davis
Category: SLD

CRAIGAVON

Brookfield Special School
65 Halfpenny Gate Road, Moira,
CRAIGAVON, Co Armagh BT67 0HN
Tel: 028 9262 2978
Head: Mr D B Gillan
Category: MLD (Coed 5-11)

DONAGHADEE

Killard House
Northfield Road, DONAGHADEE, Co
Down BT21 0BH
Tel: 028 9188 2361
Head: Mr C Miller
Category: MLD

DOWNPATRICK

Ardmore House
95A Saul Street, DOWNPATRICK, Co
Down BT30 6NJ
Tel: 028 4461 4881
Acting Head: Mr B Fettes
Category: EBD

Knockevin Special School
33 Racecourse Hill, DOWNPATRICK, Co
Down BT30 6PU
Tel: 028 4461 2167
Head: Mrs A Cooper
Category: SLD

HILLSBOROUGH

Beechlawn Special School
3 Dromore Road, HILLSBOROUGH, Co
Down BT26 6PA
Tel: 028 9268 2302
Head: Mrs B Green
Category: MLD

LISBURN

Parkview Special School
2 Brokerstown Road, LISBURN, Co
Antrim BT28 2EE
Tel: 028 9260 1197
Head: Mr J Curran
Category: SLD

SOUTHERN
EDUCATION AND LIBRARY BOARD

3 Charlemont Place, The Mall, Armagh,
Northern Ireland BT61 9AX
Tel: 028 3751 2200

ARMAGH

Lisanally School
85 Lisanally Lane, ARMAGH, Co Armagh
BT61 7HF
Tel: 028 3752 3563
Head: Ms Sandra Flynn
Category: SLD (Coed)

BANBRIDGE

Donard School
22A Castlewellan Road, BANBRIDGE, Co
Down BT32 4WY
Tel: 028 4066 2357
Head: Mrs Edel Lavery
Category: SLD (Coed)

CRAIGAVON

Ceara School
Sloan Street, Lurgan, CRAIGAVON, Co
Armagh BT66 8NY
Tel: 028 3832 3312
Head: Dr Peter Cunningham
Category: SLD (Coed)

DUNGANNON

Sperrinview School
8 Coalisland Road, DUNGANNON, Co
Tyrone BT71 6FA
Tel: 028 8772 2467
Principal: Miss Paula Jordan
Category: SLD (Coed)

NEWRY

Rathore School
23 Martin's Lane, Carnagat, NEWRY, Co
Down BT35 8PJ
Tel: 028 3026 1617
Head: Mr Raymond Cassidy
Category: SLD (Coed)

WESTERN
CHILDREN AND YOUNG PEOPLE'S SERVICES

SEN Team, Headquarters Office, 1
Hospital Road, Omagh, Northern Ireland
BT79 0AW
Tel: 028 8241 1456

ENNISKILLEN

Willowbridge School
Derrygonnelly Road, ENNISKILLEN, Co
Fermanagh BT74 7EY
Principal: Mrs J Murphy
Category: SLD MLD (Coed)

LIMAVADY

Rossmar Special School
2 Ballyquin Road, LIMAVADY, Co
Londonderry BT49 9ET
Tel: 028 7776 2351
Head: Mr B McLaughlin
Category: MLD (Coed)

LONDONDERRY

Belmont House Special School
17 Racecourse Road, LONDONDERRY, Co
Londonderry BT48 7RE
Tel: 028 7135 1266
Head: Mrs N Begley
Category: EBD MLD (Coed)

Foyleview Special School
15 Racecourse Road, LONDONDERRY, Co
Londonderry BT48 7RE
Tel: 028 7126 3270
Head: Dr M Dobbins
Category: SLD (Coed)

OMAGH

Arvalee School and Resource Centre
17 Deverney Road, OMAGH, Co Tyrone
BT79 0ND
Tel: 028 8224 9182
Head: Mr J Gray
Category: MLD SLD (Coed)

STRABANE

Knockavoe School and Resource Centre
10A Melmount Gardens, STRABANE, Co
Tyrone BT82 9EB
Tel: 028 7188 3319
Head: Ms Martina McCornish
Category: SLD MLD (Coed)

SCOTLAND

ABERDEEN
EDUCATION, CULTURE & SPORT

Additional Support Needs, Business
Hub 13, Second Floor North, Marischal
College, Broad Street, Aberdeen
AB10 1AB
Tel: 01224 522695

ABERDEEN

Aberdeen School for the Deaf
c/o Sunnybank School, Sunnybank Road,
ABERDEEN AB24 3NJ
Tel: 01224 261722
Acting Head: MS Alison Martin
Category: HI

Cordyce School
Riverview Drive, Dyce, ABERDEEN
AB21 7NF
Tel: 01224 724215
Acting Head: Ms Maureen Simmers
Category: EBD

Hazlewood School
Fernielea Road, ABERDEEN AB15 6GU
Tel: 01224 321363
Head: Ms Jill Barry
Category: SLD MLD PMLD

Hospital and Home Tuition Service
Royal Aberdeen Children's Hospital,
Lowit Unit, Westburn Road, ABERDEEN
AB25 2ZG
Tel: 01224 550317
Acting Head: Ms Maureen Simmers
Category: HS

Woodlands School
Regent Walk, ABERDEEN AB24 1SX
Tel: 01224 524393
Head: Ms Caroline Stirton
Category: PMLD

ABERDEENSHIRE
EDUCATION, LEARNING AND LEISURE SERVICE

Woodhill House, Westburn Road,
Aberdeen AB16 5GB
Tel: 01224 664630

FRASERBURGH

Westfield School
Argyll Road, FRASERBURGH,
Aberdeenshire AB43 9BL
Tel: 01346 518699
Acting Head: Ms Kerri Dalton
Category: PH MLD (Coed 3-11)

INVERURIE

St Andrew's School
St Andrew's Garden, INVERURIE,
Aberdeenshire AB51 3XT
Tel: 01467 621215
Acting Head: Ms Susan Stewart
Category: AUT SP&LD GLD (Coed 3-18)

PETERHEAD

Anna Ritchie School
Grange Gardens, PETERHEAD,
Aberdeenshire AB42 2AP
Tel: 01779 473293
Head: Mrs I Cruikshank
Category: LD (3-16)

STONEHAVEN

Carronhill School
Mill of Forest Road, STONEHAVEN,
Kincardineshire AB39 2GZ
Tel: 01569 763886
Head: Mrs Glenda Fraser
Category: CLD (3-16)

EAST AYRSHIRE
EDUCATION & SOCIAL SERVICES

Council Headquarters, London Road,
Kilmarnock KA3 7BU
Tel: 01563 576000

CUMNOCK

Hillside School
Dalgleish Avenue, CUMNOCK, East
Ayrshire KA18 1QQ
Tel: 01290 423239
Head: Ms Debbie Skeoch
Category: SLD PMLD (Coed 6-17)

KILMARNOCK

Park School
Beech Avenue, KILMARNOCK, East
Ayrshire KA1 2EW
Tel: 01563 549988
Head: Ms Carol Anne Burns
Category: LD PD (Coed 5-18)

**Willowbank School (with effect from 1
August 2013)**
Grassyards Road, KILMARNOCK, East
Ayrshire KA3 7BB
Head: Ms Tracy Smallwood
Category: SLD PMLD

SOUTH AYRSHIRE
COUNCIL

Children & Community, County
Buildings, Wellington Square, Ayr
KA7 1DR
Tel: 0300 123 0900

AYR

Southcraig Campus
Belmont Avenue, AYR, South Ayrshire
KA7 2ND
Tel: 01292 612146
Head: Mrs Lorraine Stobie
Category: SLD CLD (Coed 1-5)

GIRVAN

Invergarven School
15 Henrietta Street, GIRVAN, South
Ayrshire KA26 9EB
Tel: 01465 716808
Head: Mrs Jane Gordon
Category: SLD CLD PD MSI (Coed 3-16)

CLACKMANNANSHIRE
COUNCIL

Facilities, Schools & Welfare Team,
Kilncraigs, Greenside Street, Alloa,
Clackmannanshire FK10 1EB
Tel: 01259 452499

SAUCHIE

Lochies School
Gartmorn Road, SAUCHIE,
Clackmannanshire FK10 3PB
Tel: 01259 216928
Head: Rhoda MacDougall
Category: CLD SLD ASD (Coed 5-11))

COMHAIRLE NAN EILEAN SIAR
DEPARTMENT OF EDUCATION & CHILDREN'S SERVICES

Sandwick Road, Stornoway, Isle of Lewis
HS1 2BW
Tel: 0845 600 7090

SANDWICK

Sandwickhill Learning Centre
, SANDWICK, Isle of Lewis HS2 0AG
Tel: 01851 703300
Principal Teacher: Mrs A Campbell
Category: SLD PMLD (Coed 3-11)

EAST DUNBARTONSHIRE
COUNCIL

12 Strathkelvin Place, Kirkintilloch,
Glasgow, Lanarkshire G66 1TJ
Tel: 0300 123 4510

KIRKINTILLOCH

Merkland School
Langmuir Road, KIRKINTILLOCH, East
Dunbartonshire G66 2QF
Tel: 0141 955 2336
Head: Ms Anne Mulvenna
Category: MLD PH

LENZIE

Campsie View School
Boghead Road, LENZIE, East
Dunbartonshire G66 4DP
Tel: 0141 955 2339
Head: Mrs C Bowie
Category: SCLD

WEST DUNBARTONSHIRE
COUNCIL

Garshake Road, Dumbarton G82 3PU
Tel: 01389 738282

CLYDEBANK

Cunard School
Cochno Street, Whitecrook, CLYDEBANK,
West Dunbartonshire G81 1RQ
Tel: 0141 952 1621
Head: Lousie Finch
Category: SEBD (Primary)

Kilpatrick School
Mountblow Road, Dalmuir, CLYDEBANK,
West Dunbartonshire G81 4SW
Tel: 01389 872171/872168
Head: Debbie Queen
Category: SCLD (Primary/Secondary)

CITY OF EDINBURGH COUNCIL

Waverley Court, 4 East Market Street,
Edinburgh, Midlothian EH8 8BG
Tel: 0131 200 2000

EDINBURGH

Braidburn Special School
107 Oxgangs Road North, EDINBURGH
EH14 1ED
Tel: 0131 312 2320
Head: Mrs Arlene Mooney
Category: EPI PH (Coed 2-16)

Gorgie Mills Special School
97 Gorgie Park Road, EDINBURGH
EH11 2QL
Tel: 0131 313 3848
Head: Ms Terri Dwyer
Category: EBD

Howdenhall and St Katharine's Special School
39 Howdenhall Road, EDINBURGH
EH16 6PG
Tel: 0131 664 8488

Kaimes Special School
140 Lasswade Road, EDINBURGH
EH16 6RT
Tel: 0131 664 8241
Head: Ms Kath Togneri
Category: SP&LD ASD (Coed 5-18)

Oaklands Special School
750 Ferry Road, EDINBURGH EH4 4PQ
Tel: 0131 315 8100
Head: Ms Maureen Mathieson
Category: SLD CLD PD MSI

Panmure St Ann's
6 South Grays Close, EDINBURGH
EH1 1TQ
Tel: 0131 556 8833
Acting Head: Angelina Lombardo

Pilrig Park Special School
12 Balfour Place, EDINBURGH EH6 5DW
Tel: 0131 467 7960
Head: Ms Ellen Muir
Category: MLD SLD (Coed 11-16)

Prospect Bank Special School
81 Restalrig Road, EDINBURGH EH6 8BQ
Tel: 0131 553 2239
Head: Ms Kirsty Rosie
Category: LD SP&LD (Coed 5-12)

Redhall Special School
3c Redhall Grove, EDINBURGH EH14 2DU
Tel: 0131 443 1256
Head: Ms Susan Shipway

Rowanfield Special School
67c Groathill Road North, EDINBURGH
EH4 2SA
Tel: 0131 343 6116
Head: Ms Leanne Sharpe
Category: EBD

St Crispin's Special School
19 Watertoun Road, EDINBURGH
EH9 3HZ
Tel: 0131 667 4831
Head: Ms Ruth Hendery
Category: SLD AUT (Coed 5-16)

Wellington Residential School
Peebles Road, Penicuik, EDINBURGH
EH26 8PT
Tel: 01968 672515
Head: Ronnie Wells
Category: SEBD (Boys Day/boarding 13-16)

Woodlands Special School
36 Dolphin Avenue, EDINBURGH
EH14 5RD
Tel: 0131 449 3447
Head: Aisling Boyle

FALKIRK COUNCIL

Education Services, Sealock House, 2
Inchyra Road, Grangemouth FK3 9XB
Tel: 01324 506600, *Fax:* 01324 506601

FALKIRK

Falkirk Day Unit
Camelon Education Centre, Abercrombie
Street, Camelon, FALKIRK FK1 4HA
Tel: 01324 501650
Head: Ms Gillian Wilson
Category: SEBD (Secondary)

Windsor Park School
Bantaskine Road, FALKIRK FK1 5HT
Tel: 01324 508640
Head: Mrs Catherine Finestone
Category: D (Coed 3-16)

GRANGEMOUTH

Oxgang School
c/o Moray Primary School, Moray Place,
GRANGEMOUTH FK3 9DL
Tel: 01324 501311
Head: Mrs Sharon Wilson
Category: BESD (5-11)

LARBET

Carrongrange School
Carrongrange Avenue, LARBET, Falkirk
FK5 3BH
Tel: 01324 555266
Head: Mrs Gillian Roberston
Category: CLD MLD (Secondary)

FIFE EDUCATION SERVICE

Rothesay House, Rothesay Place,
Glenrothes, Fife KY7 5PQ
Tel: 08451 55 55 55

CUPAR

Kilmaron School
Balgarvie Road, CUPAR, Fife KY15 4PE
Tel: 01334 659480
Head: Ms Isla Lumsden
Category: CLD PD (Coed 3-18)

DUNFERMLINE

Calaiswood School
Nightingale Place, DUNFERMLINE, Fife
KY11 8LW
Tel: 01383 602481
Head: Deborah Davidson
Category: CLD (Coed 3-18)

Pupil Support Service - Dunfermline
The Bridges Centre, 8a MacGrigor Road,
Rosyth, DUNFERMLINE, Fife KY11 2AE
Tel: 01383 602337
Head: C Gover
Category: SEBD

GLENROTHES

John Fergus School
2 Erskine Place, GLENROTHES, Fife
KY7 4JB
Tel: 01592 583489
Head: Pamela Kirkum
Category: CD PD (Coed Day 3-18)

Pupil Support Service - Glenrothes
Rimbleton House, 4-5 Rimbleton Park,
GLENROTHES, Fife KY6 2BZ
Tel: 01592 583368
Head: E Watson
Category: SEBD

KENNOWAY

East Area Pupil Support Service
East Wing Sandy Brae Centre, Sandy
Brae, KENNOWAY, Fife KY8 5JW
Tel: 01592 583332
Head: Mr R Duncan

Levenmouth Enhanced Support Centre
Kennoway Primary School, Langside
Crescent, KENNOWAY, Fife KY8 5LW
Tel: 01334 659420
Head: Catherine Stewart
Category: SEBD (5-16)

KIRKCALDY

Rosslyn School
Viewforth Terrace, KIRKCALDY, Fife
KY1 3BW
Tel: 01592 583482
Head: N Caiger
Category: SLD PMLD PD (Coed 3-19)

LEVEN

Hyndhead School
Barncraig Street, Buckhaven, LEVEN, Fife
KY8 1JE
Tel: 01592 583480
Head: Ms A Lindsay
Category: SLD (Coed 5-18)

LOCHGELLY

Lochgelly North School
6 McGregor Avenue, LOCHGELLY, Fife
KY5 9PE
Tel: 01592 583481
Head: M Sparling
Category: SLD PMLD GLD MSI (Coed 11-19)

GLASGOW
EDUCATION SERVICES

40 John Street, Glasgow G1 1JL
Tel: 0141 287 2000

GLASGOW

Abercorn Secondary School
195 Garscube Road, GLASGOW G4 9QH
Tel: 0141 332 6212
Acting Head: Ms Elizabeth Murphy
Category: MLD

Ashcraig Secondary School
100 Avenue End Road, GLASGOW
G33 3SW
Tel: 0141 774 3428
Head: Mr Danny McGrorry
Category: PH

Broomlea Primary School
Keppoch Campus, 65 Stonyhurst Street,
GLASGOW G22 5AX
Tel: 0141 336 8428
Head: Ms Fiona Shields
Category: CLD

Cardinal Winning Secondary School
30 Fullarton Avenue, GLASGOW G32 8NJ
Tel: 0141 778 3714
Head: Gerard Mc Donald
Category: MLD

Cartvale Secondary School
3 Burndyke Court, GLASGOW G51 2BG
Tel: 0141 445 1767
Head: Ms Pauline Harte

Croftcroighn Primary School
290 Mossvale Road, GLASGOW G33 5NY
Tel: 0141 774 3760
Head: Mrs Margaret McFadden
Category: CLD

Drummore Primary School
129 Drummore Road, GLASGOW G15 7NH
Tel: 0141 944 1323
Head: Ms Patricia Podmore
Category: MLD

Eastmuir Primary School
211 Hallhill Road, GLASGOW G33 4QL
Tel: 0141 771 3464
Head: Mrs Lorraine Campbell
Category: MLD

Gadburn School
70 Rockfield Road, GLASGOW G21 3DZ
Tel: 0141 558 5373
Category: MLD (Primary)

Glasgow Dyslexia Support Service
Floor 2 Room 9, Thornwood Primary
School, 11 Thornwood Avenue,
GLASGOW G11 7QZ
Tel: 0141 334 5700
Category: DYS DYSP

Greenview Learning Centre
384 Drakemire Drive, GLASGOW G45 9SR
Tel: 0141 634 1551
Category: SEBD

Hampden Primary School
18 Logan Gardens, GLASGOW G5 0LJ
Tel: 0141 429 6095
Head: Ms Mary Cloughley
Category: PH

Hazelwood School
50 Dumbreck Court, GLASGOW G41 5NG
Tel: 0141 427 9334
Head: Ms Monica McGeever
Category: HI VIS (2-19)

Hollybrook Academy
135 Hollybrook Street, GLASGOW
G42 7HU
Tel: 0141 423 5937
Head: Mrs Mary Farrell
Category: MLD (Secondary)

Howford Primary School
487 Crookston Road, GLASGOW G53 7TX
Tel: 0141 882 2605
Head: Ms Karen Keith
Category: MLD

Kelbourne Park Primary School
109 Hotspur Street, GLASGOW G20 8LH
Tel: 0141 946 1405
Head: Ms Andrea MacBeath
Category: PH

Kirkriggs Primary School
500 Croftfoot Road, GLASGOW G45 0NJ
Tel: 0141 634 7158
Head: Ms Elena Convery
Category: MLD

Ladywell School
12A Victoria Park Drive South, GLASGOW
G14 9RU
Tel: 0141 959 6665
Head: Ms Karen Muir
Category: SEBD (10-14)

Langlands Primary School
Glenside Avenue, GLASGOW G53 5FD
Tel: 0141 892 0952
Head: Johann Dunable
Category: CLD

Linburn Academy
77 Linburn Road, GLASGOW G52 4EX
Tel: 0141 883 2082
Head: Ms Jinty Stewart
Category: CLD (Secondary)

Middlefield Residential School
26 Partickhill Road, GLASGOW G11 5BP
Tel: 0141 334 0159
Category: ASD (Day & residential)

Milton School
6 Liddesdale Terrace, GLASGOW G22 7HL
Tel: 0141 762 2102
Head: Ms Bernadette Casey
Category: CLD

Newhills Secondary School
Newhills Road, GLASGOW G33 4HJ
Tel: 0141 773 1296
Head: Alison Lochrie
Category: CLD

Parkhill Secondary School
375 Cumbernauld Road, GLASGOW
G31 3LP
Tel: 0141 554 2765
Head: Ms Bernadette Casey
Category: MLD

Rosevale Primary School
48 Scalpay Street, GLASGOW G22 7DD
Tel: 0141 772 1756
Acting Head: Mary Dunwoody
Category: SEBD

St Kevin's Primary School
25 Fountainwell Road, GLASGOW
G21 1TN
Tel: 0141 557 3722
Head: Ms Elizabeth Murphy
Category: MLD

St Oswald's Secondary School
83 Brunton Street, GLASGOW G44 3NF
Tel: 0141 637 3952
Head: Mr Gerald MacDonnell
Category: MLD

Westmuir High School
255 Rigby Street, GLASGOW G32 6DJ
Tel: 0141 556 6276
Head: Ms Pauline Harte
Category: SEBD

HIGHLAND
EDUCATION, CULTURE & SPORT SERVICE

Glenurquhart Road, Inverness IV3 5NX
Tel: 01463 702801

INVERNESS

Drummond School
Drummond Road, Inverness, INVERNESS,
Highland IV2 4NZ
Tel: 01463 701050
Head: Mrs L Schubert
Category: SLD PMLD CLD (Coed 3-16)

ROSS-SHIRE

St Clement's School
Tulloch Street, Dingwall, ROSS-SHIRE,
Highland IV15 9JZ
Tel: 01349 863284
Head: Mrs M MacKenzie
Category: SP&LD VIS HI PD (Coed 5-11)

St Duthus School
Academy Street, Tain, ROSS-SHIRE,
Highland IV19 1ED
Tel: 01862 894407
Head: Mr J Eggermont
Category: SLD PLD CLD (Coed 3-18)

INVERCLYDE
COUNCIL

Special Needs, Municipal Buildings,
Greenock PA15 1LY
Tel: 01475 714100

GOUROCK

Garvel Deaf Centre
c/o Moorfoot Primary School, GOUROCK,
Inverclyde PA19 1ES
Tel: 01475 715642
Acting Head: Ms Eileen Burns
Category: D

GREENOCK

Glenburn School
Inverkip Road, GREENOCK, Inverclyde
PA16 0QG
Tel: 01475 715400
Head: Mrs Eileen McGeer
Category: PH MLD SLD

PORT GLASGOW

Lilybank School
Birkmyre Avenue, PORT GLASGOW,
Inverclyde PA14 5AN
Tel: 01475 715703/4
Head: Mrs Eileen Stewart
Category: SLD PMLD

NORTH LANARKSHIRE
COUNCIL

Learning and Leisure Services, Municipal
Buildings, Kildonan Street, Coatbridge
ML5 3BT
Tel: 01236 812222, *Fax:* 01698 403022

AIRDRIE

Mavisbank School and Nursery
Mitchell Street, AIRDRIE, North
Lanarkshire ML6 0EB
Tel: 01236 752725
Head: Mr John Lochrie
Category: PMLD (Coed 2-18)

COATBRIDGE

Drumpark School
Albert Street, COATBRIDGE, North
Lanarkshire ML5 3ET
Tel: 01236 794884
Head: Mrs Theresa Collins
Category: MLD PH SP&LD (3-18)

Pentland School
Tay Street, COATBRIDGE, North
Lanarkshire ML5 2NA
Tel: 01236 794833
Head: Mr I Porteous
Category: SEBD (Coed 5-11)

Portland High School
31-33 Kildonan Street, COATBRIDGE,
North Lanarkshire ML5 3LG
Tel: 01236 440634
Head: Mr Martin McGovern
Category: SEBD (Coed 11-16)

Willowbank School
299 Bank Street, COATBRIDGE, North
Lanarkshire ML5 1EG
Tel: 01236 421911
Head: Mr V Jack
Category: SEBD (Coed 11-18)

CUMBERNAULD

Glencryan School
Greenfaulds Road, CUMBERNAULD,
North Lanarkshire G67 2XJ
Tel: 01236 794866
Head: Ms Angela Moore
Category: MLD PH ASD (Coed 5-18)

Redburn School and Nursery
Kildrum Ring Road, CUMBERNAULD,
North Lanarkshire G67 2EL
Tel: 01236 736904
Head
Category: SLD CLD PH (Coed 2-18)

MOTHERWELL

Bothwellpark High School
Annan Street, MOTHERWELL, North
Lanarkshire ML1 2DL
Tel: 01698 274939
Head: Mrs Trisha Docherty
Category: SLD (Coed 11-18)

Clydeview School and Nursery
Magna Street, MOTHERWELL, North
Lanarkshire ML1 3QZ
Tel: 01698 264843
Head: Mrs Marie Jo McGurl
Category: SLD (Coed 5-11)

Firpark Secondary
Firpark Street, MOTHERWELL, North
Lanarkshire ML1 2PR
Tel: 01698 251313
Head: Mr John Morley
Category: MLD PH (Coed 11-18)

UDDINGSTON

Fallside Secondary
Sanderson Avenue, Viewpark,
UDDINGSTON, North Lanarkshire G71 6JZ
Tel: 01698 747721
Head
Category: EBD (Coed 11-16)

SOUTH LANARKSHIRE COUNCIL

Council Offices, Almada Street, Hamilton
ML3 0AA
Tel: 0303 123 1015

CAMBUSLANG

Rutherglen High School
Langlea Road, CAMBUSLANG, South
Lanarkshire G72 8ES
Tel: 0141 643 3480
Head: Jan Allen

CARLUKE

Victoria Park School
Market Road, CARLUKE, South
Lanarkshire ML8 4BE
Tel: 01555 750591
Head: Miss Anne Fisher
Category: PMLD SLD

EAST KILBRIDE

Greenburn School
Maxwellton Avenue, EAST KILBRIDE,
South Lanarkshire G74 3DU
Tel: 01355 237278
Head: Mrs Helen Nicol
Category: PMLD

Kittoch School
Livingstone Drive, Murray, EAST
KILBRIDE, South Lanarkshire G75 0AB
Tel: 01355 244348/9
Acting Head: Mr Chris Downing
Category: EBD

Sanderson High School
High Common Road, St Leonard's, EAST
KILBRIDE, South Lanarkshire G74 2LP
Tel: 01355 588625
Head: Mr John McEnaney

West Mains School
Logie Park, EAST KILBRIDE, South
Lanarkshire G74 4BU
Tel: 01355 249938
Head: Mrs Rosemary Payne
Category: SLD

HAMILTON

Hamilton School for the Deaf
Anderson Street, HAMILTON, South
Lanarkshire ML3 0QL
Tel: 01698 823377
Acting Head: Ms Joyce Larson
Category: D

LANARK

Ridgepark School
Mousebank Road, LANARK, South
Lanarkshire ML11 7RA
Tel: 01555 662151
Acting Head: Mrs Jane Sludden
Category: EBD

MIDLOTHIAN EDUCATION AND CHILDREN'S SERVICES

Midlothian House, Buccleuch Street,
Dalkeith, Midlothian EH22 1DN
Tel: 0131 271 6697

DALKEITH

Saltersgate School
3 Cousland Road, DALKEITH, Midlothian
EH22 2PS
Tel: 0131 654 4703
Head: Mrs Jean Loughlin
Category: GLD

WEST LOTHIAN EDUCATION & LEARNING

West Lothian Civic Centre, Howden
South Road, Livingston, West Lothian
EH54 6FF
Tel: 01506 775000

BATHGATE

Pinewood Special School
Elm Grove, Blackburn, BATHGATE, West
Lothian EH47 7QX
Tel: 01506 656374
Head: Ms Pam Greig
Category: MLD SLD

LIVINGSTON

Beatlie School Campus
The Mall, Craigshill, LIVINGSTON, West
Lothian EH54 5EJ
Tel: 01506 777598
Acting Head: Mrs Carol Robbie
Category: CLD MSI PD (Coed 3-16)

Cedarbank School
Cedarbank, Ladywell East, LIVINGSTON,
West Lothian EH54 6DR
Tel: 01506 442172
Acting Head: Ms Fiona Barber
Category: ASD LD (Coed 12-18)

Ogilvie School Campus
Ogilvie Way, Knightsbridge, LIVINGSTON,
West Lothian EH54 8HL
Tel: 01506 777489
Head: Mrs Catriona Grant
Category: EBD (Primary)

LIVINGSTONE

Willowgrove House
1/6 Willowgrove, Craigshill,
LIVINGSTONE, West Lothian EH54 5LU
Tel: 01506 434274
Head: Ms Denise McPhail

WHITBURN

Burnhouse School
The Avenue, WHITBURN, West Lothian
EH47 0BX
Tel: 01501 678100
Head: Mrs Laura Quilter
Category: EBD (Secondary)

PERTH & KINROSS
EDUCATION & CHILDREN'S SERVICES

Pullar House, 35 Kinnoull Street, Perth
PH1 5GD
Tel: 01738 476200

PERTH

Fairview School
Oakbank Crescent, PERTH, Perthshire &
Kinross PH1 1DF
Tel: 01738 473050
Head: Ms Fiona Gillespie
Category: SLD CLD (Coed 2-18)

RENFREWSHIRE
EDUCATION & LEARNING

LINWOOD

Clippens School
Brediland Road, LINWOOD, Renfrewshire
PA3 3RX
Tel: 01505 325333
Head: Ms Isabell Gibb
Category: ASD CLD PI MSI (Coed 5-19)

PAISLEY

Kersland School
Ben Nevis Road, PAISLEY, Renfrewshire
PA2 7BU
Tel: 0141 889 8251
Head: Mrs Carol Jackson
Category: SLD (Coed 5-18)

Mary Russell School
Hawkhead Road, PAISLEY, Renfrewshire
PA2 7BE
Tel: 0141 889 7628
Head: Ms Jane Dorby
Category: MLD (Coed 5-18)

EAST RENFREWSHIRE
EDUCATION DEPARTMENT

Council Offices, 211 Main Street,
Barrhead, East Renfrewshire G78 1SY
Tel: 0141 577 3001

NEWTON MEARNS

The Isobel Mair School
58 Stewarton Road, NEWTON MEARNS,
East Renfrewshire G77 6NB
Tel: 0141 570 7600
Head: Mrs Mari Wallace
Category: CLD (Coed 5-18)

STIRLING
COUNCIL

Education Services, Viewforth, Stirling
FK8 2ET
Tel: 0845 277 7000

BANNOCKBURN

Brucefield Resource Centre
Resource Centre, 50A Park Drive,
BANNOCKBURN FK7 0EH
Tel: 01786 812386
Head: Ms Cath McRorie

STIRLING

Castleview School
Drip Road, Kildean, STIRLING FK8 1SD
Tel: 01786 272326
Head: Mrs Maureen Howie
Category: SLD PH CLD

Wallace High School
Ochil House, Airthrey Road, STIRLING
FK9 5HW
Tel: 01786 462166/7
Head: Mr Scott Pennock

Young Persons Unit
84 Glasgow Road, St Ninian's, STIRLING
FK7 0PQ
Tel: 01786 816759
Head: Ms Cath McRorie

WALES
BLAENAU GWENT
COUNTY BOROUGH COUNCIL

Education & Leisure Department,
Central Depot, Barleyfield Industrial
Estate, Brynmawr NP23 4YF
Tel: 01495 311556

EBBW VALE

Pen-y-Cwm Special School
Strand Annealing Lane, EBBW VALE,
Blaenau Gwent NP23 6AN
Tel: 01495 357755
Head: Mrs D Williams
Category: SLD PMLD

BRIDGEND
COUNTY BOROUGH COUNCIL

Children's Directorate, Sunnyside, Bridgend CF31 4AR
Tel: 01656 642647

BRIDGEND

Heronsbridge Special School
Ewenny Road, BRIDGEND CF31 3HT
Tel: 01656 653974
Head: Mrs G James
Category: PMLD VIS AUT (Coed Day & boarding 3-18)

Ysgol Bryn Castell
Llangewydd Road, Cefn Glas, BRIDGEND CF31 4JP
Tel: 01656 815595
Head: Mr S O'Callaghan
Category: EBD LD HI ASD MLD SLD SP&LD (Coed 3-19)

CAERPHILLY
COUNTY BOROUGH COUNCIL

Directorate of Education & Lifelong Learning, Penallta House, Tredoman Park, Ystrad Mynach, Hengoed CF82 7PG
Tel: 01443 864870

CAERPHILLY

Trinity Fields School & Resource Centre
Caerphilly Road, Ystrad Mynach, CAERPHILLY CF82 7XW
Tel: 01443 866000
Head: Mr I Elliott
Category: SLD VIS HI CLD SP&LD (Coed 3-19)

CARDIFF
EDUCATION SERVICE

Achievement & Inclusion, County Hall, Cardiff CF10 4UW
Tel: 029 2087 2000

CARDIFF

Greenhill School
Heol Brynglas, Rhiwbina, CARDIFF CF14 6UJ
Tel: 029 2069 3786
Head: Mrs Jane Counsell
Category: SEBD (Coed 11-16)

Meadowbank School
Colwill Road, Llandaff North, CARDIFF CF14 2QQ
Tel: 029 2061 6018
Head: Mrs L Felstead
Category: SLCD (Coed 4-11)

Riverbank School
Vincent Road, Caerau, CARDIFF CF5 5AQ
Tel: 029 2056 3860
Head: Mrs Amanda Gibson-Evans
Category: MLD SLD (Coed 4-11)

The Court School
Station Road, Llanishen, CARDIFF CF14 5UX
Tel: 029 2075 2713
Head: Mr P Owen
Category: SEBD (Coed 4-11)

The Hollies School
Brynheulog, CARDIFF CF23 7XG
Tel: 029 2073 4411
Head: Ms Kath Keely
Category: ASD PMED (Coed 4-11)

Ty Gwyn School
Vincent Road, CARDIFF CF5 5AQ
Tel: 029 2083 8560
Head: Mr K Tansley
Category: PMLD ASD (Coed 4-19)

Woodlands High School
Vincent Road, Caerau, CARDIFF CF5 5AQ
Tel: 029 2056 1279
Head: Mr R Webb
Category: MLD SLD (Coed 11-19)

CARMARTHENSHIRE
COUNTY COUNCIL

The Department for Education and Children, Building 2, St David's Park, Jobswell Road, Carmarthen, Carmarthenshire SA31 3HB
Tel: 01267 246500

CARMARTHEN

Rhyd-y-gors School & Support Services
Rhyd-y-gors, Johnstown, CARMARTHEN, Carmarthenshire SA31 3QU
Tel: 01267 231171
Head: Mr S C Saunders
Category: EBD

LLANELLI

Ysgol Heol Goffa
Heol Goffa, LLANELLI, Carmarthenshire SA15 3LS
Tel: 01554 759465
Head: Mrs N Symmons
Category: SLD PMLD

CONWY
EDUCATION SERVICES

Education Services, ALN Services, Government Buildings, Dinerth Road, Colwyn Bay LL28 4UL
Tel: 01492 575030

ABERGELE

Ysgol Cedar Court (NWAS)
North Wales Adolescent Service, Abergele Hospital, ABERGELE LL22 8DP
Tel: 01745 448742
Head: Mrs V Roberts
Category: HS (11-16)

LLANDUDNO

Ysgol Y Gogarth
Ffordd Nant y Gamar, Craig y Don, LLANDUDNO, Conwy LL30 1YF
Tel: 01492 860077
Head: Mr J Morgan
Category: General SEN (2-19)

DENBIGHSHIRE
COUNTY COUNCIL

Education Services, County Hall, Wynnstay Road, Ruthin, Denbighshire LL15 1YN
Tel: 01824 712777, *Fax:* 01824 712664

DENBIGH

Plas Brondyffryn
Rhyl Road, DENBIGH, Denbighshire LL16 3DP
Tel: 01745 813914
Head: Dr I Barros-Curtis
Category: AUT SLD (Coed 4-19)

RHYL

Tir Morfa School
Derwen Road, RHYL, Denbighshire LL18 2RN
Tel: 01745 350388
Head: Mrs Carol Edwards
Category: MLD SLD (Coed 4-19)

FLINTSHIRE
COUNTY COUNCIL

Education & Learning, County Hall, Mold, Flintshire CH7 6NB
Tel: 01352 704017

FLINT

Ysgol Maes Hyfryd
Fifth Avenue, FLINT, Flintshire CH6 5QL
Tel: 01352 792720
Head: Ms Jane Kelly
Category: (Coed 11-16)

Ysgol Pen Coch
Prince of Wales Avenue, FLINT, Flintshire CH6 5NF
Tel: 01352 792730
Head: Ms A Anderson
Category: (Coed 5-11)

GWYNEDD
COUNCIL

Education Department, Council Offices, Caernarfon, Gwynedd LL55 1SH
Tel: 01766 771000

CAERNARFON

Ysgol Pendalar
Ffordd Bethel, CAERNARFON, Gwynedd LL55 1DU
Tel: 01248 672141
Head: Mr Ieuan Roberts
Category: SLD

PWLLHELI

Ysgol Hafod Lon
Y FfÙr, PWLLHELI, Gwynedd LL53 6UP
Tel: 01766 810626
Head: Mrs Donna Rees-Roberts
Category: SLD

MERTHYR TYDFIL
INTEGRATED CHILDREN'S SERVICES

Additional Learning Needs Service, 3rd floor, Ty Keir Hardie, Avenue De Clichy, Merthyr Tydfil CF 48 8XD
Tel: 01685 724616, *Fax:* 01685 724642

MERTHYR TYDFIL

Greenfield Special School
Duffryn Road, Pentrebach, MERTHYR TYDFIL CF48 4BJ
Tel: 01443 690468
Head: Mr Anthony Blake
Category: SLD MLD PMLD ASD EBD MSI SP&LD (Coed 3-19)

MONMOUTHSHIRE
COUNTY COUNCIL

SEN Department, @ Innovations House, Wales 1 Business Park, Magor, Monmouthshire NP26 3DG
Tel: 01633 644644

CHEPSTOW

Mounton House School
Pwyllmeyric, CHEPSTOW, Monmouthshire NP6 6LA
Tel: 01291 635642
Head: Mr P Absolom
Category: EBD (Boys 11-16)

NEATH PORT TALBOT
THE CHILD CARE (DISABILITY) TEAM

2nd Floor, Neath Port Talbot CBC, Civic Centre, Neath SA11 3QZ
Tel: 01639 685862

NEATH

Ysgol Hendre Residential School
Heol Hendre, Bryncoch, NEATH SA10 7TY
Tel: 01639 642786
Acting Head: Mr Jonathan Roberts
Category: GLD (Coed 2-19)

Ysgol Maes Y Coed
Hoel Hendre, Brynoch, NEATH SA10 7TY
Tel: 01639 643648
Head: Mrs Helen Glover
Category: GLD (Coed 2-19)

PORT TALBOT

Velindre Community School
Reginald Street, PORT TALBOT SA13 1YY
Tel: 01639 880010
Acting Head: Mrs Susan Coyne

NEWPORT
CITY COUNCIL

Education Department, Education Inclusion Department, Civic Centre, Newport NP20 4UR
Tel: 01633 656656

NEWPORT

Maes Ebbw School
Maesglas Road, NEWPORT, Newport NP20 3DG
Tel: 01633 815480
Head: Ms Julie Nichols
Category: SLD PMLD AUT PH

PEMBROKESHIRE
EDUCATION DEPARTMENT

Inclusion and SEN Service, County Hall, Haverfordwest, Pembrokeshire SA61 1TP
Tel: 01437 775012

HAVERFORDWEST

Portfield School
off Portfield, HAVERFORDWEST, Pembrokeshire SA61 1BS
Tel: 01437 762701
Head: Mrs S Painter
Category: SLD PMLD CLD (Coed 4-18+)

POWYS
COUNTY COUNCIL

Schools Service, Powys County Hall, Llandrindod Wells, Powys LD1 5LG
Tel: 01597 826000, *Fax:* 01597 826475

BRECON

Penmaes School
Canal Road, BRECON, Powys LD3 7HL
Tel: 01874 623508
Head: Mrs Julie Kay
Category: SLD ASD PMLD

NEWTOWN

Brynllywarch Hall School
Kerry, NEWTOWN, Powys SY16 4PB
Tel: 01686 670276
Head: Mr Gavin Randell
Category: MLD EBD

Cedewain School
Maesyrhandir, NEWTOWN, Powys SY16 1LH
Tel: 01686 627454
Head: Mrs Pippa Sillitoe
Category: SLD ASD PMLD

RHONDDA CYNON TAFF
COUNTY BOROUGH COUNCIL

Special Educational Needs (SEN), Ty Trevithick, Abercynon, Mountain Ash CF45 4UQ
Tel: 01443 744000

ABERDARE

Maesgwyn Special School
Cwmdare Road, Cwmdare, ABERDARE, Rhondda Cynon Taf CF44 8RE
Tel: 01685 873933
Head: Mr S K Morgan
Category: MLD (Coed 11-18)

Park Lane Special School
Park Lane, Trecynon, ABERDARE, Rhondda Cynon Taf CF44 8HN
Tel: 01685 874489
Head: Mrs J Davies
Category: SLD (3-19)

PENTRE

Ysgol Hen Felin
Gelligaled Park, Ystradyfodwg, PENTRE, Rhondda Cynon Taf CF41 7SZ
Tel: 01443 431571
Head: Mr A Henderson
Category: SLD (3-19)

PONTYPRIDD

Ysgol Ty Coch
Lansdale Drive, Tonteg, PONTYPRIDD, Rhondda Cynon Taf CF38 1PG
Tel: 01443 203471
Head: Ms H Hodges
Category: SLD (3-19)

CITY AND COUNTY OF SWANSEA

Education Directorate, Civic Centre, Oystermouth Road, Swansea SA1 3SN
Tel: 01792 636000

SWANSEA

Ysgol Crug Glas
Croft Street, SWANSEA SA1 1QA
Tel: 01792 652388
Head: Mr P Martin
Category: SLD PMLD

Ysgol Pen-y-Bryn
Glasbury Road, Morriston, SWANSEA SA6 7PA
Tel: 01792 799064
Head: Mrs Ann Williams-Brunt
Category: MLD SLD AUT

TORFAEN
COUNTY BOROUGH COUNCIL

Education Service, Civic Centre, Pontypool, Torfaen NP4 6YB
Tel: 01495 762200

CWMBRAN

Crownbridge School
Turnpike Road, Croesyceiliog, CWMBRAN, Torfaen NP44 2BJ
Tel: 01633 624201
Head: Mrs Lesley Bush
Category: SLD

VALE OF GLAMORGAN COUNCIL

Learning & Skills, Provincial House, Kendrick Road, Barry CF62 8BF
Tel: 01446 700111

BARRY

Ysgol Maes Dyfan
Gibbonsdown Rise, BARRY, Vale of Glamorgan CF63 1DT
Tel: 01446 732112
Head: Mr C Britten
Category: SLD (Coed 5 Day 3-19)

PENARTH

Ashgrove School
Sully Road, PENARTH, Vale of Glamorgan CF64 2TP
Tel: 029 2070 4212
Head: Mr C Britten
Category: AUT (Coed 5 Day/boarding 4-19)

Ysgol Erw'r Delyn
St Cyres Road, PENARTH, Vale of Glamorgan CF64 2WR
Tel: 029 2070 7225
Headteacher: Mike Farrell
Category: PD PMLD (Coed 5 Day 3-19)

WREXHAM COUNTY BOROUGH COUNCIL

Learning and Achievement Department, Lambpit Street, Wrexham LL11 1AR
Tel: 01978 297505

WREXHAM

St Christopher's School
Stockwell Grove, WREXHAM LL13 7BW
Tel: 01978 346910
Head: Mrs M Pittaway
Category: MLD SLD PMLD (Coed 8-19)

Glossary

ACLD	Autism, Communication and Associated Learning Difficulties	CRB	Criminal Records Bureau
ADD	Attention Deficit Order	CReSTeD	Council for the Registration of Schools Teaching Dyslexic Pupils
ADHD	Attention Deficit and Hyperactive Disorder (Hyperkinetic Disorder)	CSSE	Consortium of Special Schools in Essex
AdvDip SpecEduc	Advanced Diploma in Special Education	CSSIW	Care and Social Services Inspectorate for Wales
AFBPS	Associate Fellow of the British Psychological Society	CTEC	Computer-aided Training, Education and Communication
ALAN	Adult Literacy and Numeracy	D	Deaf
ALCM	Associate of the London College of Music	DDA	Disability Discrimination Act
ALL	Accreditation of Lifelong Learning	Del	Delicate
AOC	Association of Colleges	DfE	Department for Education
AQA	Assessment and Qualification Alliance/Northern Examinations and Assessment Board	DIDA	Diploma in Digital Applications
ASC	Autistic Spectrum Conditions	DipAppSS	Diploma in Applied Social Sciences
ASD	Autistic Spectrum Disorders	DipEd	Diploma of Education
ASDAN	Qualifications for 11-16 age range	DipSEN	Diploma in Speial Educational Needs
ASP	Asperger syndrome	DipSpEd	Diploma in Special Education
AUT	Autism	DT	Design and Technology
AWCEBD	now SEBDA	DYC	Dyscalculia
BA	Bachelor of Arts	DYS	Dyslexia
BDA	British Dyslexic Association	DYSC	Dyscalculia
BESD	Behavioural, Emotional and Social Difficulties	DYSP	Dyspraxia
BMET	Biomedical Engineering Technologist	EASIE	Exercise and Sound in Education
BPhil	Bachelor of Philosophy	EBSD	Emotional, Behavioural and/or Social Difficulties
BSc	Bachelor of Science	ECDL	European Computer Driving Licence
BSL	British Sign Language	ECIS	European Council of International Schools
BTEC	Range of practical work-related programmes; which lead to qualifications equivalent to GCSEs and A levels (awarded by Edexcel)	ECM	Every Child Matters (Government Green Paper)
		EdMng	Educational Management
		ELC	Early Learning Centre
C & G	City & Guilds Examination	ELQ	Equivalent or Lower Qualification
C(Ed) Psychol	Certificate in Educational Psychology	EPI	Epilepsy
CACDP	Council for the Advancement of Communication with Deaf People	EQUALS	Entitlement and Quality Education for Pupils with Learning Difficulties
CAMHS	Child and Adolescent Mental Health Service	FLSE	Federation of Leaders in Special Education
CB	Challenging Behaviour	GCSE	General Certificate of Secondary Education
CD	Communcation Difficulties	GLD	General Learning Difficulties
CertEd	Certificate of Education	HA	High Ability
CF	Cystic Fibrosis	HANDLE	Holistic Approach to Newuro-DEvelopment and Learning Efficiency
CLAIT	Computer Literacy and Information Technology	HEA	Higher Educaiton Authority/Health Education Authority
CLD	Complex Learning Difficulties	HI	Hearing Impairment
CNS	Central Nervous System	HS	Hospital School
COPE	Certificate of Personal Effectiveness	ICT	Information Communication Technology
CP	Cerebral Palsy	IEP	Individual Education Plan
CPD	Continuing Professional Development	IIP	Investors in People
		IM	Idiopathic Myelofibrosis

Glossary

ISI	Independent Schools Inspectorate		PGTC	Post Graduate Teaching Certificate
IT	Information Technology		PH	Physical Impairment
KS	Key Stage		PhD	Doctor of Philosophy
LA	Local Authority		Phe	Partially Hearing
LD	Learning Difficulties		PMLD	Profound and Multiple Learning Difficulties
LDD	Learning Difficulties and Disabilities		PNI	Physical Neurological Impairment
LISA	London International Schools Association		PRU	Pupil Referral Unit
MA	Master of Arts		PSHCE	Personal Social Health, Citizenship and Economics
MAPA	Management of Actual or Potential Aggression			
MBA	Master of Business Administration		RE	Religious Education
MD	Muscular Dystrophy		SAT	Standard Asessment Test
MDT	Multidisciplinary Team		SCD	Social and Communication Difficulties
MEd	Master of Education		SCLD	Severe and Complex Learning Difficulties
MLD	Moderate Learning Difficulties		SEAL	Social and Emotional Aspects of Learning
MS	Multiple Sclerosis		SEBD	Severe Emotional and Behavioural Disorders
MSc	Master of Science		SEBDA	Social, Emotional and Behavioural Difficulties Association
MSI	Multi-sensory Impairment			
NAES	National Association of EBD Schools		SEBN	Social, Emotional and Behavioural Needs
NAS	National Autistic Society		SHB	Sexually Harmful Behaviour
NASEN	Northern Association of Special Educational Needs		SLCN	Speech, Language and Communicational Needs
			SLD	Severe Learning Difficulties
NASS	National Association of Independent Schools & Non-maintained Special Schools		SLI	Specific Language Impairment
			SLT	Speech and Language Teacher
NATSPEC	National Association of Specialist Colleges		SP	Special Purpose/Speech Processing
NOCN	National Open College Network		SpEd	Special Education
NPQH	National Professional Qualification for Headship		SPLD	Specific Learning Difficulties
NVQ	National Vocational Qualifications		SP&LD	Speech and Language Difficulties
OCD	Obsessive Compulsive Disorder		STREAM	Strong Therapeutic, Restoring Environment and Assesssment Model
OCN	Open Course Network			
ODD	Oppositional Defiant Disorder		SWALSS	South and West Association of Leaders in Special Schools
OT	Occupational Therapist			
P scales	method of recording the achievements of SEN students who are working towards the first levels of the National Curriculum		SWSF	Steiner Waldorf Schools Foundation
			TAV	Therapeutic, Academic and Vocational
			TEACCH	Treatment and Education of Autistic and related Communication Handicapped Children (also sometimes written as TEACHH)
PACT	Parents Association of Children with Tumours			
PACT	Parents and Children Together			
PCMT	Professional and Clinical Multidisciplinary Team		TCI	Therapeutic Crisis Intervention
PD	Physical Difficulties		ToD	Teacher of the Deaf
PE	Physical Education		TOU	Tourette syndrome
PECS	Picture Exchange Communication System		VB	Verbal Reasoning
PGCE	Post Graduate Certificate in Education		VIS	Visually Impaired
PGCertSpld	Post Graduate Certificate in Specific Learning Difficulties		VOCA	Voice Output Communication Aid
			WMLG	West Midlands Lupus Group

Index